A Reader/Study Guide for FOOTHILL COLLEGE

COSMOS

Carl Sagan

Prepared by

Ann Elwood
and
Linda Wood

A Project of
National Media Programs
University Extension
University of California, San Diego
and
Telecourse Design and Development
Coast Community Colleges
Orange County, California

RANDOM HOUSE   NEW YORK

ACKNOWLEDGMENTS

I. THE SHORES OF THE COSMIC OCEAN

George A. Seielstad, "Cosmic Ecology: A View from the Outside In," reprinted from the November/December 1978 issue of *Mercury* magazine. © Copyright 1978, Astronomical Society of the Pacific, 1290 24th Avenue, San Francisco, CA 94122.

Carl Sagan, "The Cosmic Calendar," from *The Dragons of Eden* by Carl Sagan. Copyright © 1977 by Carl Sagan. Reprinted by permission of Random House, Inc.

George Sarton, "The Library," reprinted by permission of the publishers from *A History of Science: Hellenistic Science and Culture in the Last Three Centuries B.C.* by George Sarton, Cambridge, Mass.: Copyright © 1959 by the President and Fellows of Harvard College.

II. ONE VOICE IN THE COSMIC FUGUE

Lewis Thomas, "The Lives of a Cell," from *The Lives of a Cell* by Lewis Thomas. Copyright © 1971, 1972, 1973 by the Massachusetts Medical Society. Originally appeared in the *New England Journal of Medicine*. Reprinted by permission of Viking Penguin Inc.

Guy Murchie, "Cells," from *The Seven Mysteries of Life* by Guy Murchie, published by Houghton Mifflin Company. Copyright © 1978 by Guy Murchie. Reprinted by permission of Houghton Mifflin Company.

Stephen Jay Gould, "Ever Since Darwin," prologue from *Ever Since Darwin* by Stephen Jay Gould. Reprinted by permission of W.W. Norton & Company. Copyright © 1977 by Stephen Jay Gould.

Charles Darwin, excerpts from *The Origin of Species* reproduced from *Darwin, A Norton Critical Edition*, Edited by Philip Appleman, by permission of W.W. Norton & Company, Inc. Copyright © 1979, 1980, 1970, by W.W. Norton & Company, Inc.

Loren Eiseley, "How Flowers Changed the World," from *Immense Journey*, by Loren Eiseley. Copyright © 1957 by Loren Eiseley. Reprinted by permission of Random House, Inc.

III. HARMONY OF THE WORLDS

George O. Abell, "The Age of Astrology," from *Drama of the Universe* by George O. Abell. Copyright © 1978 by George O. Abell. Reprinted by permission of Holt, Rinehart and Winston.

Charles A. Whitney, "Kepler: The First of the Modern Mystics," from *The Discovery of Our Galaxy* by Charles A. Whitney. Copyright © 1971 by Charles A. Whitney. Reprinted by permission of Alfred A. Knopf, Inc.

Sir William Dampier, "The Newtonian Epoch," from *A History of Science*, 4th edition, by Sir William Dampier. Cambridge University Press, 1958. Reprinted by permission of the publisher.

William J. Kaufmann, III, "The Foundations of Gravitational Theory," from *Relativity and Cosmology*, Second Edition (pp. 1–9) by William J. Kaufmann, III. Copyright © 1977 by Kaufmann Industries, Inc. Reprinted by permission of Harper & Row, Publishers, Inc.

IV. HEAVEN AND HELL

Dorothy B. Vitaliano, "Minoan Eruption of Santorin," from *Legends of the Earth: Their Geologic Origins* by Dorothy B. Vitaliano. Copyright © 1973. Reprinted by permission of Indiana University Press.

Richard Goody, "Climate and the Planets," with permission from *Natural History*, January, 1978. Copyright American Museum of Natural History, 1978.

Lewis Thomas, "The World's Biggest Membrane," from *The Lives of a Cell* by Lewis Thomas. Copyright © 1971, 1972, 1973 by the Massachusetts Medical Society. Originally appeared in the *New England Journal of Medicine*. Reprinted by permission of Viking Penguin, Inc.

V. BLUES FOR A RED PLANET

Percival Lowell, excerpts from *Mars*. Published by Houghton Mifflin and Company, Boston, 1895.

Alfred Russel Wallace, excerpt from *Is Mars Habitable?* Published by Macmillan and Company, Ltd., London, 1907.

George Alexander, "Viking Science: Tantalizing Viking Scientists: Cautious," from *Today*, the quarterly magazine of the Martin Marietta Corporation. Reprinted by permission.

James Oberg, "Terraforming," from *Astronomy*, May 1978. Reproduced by permission of *Astronomy* Magazine, copyright © 1978 by AstroMedia Corp.

VI. TRAVELERS' TALES

Christiaan Huygens, excerpts from *The Celestial Worlds Discover'd: or, Conjectures Concerning the Inhabitants, Plants and Productions of the Worlds in the Planets* (1698, reprinted Frank Cass 1968).

William K. Hartmann, "Moons of the Outer Solar System Become Real, Although Weird, Places," from *Smithsonian*, January 1980. Reprinted by permission of *Smithsonian* magazine and the author.

James L. Elliot, Edward Dunham, and Robert L. Millis, "Discovering the Rings of Uranus," from *Sky and Telescope*, June 1977. Reproduced courtesy of *Sky and Telescope* and the authors. Copyright © Sky Publishing Corporation 1977; copyright returned to J.L. Elliot.

VII. THE BACKBONE OF NIGHT

Benjamin Farrington, "Greek Science," from *Greek Science* (London: Penguin Books Ltd., 1944), pp. 72–74. Copyright © Benjamin Farrington, 1944. Reprinted by permission of Penguin Books Ltd.

Sir William Dampier, "The Ionians," from *A History of Science*, 4th edition, by Sir William Dampier. Cambridge University Press, 1958. Reprinted by permission of the publisher.

Lucretius, "Movements and Shapes of Atoms," from *On the Nature of the Universe*, translated by Ronald Latham (London: Penguin Classics, 1951), pp. 60–70, 90–95. Copyright © R.E. Latham, 1951. Reprinted by permission of Penguin Books Ltd.

VIII. TRAVELS IN SPACE AND TIME

Jeremy Bernstein, "Einstein: The Early Years," from *Einstein* by Jeremy Bernstein. Copyright © 1973 by Jeremy Bernstein. Reprinted by permission of Viking Penguin Inc.

Lincoln Barnett, "Special Theory of Relativity," from pp. 38–49 of *The Universe and Dr. Einstein* by Lincoln Barnett. Copyright 1948 by Harper & Brothers. Copyright 1950, 1957 by Lincoln Barnett. By permission of William Morrow & Co.

Donald Goldsmith, "When Time Slows Down," reprinted from the May/June 1975 issue of *Mercury* magazine. © Copyright 1975 by the Astronomical Society of the Pacific, 1290 24th Avenue, San Francisco, CA 94122.

IX. THE LIVES OF THE STARS

David H. Clark and F. Richard Stephenson, "The Historical Supernovae," reprinted with permission from *The Historical Supernovae* by David H. Clark and F. Richard Stephenson. Copyright 1977, Pergamon Press, Ltd.

Susan Wyckoff, "Red Giants: The Inside Scoop," reprinted from the Jan./Feb. 1979 issue of *Mercury* magazine. © Copyright 1979 by the Astronomical Society of the Pacific, 1290 24th Avenue, San Francisco, CA 94122.

Timothy Ferris, excerpt from *The Red Limit: The Search for the Edge of the Universe* (pp. 211–218) by Timothy Ferris. Copyright © 1977 by Timothy Ferris. By permission of William Morrow & Company.

Dennis Overbye, "The Wizard of Space and Time," from *Omni*, February 1979. Copyright 1979 by *Omni* Publications International, Ltd. and reprinted with the permission of the copyright owner.

X. THE EDGE OF FOREVER

Martin Rees, "The Unfolding Universe" from *Current*, February 1977. First appeared as "The 13,000,000,000 Year Bang" in *New Scientist* (December 2, 1976), London, the weekly review of science and technology. Reprinted by permission.

Timothy Ferris, "Crucibles of the Cosmos," from *The New York Times Magazine*, January 14, 1979. Copyright © 1979 by The New York Times Company. Reprinted by permission.

Edwin A. Abbott, excerpts from *Flatland* by Edwin A. Abbott. Copyright 1952 by Dover Publications, Inc. Reprinted by permission of the publisher.

XI. THE PERSISTENCE OF MEMORY

Roger Payne, "Humpbacks: Their Mysterious Songs," from *National Geographic*, January 1979. Excerpts reprinted courtesy of *National Geographic* Magazine.

Gordon Rattray Taylor, "Wond'rous Machine" from *The Natural History of the Mind* by Gordon Rattray Taylor. Copyright © 1979 by Gordon Rattray Taylor. Reprinted by permission of the publisher, E.P. Dutton. Reprinted by permission of A.D. Peters & Company Ltd.

C. Wetherill and W.T. Sullivan III, "Eavesdropping on the Earth," reprinted from the March/April 1979 issue of *Mercury* magazine. © Copyright 1979 by the Astronomical Society of the Pacific, 1290 24th Avenue, San Francisco, CA 94122. Excerpted with the permission of the authors.

Ann Druyan, "Earth's Greatest Hits," from *The New York Times Magazine*, September 4, 1977. Copyright © 1977 by the New York Times Company. Reprinted by permission.

XII. ENCYCLOPEDIA GALACTICA

Chang Hsieh, "Touching the Left Horn of a Snail," from *Science and Civilization*, Volume 4, by Joseph Needham. Cambridge University Press, 1971. Reprinted courtesy of the publisher.

Samuel Eliot Morison, excerpt from *Admiral of the Ocean Sea* by Samuel Eliot Morison. Copyright 1942 by Samuel Eliot Morison. By permission of Little, Brown and Company in association with the Atlantic Monthly Press.

James Oberg, "The Failure of the Science of Ufology," from *New Scientist*, October 11, 1979. This article first appeared in *New Scientist*, London, the weekly review of science and technology and is reprinted by permission.

Trudy E. Bell, "The Grand Analogy: History of the Idea of Extraterrestrial Life," from *Cosmic Search*, January 1980. First appeared in *Griffith Observer* monthly magazine, first prize, 1978 Hughes Aircraft Writing Contest. Reprinted by permission.

Freeman Dyson, "Extraterrestrials," from *Disturbing the Universe* by Freeman Dyson. Copyright © 1979 by Freeman J. Dyson. By permission of Harper and Row Publishers, Inc.

(continued on p. 278)

Preface

THIS READER/STUDY GUIDE is the key component of the television course designed to accompany the public broadcasting series COSMOS. Developed by National Media Programs at University Extension, University of California, San Diego, and the Coast Community Colleges, Orange County, California, this course is aimed at the student with an interest, but no prior background, in science.

The television series COSMOS deals with a variety of subjects pertaining to the universe and our place in it. The purpose of the course and of this *Reader/Study Guide* is to give the student an historical perspective on the human relationship to the universe, an understanding of the development of the scientific method of inquiry, and a knowledge of the processes that led to the discovery of the laws that govern space and the entities within it. The course also strives to impart an appreciation of the vastness of the cosmos and of its constituents, and some notion of how we can use what we learn about our solar system and beyond to improve the quality of life on earth.

The thirteen-part series COSMOS is a joint production of Carl Sagan Productions and KCET-TV/Los Angeles. Adrian Malone is Executive Producer/Series Director. The series is made possible by grants from Atlantic Richfield Company, the Corporation for Public Broadcasting and the Arthur Vining Davis Foundations. The British Broadcasting Corporation and Polytel International are co-producers.

The authors wish to thank the many people involved in the development of this *Reader/Study Guide*. The academic consultant for this project, Dr. Harding E. Smith of the Department of Physics, University of California, San Diego, provided invaluable assistance in determining the design and content of the course and this book. Trudy E. Bell, editorial consultant for the *Reader/Study Guide* and contributing editor for *Science 80*, gave an enormous amount of time and energy to both the development and final editing of the manuscript and her enthusiastic input is deeply appreciated. Thanks are also due to the staff of Carl Sagan Productions, notably Dr. Steven Soter, Dr. Gentry Lee, and Deane Rink for their perceptive suggestions as to the readings; to Adrian Malone and especially his assistant, Susan Stribling, for their aid in interfacing with the television series; and to Geoffrey Haines-Stiles, one of the producers for COSMOS.

Finally, the authors wish to thank the staff at National Media Programs, particularly Susan Graff and Jane Scheiber, and the telecourse design group at Coast Telecourses, especially Michael Olds and Leslie Purdy.

The views expressed in this book are those of the authors alone and do not necessarily reflect those of the University of California nor The Coast Community Colleges.

Contents

An Introduction to the COSMOS Telecourse

THIS BOOK IS intended to serve as your guide for the course accompanying the television series COSMOS. Besides providing material to supplement the television programs, this *Reader/Study Guide* is designed to aid you in using the various components of the course to better understand the ideas and concepts you will encounter.

It is hoped that, by the end of this course, you will be able to:

1. Identify the major thinkers and scientists discussed in the telecourse and list the key ideas or advances in human knowledge with which they are associated.

2. Identify and describe the major periods of human history which, according to Dr. Sagan, have been characterized by open inquiry and the scientific method.

3. Define what is meant by "the scientific method" and cite examples of its application in the quest for an understanding of the unknown.

4. Describe the "Copernican principle" and give examples of how human understanding of the universe and the advance of scientific knowledge has been affected by its application or neglect.

5. Describe the interplay between science and cultural beliefs, and cite examples illustrating how philosophical and religious tenets have enhanced or conflicted with scientific principles.

6. Define what is meant by "cosmic evolution," and trace its path chronologically from what we now believe to have been the origin of the universe to the present—including the evolution of life on Earth—and into what we know of the future of the universe.

7. Describe the influence of past contact between terrestrial civilizations and their implication of future contact and communication with extraterrestrial civilizations.

8. Identify and describe areas in which the ecology of the Earth is presently being affected significantly by human activity, and suggest some of the implications of this activity for the future of the planet as a human habitat and for the activity of man on other heavenly bodies in the solar system and elsewhere.

9. Become familiar with and be able to use the specialized terminology of this telecourse, as indicated by the words selected for the Key Terms and Names of the *Reader/Study Guide*. The principal components of this telecourse are the COSMOS television programs, the companion text by Dr. Carl Sagan or a related book, and this *Reader/Study Guide*.

• THE TELEVISION PROGRAMS •

The television series COSMOS is a spectacular voyage through space and time, exploring our past, present, and future relationship with the universe. The thirteen one-hour programs were filmed at 40 locations in over a dozen different countries and incorporate more than 70 special effects sequences, enabling the viewer to "travel" with host Carl Sagan from far away galaxies to the inside of the human brain.

Dr. Sagan, writer as well as host of the series, is well known for his books (*The Cosmic Connection, The Dragons of Eden*, and *Broca's Brain*, among others) and personal appearances on television. He is the director of the Laboratory for Planetary Studies and the David Duncan Professor of Astronomy at Cornell University, Ithaca, New York, where he also serves as associate director of the Center for Radiophysics and Space Research.

Science is the subject of COSMOS, and while many of the programs deal with astronomy and cosmology, topics range from comparative religions to biology and genetics. Interstellar communication and Egyptian hieroglyphics are explored, as are the Voyager missions in our solar system and expeditions of the Dutch in the 17th century. Hindu mythology, Ionian science, and Einsteinian physics are all part of COSMOS.

Scientific accuracy is the hallmark of the series, and while in production, many segments were updated to incorporate new information. Accuracy was also the byword for the special effects: the locations of more than 6,000 stars and planets were programmed into a computer for the "Cosmic Zoom" sequence (a journey through the universe to Earth from ten billion light years away), and planetary landscapes were constructed with the help of 35 space consultants and NASA photographs.

One item in COSMOS not conforming to known fact is the vehicle by which Dr. Sagan traverses the heavens. This "spaceship of the imagination" is driven by music, has few controls, and is capable of traveling one million times faster than the speed of light. Computer-programmed light glows through its translucent skin as Dr. Sagan guides the ship around galaxies and stars.

The thirteen lessons of the telecourse and the thirteen chapters of this *Reader/Study Guide* correspond to the thirteen one-hour episodes of the COSMOS television series.

• THE BOOK •

Dr. Sagan has written a book, also titled *Cosmos*, as a companion to the television series. This elaborately illustrated book corresponds by chapter to the thirteen programs of the television series. Concepts and themes presented in the television programs are expanded upon in the book, highlighted by excerpts from the writings of scientists past and present.

The book *Cosmos* may be used as a text for this telecourse, or may be substituted with another book assigned or suggested by your instructor. Some excellent texts suitable for this course are listed in the Appendix.

• THE READER/STUDY GUIDE •

The *Reader/Study Guide* is the key element in the instructional package for COSMOS. The purpose of the *Reader/Study Guide* is to provide materials that support the information presented in the television series and direction for students taking the course. Each chapter of the guide corresponds to an episode of the series and contains seven sections: Overview, Learning Objectives, Key Terms and Names, Assignment, Discussion Questions, and Additional Activities.

The Overview section summarizes the major themes of the corresponding television program and alerts you to those things for which you should be watching. This section is followed by the Learning Objectives—the learning performance goals you will be expected to achieve and which will serve as your measure of achievement. These objectives are tailored to each lesson and therefore will vary greatly from lesson to lesson.

The Key Terms and Names section lists those terms and names you will encounter in the television program and related readings with which you may not be familiar. These terms and names are defined in the Glossary at the end of the *Reader/Study Guide.*

The Assignment section gives you the appropriate television program to watch and book chapter to read for each lesson/chapter in the *Reader/Study Guide.*

The major portion of each chapter is devoted to three to five Selected Readings from various sources that support and enhance the topics presented in the television program. The readings are accompanied by headnotes which relate them to the program and to each other.

Following the selected Readings are Discussion Questions and Additional Activities. Reading and thinking about the Discussion Questions will aid you in understanding the material in the program and readings, and in achieving the lesson and course learning objectives. The activities, while optional, are an interesting means by which you can increase your comprehension of certain concepts presented.

If you wish to explore any topics in greater depth, a Supplementary Bibliography is included in each chapter.

There are several other sections in the *Reader/Study Guide* that you will find very useful. Following this Introduction are the Lesson Assignments which suggest the order in which you should use both the television and print materials. Following the thirteen lesson chapters is a Glossary of terms and names, a Timeline placing persons and events referred to in COSMOS in chronological order, and a list of the related books and periodicals.

Lesson Assignments

THERE ARE THIRTEEN lessons in the COSMOS course corresponding to the thirteen programs of the COSMOS television series. The chapters in the *Reader/Study Guide* also parallel the television series.

For each lesson, we suggest you follow these steps in order to better understand the material presented:

1. Before viewing the television program, study the Overview, Learning Objectives, and Key Terms and Names in the corresponding chapter of the *Reader/Study Guide*. Use the Glossary at the back of this book for definitions of the terms and names.

2. Read the appropriate chapter from Carl Sagan's book *Cosmos* (which also parallels the television series) or from a textbook assigned or suggested by your instructor.

3. Watch the television program, paying special attention to the ideas and concepts presented in the Overview and Learning Objectives sections.

4. Read the selected Readings in the corresponding chapter of the *Reader/Study Guide*. To orient yourself chronologically, you may wish to refer to the Timeline at the back of this book.

5. Read the Discussion Questions; think and/or talk about the questions and their answers.

6. If you wish, try one or more of the Optional Projects and follow up on your special interests by reading selections from the Supplementary Bibliography.

Prologue

PEOPLE HAVE ALWAYS been star-gazers. In the beginning the night sky was considered to be young and comfortingly close, if often menacing. The ancients traced lines from star to star in the canopy of the heavens to show that earthly and mythological creatures existed there. In the movements of stars and planets they read their fates, and if their naked-eye observations were amazingly accurate, it was because they were keeping track of yearly flooding and other practical matters as well as life-and-death messages from the gods. They were warmed by a sun circling earth. The universe was there for them, and they were its center.

Starting with the Ionians of Greece about 600 B.C., science shared the celestial vigil with myth and magic, so that Ptolemy fitted his meticulous astronomical measurements into the straitjacket of astrology, Copernicus and later Galileo were criticized by clerics for shoving man out of his central position in the universe and replacing him with the sun, and Newton dabbled with alchemy even as he was discovering the laws of interplanetary motion. Instruments were invented. Galileo was the first to look at a planet through the telescope, and as time went on scientists surveyed the sky and saw new phenomena, some of which, like Percival Lowell's Martian canals, were no more there than the ancients' zodiac figures. But others, like Pluto, were.

Our knowledge of the universe has made a huge leap in the last 50 years. Most astronomers now place the beginning of the universe at 15 to 20 billion years ago, with the Big Bang, making it much older than previously thought. It's also much bigger and grander. The price we have paid for our knowledge is seeing ourselves rudely displaced from some close-to-central spot in the cosmos to an obscure corner of an obscure galaxy. Discoveries made concerning the very nature of life and its rise from an organic soup millions of years ago lend credence to the notion that life may exist elsewhere in the universe. Though we run on wristwatch time, in the back of our heads is a vague conception of Einstein's theory of relativity so that we know that time, space, and matter are not so absolute as we would like to think they are. With a certain uneasiness, we realize that the cosmos, which has surprised us before, will surprise us again, and that things are not as they seem.

Astrophysicists analyze the secrets of the life cycles of the stars and the motions of galaxies and the blinkings of pulsars. They speculate about quasars. The gold Newton hoped to create in his crucible was created, we find, in a supernova explosion, and all the elements except hydrogen were born in stellar furnaces.

The technology of space science has thrust us out beyond Earth's atmosphere. We are explorers of new frontiers. Our robot surrogates, carried by far-ranging spaceships, have picked up rocks from the moon, studied Martian soil for signs of life, penetrated Venus' poisonous atmosphere, sent us images of Jupiter's Great Red Spot, volcanoes on Io, and other planetary marvels.

We are still star-gazers.

Chapter I
THE SHORES OF THE COSMIC OCEAN

• OVERVIEW •

DURING THE COURSE of our relatively brief tenure on earth, human beings have made considerable strides toward understanding the laws that govern the universe. The spirit of inquisitiveness and exploration that has always characterized our species has finally brought us to a point in history where we can more clearly identify our own place in nature's scheme. In the past few centuries, we have come a long way from an era when people unquestioningly believed that the earth was the center of the universe. Only now, having discovered that the universe is much older and larger than anyone had ever imagined, that in fact our planet is only one of countless other astronomical bodies of literally awesome proportions and infinite variety, do we begin to realize how insignificant and transitory is the role we play in the cosmic drama.

When we consider that the universe is some 15 or 20 billion years old and that, if its duration were compressed into one year in a cosmic calendar, the first human beings appeared mere hours ago, we must marvel at the remarkable progress we have made. Since Eratosthenes proved in the third century B.C. that the earth was round, launching a whole new era of world exploration, we have exhausted our exploration of this planet and are now actively engaged in a large-scale exploration of outer space. Already we have sent men to the moon, set down Viking landers on the surface of Mars, launched the first interstellar spacecraft, and developed methods for communicating with other worlds. We need only stretch our imagination a bit to envision a time in the not too distant future when we will have completely explored our own solar system, and will begin setting our sights on more distant star systems.

• LEARNING OBJECTIVES •

1. Name, identify, and describe the constituent objects of the universe such as stars, planets, nebulae, galaxies, etc., and place them in their relative order of magnitude, from largest to smallest.

2. Describe the scale of the universe in terms of the common measurement of distance and cite the typical dimensions of the universe's constituents.

(Examples: distance to the nearest galaxy, diameter of a typical galaxy, distance to the nearest star, distance from the earth to the sun, and number of stars in a typical galaxy.)

3. Keeping in mind learning objectives 1 and 2 above, describe the dimensions and properties of the earth and place it in perspective with its cosmic neighbors.

4. Describe the age of the universe relative to the age of human beings in terms of a cosmic calendar one year long.

5. Describe the methods used by Eratosthenes to measure the circumference of the earth.

6. Briefly describe the historical and scientific significance of the city of Alexandria (300 B.C. to 300 A.D.) and its library.

7. Define the term "cosmos" and trace its origin.

• KEY TERMS AND NAMES •

Alexandrian Library	light year
Big Bang	Local Group
blue stars	Milky Way
cosmos	nebula
contact binaries	pulsars
Eratosthenes	red giants
galaxies	yellow dwarfs

• ASSIGNMENT •

Watch COSMOS television series Program 1, "The Shores of the Cosmic Ocean."

Read Chapter 1, "The Shores of the Cosmic Ocean," in Carl Sagan's text, *Cosmos*, or other readings assigned by your instructor.

• READINGS •

George A. Seielstad . . . . **Cosmic Ecology: A View From the Outside In**

In this provocative essay, George Seielstad traces the evolution of the universe from a cosmic perspective, and argues that unless we learn to channel our global resources into useful purposes, we may be headed toward self-destruction. Seielstad is an astronomer at the California Institute of Technology.

Imagine standing astride the entire universe, peering from the outside in. Only the most assiduous search would reveal the small planet which is our home. The search would be akin to finding one particular grain of sand from among all the beaches of

the world. Yet an outsider who spotted this tiny dwelling we call Earth would immediately recognize a planet facing a crucial decision.

Within the last tick of the cosmic clock, a species has emerged on this planet
with truly global powers. Its success or failure at using these awesome abilities
wisely will determine whether our planet's bio-system chooses the road "less traveled by", leading toward a future of unlimited, hopeful expectation, or plunges
down what is probably a well-worn cul-de-sac, ending forever the experiment in
living which it has been our planet's immense good fortune to have hosted.

Although our awareness of this dilemma is slowly growing, it is doing so from
the inside out: that is, from personal observations of our immediate surroundings
to a broadened perspective acquired via education. Thus we continue to risk thinking too small, restricting our horizons in both space and time to dimensions com-
mensurate with the human condition. Perhaps it is time to view our situation from
the outside in, to acquire a cosmic perspective.

OUR PLACE IN SPACE

Whereas not long ago "around the world in 80 days" was an impressive human
achievement, man in traveling to the moon has covered ten times that distance and
back, in one-tenth the time. Yet within a cosmic context even this accomplishment
seems miniscule. Our nearest stellar neighbor, the Sun—whose sheer bulk binds us
in an orderly path through the heavens and whose massive outpouring of energy
permits our existence—looms at almost 400 times this meager Earth-Moon distance.

Despite its critical role for Earthbound creatures, our Sun actually is only an
ordinary star. In terms of mass, size, temperature, chemical composition, power
output and several other characteristics, it exhibits rather average values. Even the
possession of planetary companions is probably just another property the Sun
shares with a sizeable fraction of other stars.

The Sun's stellar family—the ponderous Milky Way Galaxy—includes hundreds of billions of stars, many so large that millions of Earths could fit comfort-
ably within their interiors. Yet, from another vantage point, the stars are so small
that tens of millions of them could typically be strung like beads along a chain between two nearest neighbors.

To comprehend the scale of our disk-shaped Galaxy let us adopt an enormous
unit of length—the nearly 30 million solar diameters which separate the Sun from
its closest stellar companion. More than 20,000 such intervals must be laid end-to-
end to span the entire disk of the Milky Way. Within this ensemble, the Sun has an
inconspicuous galactic address. It orbits once each 250 million years around a
center twice as far from us as are we from the disk's edge.

The Milky Way itself is roughly typical of tens or hundreds of billions of
similar galaxies stretching as far as we can see in every direction with the world's
most powerful telescopes. Within a sphere of thirty times larger than the diameter
of the Milky Way lie at least seventeen galaxies, including our own, comprising
what is called the Local Group. Other groups, some many times larger and more
populous, and groups of groups stretch on and on and on, reaching distances at
least 3000 times the diameter of the Local Group. And this nearly unimaginably immense system grows ever larger as the entire universe expands.

Because we perceive an identical sky in whichever direction we search, it is
tempting to assume an ego-soothing centrality. But appearances deceive in a curved
space-time. Every location offers a similar view; none is more central than any other.

Thus the Family of Man resides on an insignificant speck of rock and metal orbiting an average star inconspicuously located within a vast collection of stars,

itself a member, unexceptionally located, of an enormous congregation of other similar stellar concentrations. How many of the hundreds of billions of star in the hundreds of billions of galaxies have planets like our own we can only estimate, but the number is likely to be huge.

OUR MOMENT IN TIME

In periods of rapid, often turbulent change people seek comfort in stability. To some, the heavens supply a soothing dependability, easily evoking feelings of eternity and immutability. But once again we distort reality by working from the inside out, by only measuring epochs against a merely human standard. Our 70-year lifespans, while relatively long for an animal species here on Earth, are hopelessly inadequate for gauging the natural flow of cosmic history. On much longer time scales the grand system in which we are such minor participants is constantly changing.

To the best of our present knowledge, it began with a bang less than 20 billion years ago. Ever since that explosive origin long ago, the entire system has expanded, while within it the initial endowment of matter and energy has repeatedly changed its composition, and assembled and reassembled in various aggregations.

Very early the matter was almost solely hydrogen, but under the incredible conditions of density and temperature prevalent in the early minutes of the universe some of it fused into helium. Meanwhile the radiative energy (heat and light) released in the original blinding flash was being continuously diluted by the expansion. Thus for perhaps a billion years or so, the universe consisted of nuclei of the two simplest chemical elements immersed in a "bath" of gradually cooling radiation.

The particulate matter did not remain homogenously distributed for long (in a cosmic sense): it may, in fact, never have been perfectly smooth. Fluctuations in density which exceeded the average tended to feed upon themselves. Every atom within such an anomaly felt the gravitational attraction of every companion atom; so they all collapsed together, the ensemble thereby isolating itself from the dispersive effect of the relentless expansion. These gigantic collections, containing hundreds or thousands of billions times the number of atoms in the Sun, became galaxies. The formation of each, including our Milky Way, required perhaps a billion years, and took place about 10 to 15 billion years ago.

The situation inside a condensing protogalaxy resembled, on a sharply diminished scale, that occurring in the Universe at large: aggregations built up around random increases in atomic density. The resultant ensembles quickly (usually in millions, or tens of millions, of years) collapsed under their own weight into stars. Within a given galaxy, the process began shortly after its formation, and in many galaxies it continues today. Thus the stellar population of the Milky Way includes senior citizens 13 billion years old, as well as proto-stars struggling to be born, and all ages in between.

The process of gravitational collapse of a protostellar cloud is unlikely to be perfectly efficient. The leftover matter may itself almost simultaneously condense into planets, the leftovers of which may in turn become their satellites.

In this way, our Sun and its minor companions came into existence some 4.6 billion years ago. The history of our home planet therefore occupies only about one-fourth of the totality of cosmic history.

CHEMICAL EVOLUTION

The awesome collapse of an atomic collection as heavy as a star does not (at least immediately) proceed without end, since as the density of matter increases, so too do its pressure and temperature. Collisions between atoms become more frequent and more violent. Eventually the temperature becomes so high and the density so great that some of the lightest atoms (the hydrogen of which most of the star is composed) interact with sufficient vigor to stick together initiating a sequence of nuclear reactions which results in the next heavier element, helium.

But the helium is a whole which is less than the sum of its parts: each helium atom which is created weighs less than the quartet of hydrogen atoms from which it was forged. The difference in mass does not disappear. It is instead converted into a form of energy—electromagnetic radiation. That radiation, created at the star's center and subsequently released from its surface into the surrounding space, eventually provides energy for the chemical reactions which constitute the process of life.

Nor is this the only debt living systems owe to the stars. For what would living matter be if it consisted only of hydrogen and helium? The richness and variety of living substances in our tiny region of the universe derives to a considerable extent from the sizeable inventory of chemical elements with which our planet is endowed. And this, nature's chemistry set, is bequeathed to us by previous generations of stars.

Inside the mighty stellar furnaces the hydrogen fuel is eventually exhausted. In the case of our Sun, we expect hydrogen depletion is about 4 to 5 billion years, but other stars, formed earlier and more consumptive, reached their demise long ago. When they did, the well-established balance between the inward crush of gravity and the outward flow of energy was destroyed. There followed a series of internal convulsions, each raising the star's central temperature, pressure, and density until the ash of the preceding reaction could become the fuel of the successor. Thus, inside some stars, helium was combined into carbon; carbon and helium into oxygen; carbon into magnesium and oxygen into sulfur; and so on, until the full complement of the chemists' inventory was stocked.

Eventually the fury of some reactions was such that their occurrence was catastrophic; the stars in which these reactions were reached imploded violently, locking up some of their matter forever in exotic stellar corpses and spewing the rest, chemically far richer in heavier elements, back into space. It is from clouds of gas enriched by such material that future stars will coalesce.

Thus, throughout this vast cosmos, stars are continually being born, living peacefully to an advanced age, and then dying, sometimes violently. The net result of such cycles is to remove some matter from the pool of raw material future stellar generations can draw upon, while enhancing the chemical variety of the remainder. As time proceeds, the chemical composition of the universe grows richer.

When these chemical elements can be mixed long enough in close proximity, the next step up in the organizational structure of matter occurs: they link together, forming molecules. When radio astronomers scan dense interstellar clouds, they detect a rapidly growing list of molecular species, which today number more than forty. Most are organic, that is, the type peculiar to living organisms, and some are surprisingly complex (witness ethyl alcohol, a compound of nine atoms). Among the simpler ones is water, the major constituent of all Earth's living systems.

Equally remarkable is the ubiquity of these molecules. These crucial links in the chain of evolution are scattered here and there throughout the Milky Way and in other galaxies as well. It appears that the raw materials from which living systems derive exist at a vast number of locations within the universe.

BIOLOGICAL EVOLUTION

Of course, multi-atom molecules—even organic ones—are a very long way from being living systems. But we know experimentally that adding some energy to a "broth" of fairly simple molecules produces amino acids, life's fundamental building units. In one of the classic experiments, an electric spark discharged in a mixture of steam, ammonia, methane, and hydrogen sufficed. And presumably these ingredients—energy from a parent star and molecules inherited from earlier stellar generations—were present in the Earth's primitive atmosphere some 4.5 billion years ago. Nor is there any reason to suspect that these conditions were unique to our planet. Meteorites, formed from the same protosolar nebula as the planets, have carried to us the message that amino acids have indeed formed elsewhere as well.

How do we progress from relatively short chains of amino-acid molecules to the long intricate spiral arrangements that constitute the essence of today's living systems? Slowly, to be sure. In fact, it took billions of years in the case of the Earth, and it is doubtful that the sequence of steps could occur significantly faster elsewhere. After all, the process is primarily statistical, with various combinations and associations of molecules randomly forming and then being subjected to the harsh tests of survival posed by their environment. Those which prove most expedient soon outnumber their competitors. Gradually systems of greater and greater complexity emerge.

The ability to assemble exact likenesses—to reproduce—is so obvious an advantage in a struggle to preserve a type of organism that, once acquired, it seems unlikely ever to be superseded. In addition, any system interacting with a variable environment will want to moderate the extremes of variation. A buffer, or wall, sealing off the system from its surroundings will obviously help do so. Thus, it seems, cells may have formed, the earliest more than 3 billion years ago. Since then, ever more complex and hardy multi-cellular organisms have arisen as natural products of the continuing interaction between a changing environment and its available gene pool.

So, although many details of the exact sequence by which life evolved here remain to be discovered, there is a growing conviction that living matter originated from the non-living; that, having once done so, all life springs from other life; and that the process seems *universal*, given only some precursor molecules, an input of energy and ample time in a suitable environment.

This is not to suggest that other people—humans, exact likenesses of ourselves—are scattered abundantly about the universe. Every living organism metabolizes, drawing raw materials and energy from its surroundings and converting them into forms of matter and energy. Since no conversion can be perfectly efficient, "waste by-products" are returned to the surroundings, thereby altering them. In other words, the possible forms of life depend upon the particular environment, *and* that environment depends upon the existing forms of life. An environment and the living inhabitants it sustains evolve together and each such interacting biosystem will probably be peculiar to its situation.

Therefore we humans can properly view ourselves as natural—perhaps, even more strongly, inevitable—products of a cosmic evolutionary scheme which was set into motion nearly 20 billion years ago. Possibly we are members of a "family of living matter" which in richness and variety exceeds even our wildest speculations, limited as we are by knowledge only of that tiny spectrum of life which is adapted to survival in one particular environment, the Earth's biosphere.

In this view, life is a continuum traceable to the beginning of all space and time at the Big Bang itself. While each of us, like all other individual living systems, lives only momentarily, a pattern and structure persists in our descendants. As individuals we are insignificant and momentary participants in a dynamic, evolving system vastly transcending us, but as a species we are necessary links between the aeons of the cosmic past and all that is yet to follow.

CULTURAL EVOLUTION

Among all the living organisms here on Earth, man does possess a unique ability: he can accumulate knowledge and transmit it to successive generations. This is a function of his intelligence, by which he has mastered the art of communication. Thus each generation starts from an informational base to which it can only add, and mankind's store of knowledge continues to be incremented.

Concomitant with this progressive accumulation of knowledge is man's ability to use it as a new form of power. Once natural phenomena are thoroughly understood, it is only a small step to manipulating or exploiting them to one's own perceived advantages. For example, radio quickly followed an understanding of electromagnetism, and atomic energy, a partial knowledge of nuclear structure. Consequently, human society—linked together by an intricate communications network binding man not only to his contemporaries but also to his predecessors—has evolved more rapidly than has the human species itself. Together we can perform tasks of which no individual is capable.

An excellent example is the modern telephone network, permitting directly dialed, long-distance, automatically billed calls. Not only is the construction of this huge and complex system beyond the capabilities of any single person, but even its operation eludes the detailed understanding of any individual. Yet it works— reliably, routinely, almost miraculously—a product of a *collective* human effort.

But bees also can jointly accomplish goals impossible individually; in particular, the construction and operation of hives. Their frenzied activities, however, are instinctively pre-programmed, and the hives are constructed precisely the same generation after generation. Man, on the other hand, can choose his projects freely and alter their design frequently, building, in addition to telephone networks, mass transit systems or grand pianos or radio telescopes or whatever. And therein lies our unique potential for greatness . . . as well as for folly.

Again, let us not be parochial. Intelligence is so great an advantage in coping with an environment that it may be an eventual development in every incipient "thread of life" blessed with sufficient evolutionary time to acquire it. That is, any living system, being wholly dependent upon its, surroundings, will have powerful incentives to acquire sensory apparatus for "mapping out" those surroundings then greater capacity for processing the flood of incoming sensory data; perhaps some memory bank to store possible reactions to different sensations; a decision making capacity for selecting a reaction; etc. May we not at least speculate that this sequence leads toward intelligence? And that it has a certain inevitability wherever evolving living systems interact with an external environment?

SUMMARY

This view of the entire universe from the outside in has revealed abundant supplies, widely distributed, of the raw materials of which living matter consists. Likewise omnipresent are sites suitable of harboring and nurturing these "seeds" of life. Wherever the seeds take root, they most likely will grow steadily toward higher levels of complexity and greater intelligence. Ultimately, if there is time, species will evolve whose intelligence permits an expanding knowledge of, and consequently power over, its surroundings.

In this progression, there are certain thresholds, some of them critical. In every such environment the dominant species may eventually acquire sufficient potential power to affect its entire bio-system. At this critical juncture, that species either learns to channel its power to useful purposes, or it self-destructs.

This is the situation in which we find the Earth precariously poised today. Mankind possesses recently acquired *global* capabilities. Our collective arsenal, for example, can destroy all life on the planet. Our potentially mushrooming numbers threaten to overburden the entire biosphere. Because of our insatiable appetite for material resources, we may irreparably scar the Earth's surface and then inundate it with unwanted debris. We can alter the global climate, or poison the Earth's entire air and water supply.

Yet so rapidly have these global powers multiplied that man's social, cultural, economic and political systems have not kept pace. In just one hundred years, the rate of communicating messages has accelerated from the Pony Express to the speed of light. In the same interval, military encounters have changed from cavalry charges to nuclear holocausts.

To conceptualize this astonishing pace of change, imagine the Earth's entire history condensed to a single year ending at the present moment. Then man's earliest, most primitive ancestors appeared only a third of a day ago. Fire was unknown until just the last hour, and art—cave paintings, stone engravings and the like—began within the last five minutes. The Christian era has been with us for a mere fourteen seconds; the Industrial Revolution for just two. On this scale the hundred years mentioned earlier occupies only two-thirds of a second. In that fleeting interval—two-millionths of one percent of Earth's history—man's population has doubled, then redoubled.

Can we accelerate our social adjustments to this bewildering pace? Or does the evolutionary thread which led to our existence end here and now on this one small planet? We have surely arrived at Frost's divergence in the road. One path dead-ends. The other might perhaps admit us into a truly universal society of advanced biocivilizations. To choose this latter "one less traveled by" will indeed make "all the difference."

Just as saguaro trees in a lifetime scatter millions of seeds by wind and water across the desert, of which but two or three attain full development, so too may seeds of life be scattered profusely throughout the universe, with few indeed able to evolve into mature cultures. But unlike the saguaro seed, adolescent bio-cultures affect their own destinies. Let us choose consciously to continue, in the hope we may blossom into a global society of as yet unimagined beneficence.

Carl Sagan . . . . **The Cosmic Calendar**

In this selection, Sagan presents a cosmic calendar and explains how it was constructed. The "dates" and "times" of his cosmic "year" differ from those presented in the previous selection; neither calendar should be construed as right or wrong but rather both should be viewed as tools with which to better comprehend the evolution of the universe.

The world is very old, and human beings are very young. Significant events in our personal lives are measured in years or less; our lifetimes in decades; our family genealogies in centuries; and all of recorded history in millenia. But we have been preceded by an awesome vista of time, extending for prodigious periods into the past, about which we know little—both because there are no written records and because we have real difficulty in grasping the immensity of the intervals involved.

Yet we are able to date events in the remote past. Geological stratification and radioactive dating provide information on archaeological, paleontological and geological events; and astrophysical theory provides data on the ages of planetary surfaces, stars, and the Milky Way Galaxy, as well as an estimate of the time that has elapsed since that extraordinary event called the Big Bang—an explosion that involved all the matter and energy in the present universe. The Big Bang may be the beginning of the universe, or it may be a discontinuity in which information about the earlier history of the universe was destroyed. But it is certainly the earliest event about which we have any record.

The most instructive way I know to express this cosmic chronology is to imagine the fifteen-billion-year lifetime of the universe (or at least its present incarnation since the Big Bang) compressed into the span of a single year. Then every billion years of Earth history would correspond to about twenty-four days of our cosmic year, and one second of that year to 475 real revolutions of the Earth about the sun. I present the cosmic chronology in three forms: a list of some representative pre-December dates; a calendar for the month of December; and a closer look at the late evening of New Year's Eve. On this scale, the events of our history books—even books that make significant efforts to deprovincialize the present—are so compressed that it is necessary to give a second-by-second recounting of the last seconds of the cosmic year. Even then, we find events listed as contemporary that we have been taught to consider as widely separated in time. In the history of life, an equally rich tapestry must have been woven in other periods—for example, between 10:02 and 10:03 on the morning of April 6th or September 16th. But we have detailed records only for the very end of the cosmic year.

PRE-DECEMBER DATES

Big Bang	January 1
Origin of the Milky Way Galaxy	May 1
Origin of the solar system	September 9
Formation of the Earth	September 14
Origin of life on Earth	~ September 25
Formation of the oldest rocks known on Earth	October 2
Date of oldest fossils (bacteria and blue-green algae)	October 9
Invention of sex (by microorganisms)	~ November 1
Oldest fossil photosynthetic plants	November 12
Eukaryotes (first cells with nuclei) flourish	November 15

~ = approximately

COSMIC CALENDAR
DECEMBER

SUNDAY	MONDAY	TUESDAY	WEDNESDAY	THURSDAY	FRIDAY	SATURDAY
	1 Significant oxygen atmosphere begins to develop on Earth.	2	3	4	5 Extensive vulcanism and channel formation on Mars.	6
7	8	9	10	11	12	13
14	15	16 First worms.	17 Precambrian ends. Paleozoic Era and Cambrian Period begin. Invertebrates flourish.	18 First oceanic plankton. Trilobites flourish.	19 Ordovician Period. First fish, first vertebrates.	20 Silurian Period. First vascular plants. Plants begin colonization of land.
21 Devonian Period begins. First insects. Animals begin colonization of land.	22 First amphibians. First winged insects.	23 Carboniferous Period. First trees. First reptiles.	24 Permian Period begins. First dinosaurs.	25 Paleozoic Era ends. Mesozoic Era begins.	26 Triassic Period. First mammals.	27 Jurassic Period. First birds.
28 Cretaceous Period. First flowers. Dinosaurs become extinct.	29 Mesozoic Era ends. Cenozoic Era and Tertiary Period begin. First cetaceans. First primates.	30 Early evolution of frontal lobes in the brains of primates. First hominids. Giant mammals flourish.	31 End of the Pliocene Period. Quaternary (Pleistocene and Holocene) Period. First humans.			

DECEMBER 31

Origin of *Proconsul* and *Ramapithecus*, probable ancestors of apes and men	1:30 P.M.
First humans	10:30 P.M.
Widespread use of stone tools	11:00 P.M.
Domestication of fire by Peking man	11:46 P.M.
Beginning of most recent glacial period	11:56 P.M.
Seafarers settle Australia	11:58 P.M.
Extensive cave painting in Europe	11:59 P.M.
Invention of agriculture	11:59:20 P.M.
Neolithic civilization; first cities	11:59:35 P.M.
First dynasties in Sumer, Ebla and Egypt; development of astronomy	11:59:50 P.M.
Invention of the alphabet; Akkadian Empire	11:59:51 P.M.
Hammurabic legal codes in Babylon; Middle Kingdom in Egypt	11:59:52 P.M.
Bronze metallurgy; Mycenaean culture; Trojan War; Olmec culture: invention of the compass	11:59:53 P.M.
Iron metallurgy; First Assyrian Empire; Kingdom of Israel; founding of Carthage by Phoenicia	11:59:54 P.M.
Asokan India; Ch'in Dynasty China; Periclean Athens; birth of Buddha	11:59:55 P.M.
Euclidean geometry; Archimedean physics; Ptolemaic astronomy; Roman Empire; birth of Christ	11:59:56 P.M.
Zero and decimals invented in Indian arithmetic; Rome falls; Moslem conquests	11:59:57 P.M.
Mayan civilization; Sung Dynasty China; Byzantine empire; Mongol invasion; Crusades	11:59:58 P.M.
Renaissance in Europe; voyages of discovery from Europe and from Ming Dynasty China; emergence of the experimental method in science	11:59:59 P.M.
Widespread development of science and technology; emergence of a global culture; acquisition of the means for self-destruction of the human species; first steps in spacecraft planetary exploration and the search for extraterrestrial intelligence	Now: The first second of New Year's Day

The chrolonogy corresponds to the best evidence now available. But some of it is rather shaky. No one would be astounded if, for example, it turns out that plants colonized the land in the Ordovician rather than the Silurian Period; or that segment worms appeared earlier in the Precambrian Period than indicated. Also, in the chronology of the last ten seconds of the cosmic year, it was obviously impossible for me to include all significant events; I hope I may be excused for not having explicitly mentioned advances in art, music and literature or the historically significant American, French, Russian and Chinese revolutions.

The construction of such tables and calendars is inevitably humbling. It is disconcerting to find that in such a cosmic year the Earth does not condense out of interstellar matter until early September; dinosaurs emerge on Christmas Eve; flowers arise on December 28th; and men and women originate at 10:30 P.M. on New Year's Eve. All of recorded history occupies the last ten seconds of December 31; and the time from the waning of the Middle Ages to the present occupies little more than one second. But because I have arranged it that way, the first cosmic year has just ended. And despite the insignificance of the instant we have so far occupied in cosmic time, it is clear that what happens on and near Earth at the beginning of the second cosmic year will depend very much on the scientific wisdom and the distinctly human sensitivity of mankind.

George Sarton . . . . **The Library**

In the following selection, George Sarton traces the history of the famed Alexandrian Library, founded around 300 B.C., and describes the series of events that finally led to its destruction some 600 years later. Sarton was a professor of the history of science at Harvard University from 1919 until 1951.

The Museum was the center of scientific research; the Library attached to it was the center of the humanities, but it was also a necesssary department of the Museum itself. Therefore, it would not be idle to discuss whether the Library was a part of the Museum or not. It is like the Library of one of our great universities, which serves not only every department of the university but also many external needs. What is certain is that the Museum and the Library were both enclosed if not in the royal park at least in the Bruchion, which was the Macedonian-Greek quarter of Alexandria, and that both were controlled by the royal will.

When the Museum was founded, it sufficed to erect a few halls and porticoes and to enroll investigators. The initial equipment was rudimentary. The growth of the Library was different. The first need was to collect manuscripts, and when these were sufficiently abundant, a building would be required to hold them and keep them in good order.

Many of the great libraries of the world grew up in the same way; that is, some of their treasures were gathered, and some of their collections well begun, before the library itself was established.

ANCIENT LIBRARIES

The Library of Alexandria was the most famous library of antiquity, but it was by no means the only one, nor the earliest . . . [but it] was undoubtedly the largest. . . . In spite of the fact that it is entirely lost, we know more about it than any other.

The characteristics of a library, we would say, are a collection of books, a building containing them, and a staff taking charge of them. That staff might be only a single person at the very beginning, but as soon as the library grew in contents and importance many employees would be needed, as well as a director or head librarian. . . . As far as its librarians are known (and what is a library without librarians) the golden age of the library lasted less than one century and a half.

Growth of the Library. Thanks to the enthusiasm of its royal patrons and the ability of their first advisers, . . . the Library grew very rapidly. The original building was already too small by the middle of the third century, and it was necessary to create a secondary library in the Serapeum. Some 42,800 rolls were given or lent to the Serapeum library by the main one; this was perhaps a way of finding more room in the latter by the rejection of imperfect copies or duplicates.

The kings of Egypt were so eager to enrich their library that they employed highhanded methods for that purpose. Ptolemaios III Evergetes (ruled 247–222) ordered that all travelers reaching Alexandria from abroad should surrender their books. If these books were not in the Library, they were kept, while copies on cheap papyrus were given to the owners. He asked the librarian of Athens to lend him the state copies of Aischylos, Sophocles, and Euripides, in order to have transcripts made of them, paying as a guarantee of return the sum of fifteen talents; then he decided to keep them, considering that they were worth more than the money he had deposited and he returned copies instead of the originals.

The Library was the memory of the scientific departments of the Museum. The physicians needed the works of Hippocrates and other predecessors; the astronomers needed the records of early observations and theories. One would like to know whether Babylonian and Egyptian observations were available there. How many of the earlier astronomical and astrological papyri did they have? The scientists of the Museum must know what had been done before them. It does not follow, however, that the early records were in the Library proper. The mass of those early scientific writings was not considerable and it was handier for men of science to keep them on their own bookshelves, either at home or in their laboratories. We may be sure that one of the nightmares of modern university librarians was already experienced in Alexandria, to wit, how can one reconcile the needs of the general readers with those of the special ones, and divide the books between the main library and the departmental ones?

When one passes from science to the humanities, however, the importance of the library increases immeasurably. For in the case of the humanities the library does not simply provide information, it contains the very masterpieces. The anatomist might find books in the library, but not bodies; the astronomer might find books, but not the stars, not the glory of heaven. On the other hand, if the humanist wanted to read the *Iliad* or the *Odyssey*, the songs of the Anacreon or the odes of Simonides, those very treasures would be available to him in the Library and perhaps nowhere else. The Library might be called the brains or the memory of the Museum; it was the very heart of the humanities.

The Library of Alexandria was really a new start, as much as the Museum was. As much work had been done before in the field of the humanities as in the field of science, and we are fully aware, as far as the Greek world is concerned, that many books were published, sold, collected, criticized at least from the fifth century on. There had been also many libraries, large and small, private and public, but now for the first time a large number of scholars were assigned to library service.

That service was enormously more complex and difficult than that of modern librarians. To keep printed books in good order is relatively easy, for each of those books is a definite and recognizable unit. The Alexandrian librarians had to struggle with an enormous number of papyrus rolls, each of which had to be identified first, then classified, catalogued, edited. The last word is the key to the main difficulties. The majority of the tests represented in the rolls were not standardized in any way, and their clear definition would remain almost impossible as long as they had not been thoroughly investigated, edited, and reduced to a canonic form.

To put it otherwise, the librarians of Alexandria were not simply custodians and cataloguers like those of today; they had to be, and were, full-fledged philologists. Indeed, the Alexandria Library was the nursery of anatomists and astronomers. This will be shown in some detail when we describe the activities of individual scholars.

The Library and its elaborate catalogue being lost, we have no idea of its contents, except that it was exceedingly rich and included many works that are no longer extant. The many thousands of papyri that have been discovered in Egypt and investigated in our century have revealed that the Greek population of Egypt (and the Greek-speaking Orientals) were fairly well acquainted with Greek literature. Homer was obviously the most popular author; Homeric papyri are more abundant than all the other literary papyri put together; then follow, in order of decreasing frequency, Demosthenes, Euripides, Menandros, Plato, Thucydides, Hesiodos, Isocrates, Aristophanes, Xenophon, Sophocles, Pindaros, Sappho. There are very few fragments of Aristotle, but that is compensated by the discovery of a whole work of his, the *Constitution of Athens*, in a British Museum papyrus. Strangely enough, Herodotos, who should have been of special interest to the Greeks of Egypt, was hardly represented. Not only did the papyri give us many fragments of known works but they revealed lost works like the *Athenaion politeia* (just mentioned) and the medical papyrus of London, and they increased considerably our knowledge of other authors, such as Menandros, Bacchylides, Hypereides, Herodas, Timotheos, Ephoros. "Toutes proportions gardees," the Greeks of Egypt were more literate than our American contemporaries.

Size of the Library. The Library was very large, but it is impossible to know how many rolls it included. The numbers mentioned by various authors vary considerably. As the Library was steadily growing, the numbers were increasing; according to one account, there were already 200,000 rolls at the end of Soter's rule; according to another, there were only 100,000 at the end of his son's rule; other accounts speak of 500,000 rolls or even 700,000 in Caesar's time. Never mind those conflicting dates. The numbers relative to definite dates may have different meanings; they may refer to works or to rolls, and there were sometimes many works to a roll or many rolls to a single work. Even today, it is difficult to answer this apparently single question, "How many books does your library contain," exactly and without ambiguities. After all, the number of books does not matter so much; the books might be very important or else trivial and worthless; they might be in perfect condition or not, there might be many imperfect or duplicate copies, or there might be few. The true richness and greatness of a library does not depend so much on the number of its books as on their quality.

It is a pity that we cannot visualize the Library. No doubt it was a fine building with elegant halls and colonnades. One would like to see the "stacks" of papyri, the desk or office where readers applied for them, the place where they were permitted to study. The halls were probably adorned with statues, bas-reliefs, or wall paintings. The most important features of a scientific institute are not the walls and fixtures, however, but the men using them; the pride of a great library is not so much its books as the distinguished scholars who are studying them, for without the latter the former are worthless.

The first librarians . . . were all men of letters. Was it finally realized that the classification and investigation of scientific books required the care of a man of science? At any rate, the [fifth] librarian, Eratosthenes of Cyrene (III–2 B.C.), was one of the greatest men of science of antiquity. He was not only a mathematician, astronomer, and geographer, but also a chronologist and even a philologist. One might even say that he was the first conscious philologist, for he was the first to assume the name *philologos*. That would be all wrong however, for many men have deserved that name before him, and more than he, not only in Greece but also in Pharaonic Egypt, in Mesopotamia, and in India.

He completed his education in Athens but was called to Alexandria by Ptolemaios III Evergetes (ruled 247–222) and appointed librarian c. 235; he probably remained in office until his death c. 192, at the age of 80. Two of his abundant writings were the by-products of his librarianship. One was his elaborate study of the Old Attic Comedy . . . and the other his *Chronographia*, an attempt to establish the chronology of ancient Greece on a scientific basis. . . . [Previous librarians] were often puzzled by chronological difficulties. These difficulties were immense in antiquity because the local chronologies were independent of each other and often discordant. It was thus natural enough for a scientific librarian like Eratosthenes to try to put some order in that chronological chaos even as he did in geodesy and the history of geography.

One might conclude that Eratosthenes was not simply a librarian, . . . but that he helped to establish the chronological basis of criticism and was possibly the first classifier of scientific books.

Readers may be curious to know right now what happened to the Library after the middle of the second century B.C. The fact that one cannot name any librarians after Aristarchos of Samothrace is already sufficient proof of the decadence of the Library, which was but one aspect of the decadence of Hellenistic Egypt.

At the time of Caesar's siege of Alexandria, in 48 B.C., the Library was still exceedingly rich. As he could not man the Egyptian fleet riding in the harbor, which might be taken by the Egyptian commander Achillas and used against him, Caesar set fire to it. The confligration extended to the wharves and is said to have destroyed part of the Library. This is difficult to believe, because the main Library was sufficiently distant from the harbor and docks, and the Serapeum was very far away on a hill. It is possible, however, that a quantity of books had been taken to the waterside to be shipped to Rome, and that it was those books that were destroyed.

This may explain why Marcus Antonius, the triumvir, gave to Cleopatra in 41 B.C. some 200,000 volumes taken from the Library of Pergamon. That story is far from certain, but it is plausible. If the Library had been diminished by Caesar's action, it would have been natural enough for the queen to complain and for Marcus Antonius to giver her a rich compensation at the expense of his enemies.

The Library was still very important at the beginning of the Roman rule, when the Romans thought of themselves as liberators of Egypt. This is not proved, however, by the account of Josephus Flavius (I–2), who does not speak of the Library as it was in his own time. During the role of Aurelian (emperor, 270–275) the greater part of the Bruchion was destroyed. Did that involve the destruction of the main Library? At any rate, the Serapeum continued to exist.

It is possible also that books of either library or of both had been sequestered by the Roman authorities and taken to the capital. Conquerors have perpetrated such dilapidations in our own century; it was much easier to get away with them at the beginning of our era. The main enemies of the Library, however, were not the Romans but the Christians. Its decline was accelerated in proportion as Alexandria was more effectively controlled by bishops. . . . By the end of the fourth century, paganism was ebbing out of Alexandria; the Museum (if it still existed) and the Serapeum were its last refuges. The old Christians and the proselytes hated the Library, because it was in their eyes a citadel of disbelief and immorality; it was gradually undermined and brought into decay.

The Library was now concentrated in the Serapeum and the latter was finally destroyed under Theodosios the Great (emperor, 379–395), by order of Theophilos (bishop of Alexandria, 385–412), whose antipagan fanaticism was extreme. Many of the books may have been salvaged but, according [to reliable accounts], the Library was virtually nonexistent in 416.

• DISCUSSION QUESTIONS •

1. About how many galaxies are estimated to be in the universe? What are the three principal types of galaxies? Can you describe the main characteristics of each? What is the typical lifetime of a galaxy? How many stars might a typical galaxy contain? Why were galaxies once called "island universes"?

2. What is the Local Group of galaxies? About how many members does it have? What are the main characteristics of galaxies in the Local Group?

3. What type of structure does the Milky Way galaxy have, and why? How many suns are in the Milky Way? Why might a star in the Milky Way be entirely invisible from the outside?

4. What is the difference between blue stars, yellow dwarfs, and red giants? Why are there so many blue-white stars inside the Orion Nebula?

5. Why is it more convenient to measure distances among objects in the universe in terms of light years? What is a light year? How far would a beam of light travel in a year? In a second?

6. How did Eratosthenes prove that the earth was round? What methods did he use to measure the earth's circumference? What initial observations led him to question the commonly held notion that the earth was flat? What can his attitude and methods tell us about the nature of scientific inquiry in general? What impact did Eratosthenes' calculations have on subsequent world exploration?

7. What is the historical and scientific significance of the Alexandrian Library? What factors led to its ultimate destruction? Can you think of any parallels between what happened in Alexandria and events that have taken place in modern times?

8. What does the simple fact of the immensity of the universe suggest about the possibility of finding life on other worlds? What does Sagan mean when he says the surface of the earth is "the shore of the cosmic ocean"? What evidence can you find to support the idea that scientific inquiry requires an equal measure of skepticism and imagination?

9. What is the origin and meaning of the word "cosmos"? What proof do we have that the laws of nature are the same everywhere in the universe?

10. In your opinion, what is the value of studying astronomy? How might advances in astronomy have a direct effect on you in your lifetime?

• ADDITIONAL ACTIVITIES •

Optional Projects

1. Using outisde sources if necessary, prepare a chart showing the hierarchical structure of the universe. In one column, list the major structures in the universe in their relative order of magnitude, from largest to smallest. In another column, list the major characteristics of each structure.

2. Referring to the selection by Carl Sagan titled "The Cosmic Calendar," develop your own cosmic chronology. Include all the major events that have occurred during the 15-billion-year lifetime of the universe, beginning with the Big Bang and working your way up to the present.

3. Design a simple experiment to illustrate the methods used by Eratosthenes to measure the circumference of the earth.

Supplementary Bibliography

George Abell, *Exploration of the Universe*. New York: Holt, Rinehart and Winston, 1964.
An excellent basic introductory text on astronomy.

Kees Boecke, *Cosmic View: The Universe in 40 Jumps*. New York: John Day, 1957.
A cosmic survey of objects in the universe, ranging from the largest clusters of galaxies down to the nucleus of an atom.

Bart J. Bok and P. Bok, *The Milky Way*. Cambridge, Mass.: Harvard University Press, 1974.
This highly readable book on galaxies, which places special emphasis on our own Milky Way, is considered a classic.

G. Field, G. Verschuur, and C. Ponnamperuma, *Cosmic Evolution*. Boston: Houghton Mifflin, 1978.
A fine new textbook written from a cosmological perspective.

Herbert Friedman, *The Amazing Universe*. Washington, D.C.: National Geographic Society, 1975.
A richly illustrated survey of astronomy, written by a pioneer in space science.

Donald H. Menzel, *Astronomy*. New York: Random House, 1970.
This lavishly illustrated, oversized book provides an excellent popular description of the universe.

Chapter II
ONE VOICE IN THE COSMIC FUGUE

• OVERVIEW •

SINCE THE DAWN of history human beings have been preoccupied with questions about life and its origins. Today, when our knowledge of science has enabled us to perform technological feats that would have been unthinkable a hundred years ago, we are more intrigued than ever with the mystery of our own existence.

In recent decades, science has turned over many stones. In contrast to our ancestors, who looked for patterns in the sky and invented elaborate mythologies to explain life's origins, we now believe we are products of a long succession of seemingly random mutations and adaptations, which Charles Darwin described in his theory of evolution by natural selection. We are also fairly certain that the first stirrings of life on earth occurred some four billion years ago when gases in the primitive atmosphere, broken apart by lightning and ultraviolet rays from the sun, gradually recombined into more and more complex molecules to form a kind of rich organic "soup" which eventually gave rise to a new molecule—thought to be the earliest ancestor DNA—that contained life as we know it.

Stanley Miller and Harold Urey demonstrated in the 1950s that it was possible to recreate the essential building blocks of life—amino acids and nucleotides—by duplicating Earth's early atmosphere in the laboratory. Some scientists speculate that perhaps similar chemical reactions might have taken place elsewhere in the universe, which could explain the abundance of organic matter found in interstellar space and the amino acids detected in meteorites. If so, then it is not implausible to think that life, in some form, may exist on other worlds. Indeed, the close relationship between the evolution of life on Earth and the evolution of the planet itself does suggest the possibility of extraterrestrial life. But, to date, there has been no real conclusive evidence to support this idea.

• LEARNING OBJECTIVES •

1. Identify and list the requirements for life in general as we know it, specifically identifying those we believe to be essential to any life and those that are applicable only to life forms like us.

2. Briefly describe the basic molecular components of terrestrial life and their methods of reproduction.

3. Describe the time scale for terrestrial evolution and list the stages of evolution in their probable chronological sequence.

4. Describe the relationship between the evolution of life on Earth and the evolution of the planet itself, and give examples of how each has influenced the other.

5. Describe what are meant by mutation, selection (natural and artificial), and the balance between these in the evolutionary process, citing examples.

6. Identify Harold Urey and Stanley Miller and describe the significance of their experiments on the origins of life on Earth and the implications for life elsewhere in the universe.

7. Identify and describe the theoretical and factual underpinnings that allow Dr. Sagan to make the statement that "evolution is a fact, not a theory."

• KEY TERMS AND NAMES •

amino acids	mutation
artificial selection	natural selection
Cambrian explosion	nucleotides
chloroplasts	photosynthesis
Charles Darwin	trilobites
DNA	Harold Urey
Stanley Miller	viroids
mitochondria	Alfred Russel Wallace

• ASSIGNMENT •

Watch COSMOS television series Program 2, "One Voice in the Cosmic Fugue."

Read Chapter 2, "One Voice in the Cosmic Fugue," in Carl Sagan's text, *Cosmos*, or other readings assigned by your instructor.

• READINGS •

Lewis Thomas . . . . The Lives of a Cell

In this brief and beautifully written essay, Lewis Thomas discusses the interrelatedness and biological uniformity of all life on Earth, and concludes with the thought that the earth itself is not unlike a single cell. Thomas is currently president of the Memorial Sloan-Kettering Cancer Center in New York City.

We are told that the trouble with Modern Man is that he has been trying to detach himself from nature. He sits in the topmost of tiers of polymer, glass, and steel, dangling his pulsing legs, surveying at a distance the writhing life of the planet. In this scenario, Man comes on as a stupendous lethal force, and the earth is pictured as something delicate, like rising bubbles at the surface of a country pond, or flights of fragile birds.

But it is illusion to think that there is anything fragile about the life of the earth; surely this is the toughest membrane imaginable in the universe, opaque to probability, impermeable to death. We are the delicate part, transient and vulnerable as cilia. Nor is it a new thing for man to invent an existence that he imagines to be above the rest of life; this has been his most consistent intellectual exertion down the millennia. As illusion, it has never worked out to his satisfaction in the past, any more than it does today. Man is embedded in nature.

The biologic science of recent years has been making this a more urgent fact of life. The new hard problem will be to cope with the dawning, intensifying realization of just how interlocked we are. The old, clung-to notions most of us have held about our special lordship are being deeply undermined.

Item. A good case can be made for our nonexistence as entities. We are not made up, as we had always supposed, of successively enriched packets of our own parts. We are shared, rented, occupied. At the interior of our cells, driving them, providing the oxidative energy that sends us out for the improvement of each shining day, are the mitochondria, and in a strict sense they are not ours. They turn out to be little separate creatures, the colonial posterity of migrant prokaryocytes, probably primitive bacteria that swam into ancestral precursors of our eukaryotic cells and stayed there. Ever since, they have maintained themselves and their ways, replicating in their own fashion, privately, with their own DNA and RNA quite different from ours. They are as much symbionts as the rhizobial bacteria in the roots of beans. Without them, we would not move a muscle, drum a finger, think a thought.

Mitochondria are stable and responsible lodgers, and I choose to trust them. But what of the other little animals, similarly established in my cells, sorting and balancing me, clustering me together? My centrioles, basal bodies, and probably a good many other more obscure tiny beings at work inside my cells, each with its own special genome, are as foreign, and as essential, as aphids in anthills. My cells are no longer the pure line entities I was raised with; they are ecosystems more complex than Jamaica Bay.

I like to think that they work in my interest, that each breath they draw for me, but perhaps it is they who walk through the local park in the early morning, sensing my senses, listening to my music, thinking my thoughts.

I am consoled, somewhat, by the thought that the green plants are in the same fix. They could not be plants, or green, without their chloroplasts, which run the photosynthetic enterprise and generate oxygen for the rest of us. As it turns out, chloroplasts are also separate creatures with their own genomes, speaking their own language.

We carry stores of DNA in our nuclei that may have come in, at one time or another, from the fusion of ancestral cells and the linking of ancestral organisms in symbiosis. Our genomes are catalogues of instructions from all kinds of sources in nature, filed for all kinds of contingencies. As for me, I am grateful for differentiation and speciation, but I cannot feel as separate an entity as I did a few years ago, before I was told these things, nor, I should think, can anyone else.

Item. The uniformity of the earth's life, more astonishing than its diversity, is accountable by the high probability that we derived, originally, from some single cell, fertilized in a bolt of lightning as the earth cooled. It is from the progeny of this parent cell that we take our looks; we still share genes around, and the resemblance of the enzymes of grasses to those of whales is a family resemblance.

The viruses, instead of being single-minded agents of disease and death, now begin to look more like mobile genes. Evolution is still an infinitely long and tedious biologic game, with only the winners staying at the table, but the rules are beginning to look more flexible. We live in a dancing matrix of viruses; they dart, rather like bees, from organism to organism, from plant to insect to mammal to me and back again, and into the sea, tugging along pieces of this genome, strings of genes from that, transplanting grafts of DNA, passing around heredity as though at a great party. They may be a mechanism for keeping new, mutant kinds of DNA in the widest circulation among us. If this is true, the odd virus disease, on which we must focus so much of our attention in medicine, may be looked on as an accident, something dropped.

Item. I have been trying to think of the earth as a kind of organism, but it is no go. I cannot think of it this way. It is too big, too complex, with too many working parts lacking visible connections. The other night, driving through a hilly, wooded part of southern New England, I wondered about this. If not like an organism, what is it like, what is it *most* like? Then, satisfactorily for that moment, it came to me: it is *most* like a single cell.

Guy Murchie . . . . Cells

In the following excerpt from The Seven Mysteries of Life, *Guy Murchie entertainingly describes the cell—how it works, how it reproduces, and how it specializes.*

Cells have not been easy to investigate, being generally invisible and therefore quite unsuspected by man until A.D. 1665 when Robert Hooke happened to notice their compartmented structure while examining pieces of cork under his low-powered pre-Leeuwenhoek "microscope." The segments presumably reminded him so much of monks' cells in a monastery that he naturally named them cells also. But although he drew detailed pictures of them, he did not realize they were present in all plants and animals. In fact is was not until 1839 that the botanist Matthias Jakob Schleiden and the zoologist Theodor Schwann propounded the startling theory that the cell is the "vessel of living matter," a new idea for which Rudolf Virchow was to win wide acceptance in 1859 by demonstrating that all cells, in both vegetables and animals, originate from the divisions of earlier cells. In other words, the cell at last was revealed as the natural unit of life, not only capable of independence as a complete one-celled animal like an ameba or a paramecium, but surprisingly independent even when part of a large multicelled organism, feeding, excreting, reproducing and in many cases moving about and making responsive decisions. In a nourishing liquid (known as a "tissue culture") almost any body cell can now be kept alive *outside* the body, like the free creature many of its ancestors must have been millions of years ago, and this discovery in the early 1930s convinced biologists that cells must be much more than the simple blobs of jelly they appeared.

If you have never seen a body cell floating by itself in a tissue culture, I might say that at first the ovoid speck usually seems inert and helpless, drifting idly off after separation from that greater organism, its multicelled body society. But as soon as the lonely cell touches a solid object it responds. Perceptibly it bulges toward it. Then a protoplasmic finger forms on the cell, pointing and reaching out in the direction it wants to go. If the solid object is the inside surface of a test tube, the fingertip usually flattens against it, gluing itself to the glass. Then the finger contracts, pulling the rest of the cell toward that glued spot. The cell then normally takes a second step as another finger reaches forward, and thus it creeps with apparent purpose on its way.

Startled to find such unexpected deliberation in human flesh, biologists have been pursuing the cell with more and more powerful microscopes ever since, eagerly exploring its mysterious spots and shadows to learn how this curious unit organism functions. In the 1940s they discovered a faint but persistent stringiness in the protoplasm near the nucleus that eventually proved to be a complicated and beautiful network of tubes and necklaces, through which the teeming cell populace of porters and messengers could be detected flowing like street traffic in all directions, delivering supplies and orders to every part of the cell and of course to a great extent beyond it among adjoining cells and the outside world. The beads on the necklaces (some of them loose beads) in turn were found to be individual chemical generators, soon named mitochondria, which are endlessly turning out the dynamic fuel adenosine triphosphate, now commonly abbreviated ATP, a very ancient kind of bio-explosive that powers all of life's material activity from growth to muscle contraction and is, as you may remember, a vital step in the chemistry of photosynthesis.

Between and all around the tubes, necklaces and other special parts is the real interior space of the cell, a sort of storage place that serves also as a lobby and reading room, where fat vacuoles loll about full of water, oil or gruel and curious enzymes are stacked like books and periodicals on library shelves. The most useful "volumes" are continually being passed and circulated about the cell corridors while an important percentage are confidently dispatched abroad like overseas mail in the form of explicit messages, in effect written, coded and posted by one cell to a fellow cell it has never seen but somehow manages to correspond with, even while they are worlds apart.

The key to this enzyme library is located, as long suspected, in the cell's nucleus in the form of a master code, a code literally made of genes and guarded like a state secret. The nucleus that encloses it turns out to be a sort of cell manager's office built like a vault, out of which painstakingly accurate copies of the cell's construction plans are rolling off the duplicating machines at speed for immediate distribution to ensure that every part of the cell knows what is expected of it and that not only all parts of the cell but all cells of a whole multicelled organism conform to the same standard. The very difficult job of cracking the cell's genetic code was only undertaken in the 1950s after scientists practically blasted their way into its nucleus and extracted the key substance of deoxyribonucleic acid which, by popular demand, was quickly abbreviated to DNA. The heart of the nucleus of every cell, they found, is essentially a tapelike coil of DNA that carries the code of life in it as surely as a magnetic tape carries a speech or a tune. DNA however is not only more indelible than magnetic tape but there is something unquestionably mystic about it. In fact, while ruling the cell by regulating its chemicals and dispatching its enzymes, DNA subtly conceals the ultimate origin of its power. In a way DNA acts as the cell's god, a designation appropriately spelled out in the Latin word *deo*, which forms the first three letters of deoxyribonucleic acid. And, godlike, it broadcasts its omnific decrees at electronic speed through a technique so intricate and awesome we must defer looking deeply into it.

I can say here, however, that DNA's decrees are translated into action with an elegance and perfection evolved over billions of years, a micro-majesty perhaps best exemplifed by the cell's oft-repeated but deliberate division into two daughter cells. This kind of dividing is called mitosis and is a normal act of growth that is happening in millions of places in your body at every moment. If you've ever wondered why big animals, say whales, don't multiply this way, splitting down the middle to produce two new half-sized whales, thereby circumventing the problems of babyhood, it's because the whales would have to be genetically the same. They would inevitably be identical twins and identical not only with each other but also with their parent. Which would be disastrous from the standpoint of evolution because evolution needs continuous variation in order to be flexible enough to adapt to changing conditions.

Mitosis, on the other hand, is just right for cells. Being in the microcosm and therefore very numerous, cells don't need to be flexible individually but only in statistical masses. Besides, the heirlooms of cells, unlike macrocosmic davenports and teapots that would be damaged by being cut in two, can safely be split into identical halves right down to the chromosome and gene levels. And that actually is how their bequests are bequeathed. It is an orderly, even stately, performance taking about an hour in each case, displaying a discipline, beauty and wisdom hard to imagine as springing solely from that microscopic cell. First there comes a sort of secret decision that whispers forth a quiet mobilization order that rapidly grips the whole cell in a state of pseudo crystallization. This begins just outside the nucleus at a spot called the centriole, from which tiny lines are seen to shoot like frost feathers across a windowpane, lines (probably representing microscopic fibers) that in a few minutes have organized the whole cell into two halves around two poles that appear as mirror images of each other. This polarity of course includes the nucleus, which, following the rest of the cell, progressively straightens and regiments its coils of DNA into duplicate forms, each paired member attached to an opposite centriole by threads that converge on it as if wound on spindles in a textile mill. When the whole cell is thus completely regimented into the mirrored double-crystal form, an equator of cleavage appears halfway between the poles, a bulbous waistline that begins to pinch inward as the upper and lower hemispheres pull apart, eventually thinning to a tight waspish shape before they finally separate into two new round cells.

You might think these twin baby cells would rest for a day or two after their birth, but no, their nature is to move and, as long as they are free, they keep moving at an average speed about equal to the hour hand of a small watch. Furthermore each one is under some mysterious compulsion to make a crucial decision within its first two or three hours: it must either begin to specialize, after which it many never divide again, or start to divide and subdivide further, in which case each time it cleaves into children it will also "conceive" grandchildren in the children's centrioles. By such rules do cells in general—vegetable as well as animal ones and including the 50 trillion cells in your body—live and renew themselves, diversifying the while into flesh, leaf, bone, wood, blood, muscle, nerves, skin, bark, hair, seed, eyes and all the other substances needed. And despite, or because of, their restless activity, each one somehow always seems to be in an appropriate place at every moment of its life, a life whose duration depends largely on the role it has chosen to play, the role in turn normally conforming to whatever specialized cells it has been associated with. Thus unspecialized vertebrate cell tissue, if exposed to a piece of spinal cord, will nearly always start producing cartilage tissue, a first step toward becoming a spine. Yet the same unspecialized tissue, embedded instead in muscle, will in more than 99 cases out of 100 rapidly specialize into muscle cells.

As to what actually makes a cell begin to specialize, very little is known, but biologists have noticed that body cells on the loose commonly sprout sensitive whiskers they call microspikes or pili, which whisk about and feel what is near them and, if it is congenial, penetrate and cling to it. Presumably it is these tentacles (more than any other factor) that enable cells to spot and scrape acquaintance with their neighbors, whereupon, assuming the neighbors "taste" good, they flock together with them into the dense masses familiar to us as flesh and bone, at the same time exchanging genetic material and perhaps exuding short-range chemical bonds for greater cohesion, like a kind of living mortar.

There is no reason to suppose the individual cell has any real choice as to whether it will specialize and settle down as part of a gut or a leg or an eye in this social development, which may resemble a well-rehearsed army mobilization, but, as I said, it obviously makes a lot of difference in the expectable life spans of its descendants. For an epithelial cell in the gut lining lives only a day or two before it dies and is sloughed off, but white blood cells can last two weeks and red ones four months. Nerve cells, however, which cannot normally be replaced at all, may survive more than a hundred years—a decidedly opportune span in the case of centenarians, who depend, like the rest of us, on irreplaceable nerves.

Although specialization commits cells to particular functions and life expectancies, it does not necessarily limit them to fixed locations, as can easily be seen in the travels of blood cells. Moreover, when flesh is bruised or cut, it is now known that millions of deeper-lying body cells (other than blood cells) apparently eagerly migrate upward to replace those lost in the injury, and skin cells detach themselves from all sides to spread individually over the wound's surface, floating upon the fluid film that automatically wets it while strewing it with scarcely perceptible fibrous "guidelines," along which the free cells have been seen to move and coagulate. In a way such semi-imaginary guidelines are like faint cattle trails on a Texas range, over which the cells amble forward about as obediently as steers steered by a proficient herdsman and, like them, almost surely playing a part in some hard-to-fathom overall plan. One can even imagine them enjoying their share in this mystic migration of mercy that is the healing of a wound.

Although muscle cells (like many other specialized ones) cannot replace themselves by dividing, new muscle cells are constantly being assembled from microscopic old fragments of muscle floating about in cell fluid. It is a process curiously like crystallization, in which the flowing bits manage to combine into filaments, which somehow bundle together into fibrils, which by the hundreds align to form fibers of striated muscle which, although more dynamic than any vegetable cells, turn out to look (under the microscope) remarkably like a piece of wood. This crystalline structure evidently is vital to the sophisticated coordination that enables many millions of muscle cells simultaneously to contract as a single muscle, gossamer layers of filaments sliding past each other inside the tiny fibrils, in some cases (as in midge flight) going through the cycle of contraction and relaxation up to 950 times per second, each muscle exactly balanced by its opposing countermuscle for perfect control. Muscles in a real sense are the body's engines, with their filaments pumping back and forth like pistons in the fibril cylinders, fueled internally with ATP generated by the hundreds of mitochondria in every cell. Mitochondria are remarkably like the chloroplasts in leaves, especially in their alternating layers of protein and fat that synthesize ATP, but of course are powered not directly from sunlight (as are chloroplasts) but indirectly from food (originally vegetable carbohydrates) created through the sunlight. And they resemble chloroplasts also in their ability to move about fairly freely within their cells and to reproduce themselves, behavior suggesting to some biologists that they may have once been independent organisms, which somehow got domesticated into their present specialized symbiotic role.

Nerve cells are also intimately involved in muscle cells, which they control more precisely than your car's distributor controls its engine, and they regulate many other types of cells while bestowing on an organism a continuous awareness through its senses. Fact is: it takes more nerve activity than you probably realize just to maintain human consciousness, for researchers have discovered that the average of billions of nerve cells sends reports to the brain at a rate that can never drop as low as one report per second per cell while the brain's owner is alive and well.

And bone cells, blood cells, germ cells, vegetable cells, etc., all have their own special natures. Skin cells begin to die almost as soon as they are born by stiffening or "crystallizing" into a callus, which may eventually become as hard as wood, bark or horn. Heart cells, even when separated from each other, are still hearty enough to continue faintly beating as individuals, apparently never quite forgetting their chosen purpose. And, if given half a chance, they will catch and cling to their fellows again, incorporating gradually into a hollow ball while synchronizing their rhythms, from there on redeveloping as best they can their full single throb and function as one vital organ in an organism they cannot help (at however primitive a level of instinctual being) feeling part of as long as they live.

Charles Darwin . . . . **Theory of Natural Selection**

In the following selection from The Origin of Species, *first published in 1859, Darwin summarizes the basic principles of natural selection and explains its role in the evolutionary process. The Origin of Species remains one of the most influential books ever written.*

If under changing conditions of life organic beings present individual differences in almost every part of their structure, and this cannot be disputed; if there be, owing to their geometrical rate of increase, a severe struggle for life at some age, season, or year, and this certainly cannot be disputed; then, considering the infinite complexity of the relations of all organic beings to each other and to their conditions of life, causing an infinite diversity in structure, constitution, and habits, to be advantageous to them, it would be a most extraordinary fact if no variations had ever occurred useful to each being's own welfare, in the same manner as so many variations have occurred useful to man. But if variations useful to any organic being ever do occur, assuredly individuals thus characterised will have the best chance of being preserved in the struggle for life; and from the strong principle of inheritance, these will tend to produce offspring similarly characterised. This principle of preservation, or the survival of the fittest, I have called Natural Selection. It leads to the improvement of each creature in relation to its organic and inorganic conditions of life; and consequently, in most cases, to what must be regarded as an advance in organisation. Nevertheless, low and simple forms will long endure if well fitted for their simple conditions of life.

Natural selection, on the principle of qualities being inherited at corresponding ages, can modify the egg, seed, or young, as easily as the adult. Amongst many animals, sexual selection will have given its aid to ordinary selection, by assuring to the most vigorous and best adapted males the greatest number of offspring. Sexual selection will also give characters useful to the males alone, in their struggles or rivalry with other males; and these characters will be transmitted to one sex or to both sexes, according to the form of inheritance which prevails.

Whether natural selection has really thus acted in adapting the various forms of life to their several conditions and stations, must be judged by the general tenor and balance of (all the) evidence. . . . But we have already seen how it entails extinction; and how largely extinction has acted in the world's history, geology plainly declares. Natural selection, also leads to divergence of character; for the more organic beings diverge in structure, habits, and constitution, by so much the more can a large number be supported on the area,—of which we see proof by looking to the inhabitats of any small spot, and to the productions naturalised in foreign lands. Therefore, during the modification of the descendants of any one species, and during the incessant struggle of all species to increase in numbers, the more diversified the descendants become, the better will be their chance of success in the battle for life. Thus the small differences distinguishing varieties of the same species, steadily tend to increase, till they equal the greater differences between species of the same genus, or even of distinct genera.

We have seen that it is the common, the widely-diffused and widely-ranging species, belonging to the larger genera within each class, which vary most; and these tend to transmit to their modified offspring that superiority which now makes them dominant in their own countries. Natural selection, as has just been remarked, leads to divergence of character and to much extinction of the less improved and intermediate forms of life. On these principles, the nature of the affinities, and the generally well-defined distinctions between the innumerable organic beings in each class throughout the world, may be explained. It is a truly wonderful fact—the wonder of which we are apt to overlook from familiarity— that all animals and all plants throughout all time and space should be related to each other in groups, subordinate to groups, in the manner which we everywhere behold—namely, varieties of the same species most closely related, species of the same genus less closely and unequally related, forming sections and sub-genera, species of distinct genera much less closely related, and genera related in different degrees, forming sub-families, families, orders, sub-classes and classes. The several subordinate groups in any class cannot be ranked in a single file, but seem clustered round points, and these round other points, and so on in almost endless cycles. If species had been independently created, no explanation would have been possible of this kind of classification; but it is explained through inheritance and the complex action of natural selection, entailing extinction and divergence of character. . . .

The affinities of all the beings of the same class have sometimes been represented by a great tree. I believe this simile largely speaks the truth. The green and budding twigs may represent existing species; and those produced during former years may represent the long succession of extinct species. At each period of growth all the growing twigs have tried to branch out on all sides, and to overtop and kill the surrounding twigs and branches, in the same manner as species and groups of species have at all times overmastered other species in the great battle for life. The limbs divided into great branches, and these into lesser and lesser branches were themselves once, when the tree was young, budding twigs, and this connection of the former and present buds by ramifying branches may well represent the classification of all extinct and living species in groups subordinate to groups. Of the many twigs which flourished when the tree was a mere bush, only two or three, now grown into great branches, yet survive and bear the other branches; so with the species which lived during long-past geological periods, very few have left living and modified descendants. From the first growth of the tree, many a limb and branch has decayed and dropped off; and these fallen branches of various sizes may represent those whole orders, families and genera which have now no living representatives, and which are known to us only in a fossil state. As we here and there see a thin straggling branch springing from a fork low down in a tree, and which by some chance has been favoured and is still alive on its summit, so we occasionally see an animal like the Ornithorhynchus or Lepidosiren, which in some small degree connects by its affinities two large branches of life, and which has apparently been saved from fatal competition by having inhabited a protected station. As buds give rise by growth to fresh buds, and these, if vigorous, branch out and overtop on all sides many a feebler branch, so by generation I believe it has been with the great Tree of Life, which fills with its dead and broken branches the crust of the earth, and covers the surface with its ever-branching and beautiful ramifications.

Stephen Jay Gould . . . . Ever Since Darwin

In this timely essay, Gould reexamines Darwin's theory of natural selection and tries to clear up some of the difficulties it presents. He suggests that the true Darwinian spirit might correct the pretentious Western notion that our species is somehow meant to have dominion over all the Earth's creatures. Stephen Jay Gould teaches biology, geology, and the history of science at Harvard University.

"One hundred years without Darwin are enough," grumbled the noted American geneticist H. J. Muller in 1959. The remark struck many listeners as a singularly inauspicious way to greet the centenary of the *Origin of Species*, but no one could deny the truth expressed in its frustration.

Why has Darwin been so hard to grasp? Within a decade, he convinced the thinking world that evolution had occurred, but his own theory of natural selection never achieved much popularity during his lifetime. It did not prevail until the 1940s, and even today, though it forms the core of our evolutionary theory, it is widely misunderstood, misquoted, and misapplied. The difficulty cannot lie in complexity of logical structure, for the basis of natural selection is simplicity itself—two undeniable facts and an inescapable conclusion:

1. Organisms vary, and these variations are inherited (at least in part) by their offspring.

2. Organisms produce more offspring than can possibly survive.

3. On average, offspring that vary most strongly in directions favored by the environment will survive and propagate. Favorable variations will therefore accumulate in populations by natural selection.

These three statements do ensure that natural selection will operate, but they do not (by themselves) guarantee for it the fundamental role that Darwin assigned. The essence of Darwin's theory lies in his contention that natural selection is the creative force of evolution—not just the executioner of the unfit. Natural selection must construct the fit as well; it must build adaptation in stages by preserving, generation after generation, the favorable part of a random spectrum of variation. If natural selection is creative, then our first statement on variation must be amplified by two additional constraints.

First, variation must be random, or at least not preferentially inclined toward adaptation. For, if variation comes pre-packaged in the right direction, then selection plays no creative role, but merely eliminates the unlucky individuals who do not vary in the appropriate way. Lamarckism, with its insistence that animals respond creatively to their needs and pass acquired traits to offspring, is a non-Darwinian theory on this account. Our understanding of genetic mutation suggests that Darwin was right in maintaining that variation is not predirected in favorable ways. Evolution is a mixture of chance and necessity—chance at the level of variation, necessity in the working of selection.

Secondly, variation must be small relative to the extent of evolutionary change in the foundation of new species. For if new species arise all at once, then selection only has to remove former occupants to make way for an improvement that it did not manufacture. Again, our understanding of genetics encourages Darwin's view that small mutations are the stuff of evolutionary change.

Thus, Darwin's apparently simple theory is not without its subtle complexities and additional requirements. Nonetheless, I believe that the stumbling block to its acceptance does not lie in any scientific difficulty, but rather in the radical philosophical content of Darwin's message—in its challenge to a set of entrenched Western attitudes that we are not yet ready to abandon. First, Darwin argues that evolution has no purpose. Individuals struggle to increase the representation of their genes in future generations, and that is all. If the world displays any harmony and order, it arises only as an incidental result of individuals seeking their own advantage—the economy of Adam Smith transferred to nature. Second, Darwin maintained that evolution has no direction; it does not lead inevitably to higher things. Organisms become better adapted to their local environments, and that is all. The "degeneracy" of a parasite is as perfect as the gait of a gazelle. Third, Darwin applied a consistent philosophy of materialism to his interpretation of nature. Matter is the ground of all existence; mind, spirit, and God as well, are just words that express the wondrous results of neuronal complexity. Thomas Hardy, speaking for nature, expressed his distress at the claim that purpose, direction, and spirit had been banished:

> When I took forth at dawning, pool,
> Field, flock, and lonely tree,
> All seem to gaze at me
> Like chastened children sitting silent in a school;
>
> Upon them stirs in lippings mere
> (As if once clear in call,
> But now scarce breathed at all)—
> "We wonder, ever wonder, why we find us here!"

Yes, the world has been different ever since Darwin. But no less exciting, instructing or uplifting; for if we cannot find purpose in nature, we will have to define it for ourselves. Darwin was not a moral dolt; he just didn't care to fob off upon nature all the deep prejudices of Western thought. Indeed, I suggest that the true Darwinian spirit might salvage our depleted world by denying a favorite theme of Western arrogance—that we are meant to have control and dominion over the earth and its life because we are the loftiest product of a preordained process.

Loren Eiseley. . . . . How Flowers Changed the World

Anthropologist Loren Eiseley reminds us of the important role green plants and flowers have played in the process of terrestrial evolution.

If it had been possible to observe the Earth from the far side of the solar system over the long course of geological epochs, the watchers might have been able to discern a subtle change in the light emanating from our planet. That world of long ago would, like the red deserts of Mars, have reflected light from vast drifts of stone and gravel, the sands of wandering wastes, the blackness of naked basalt, the yellow dust of endlessly moving storms. Only the ceaseless marching of the clouds and the intermittent flashes from the restless surface of the sea would have told a different story, but still essentially a barren one. Then, as the millenia rolled away and age followed age, a new and greener light would, by degrees, have come to twinkle across those endless miles.

This is the only difference those far watchers, by the use of subtle instruments, might have perceived in the whole history of the planet Earth. Yet that slowly growing green twinkle would have contained the epic march of life from the tidal oozes upward across the raw and unclothed continents. Out of the vast chemical bath of the sea—not from the deeps, but from the element-rich, light exposed platforms of the continental shelves—wandering fingers of green had crept upward along the meanderings of river systems and fringed the gravels of forgotten lakes.

In those first ages plants clung of necessity to swamps and watercourses. Their reproductive process demanded direct access to water. Beyond the primitive ferns and mosses that enclosed the borders of swamps and streams the rocks still lay vast and bare, the winds still swirled the dust of a naked planet. The grass cover that holds our world secure in place was still millions of years in the future. The green marchers had gained a soggy foothold upon the land, but that was all. They did not reproduce by seeds but by microscopic swimming sperm that had to wriggle their way through water to fertilize the female cell. Such plants in their higher forms had clever adaptations for the use of rain water in their sexual phases, and survived with increasing success in a wet land environment. They now seem part of man's normal environment. The truth is, however, that there is nothing very "normal" about nature. Once upon a time there were no flowers at all.

A little while ago—about one hundred million years, as the geologist estimates time in the history of our four-billion-year-old planet—flowers were not to be found anywhere on the five continents. Wherever one might have looked, from the poles to the equator, one would have seen only the cold dark monotonous green of a world whose plant life possessed no other color.

Somewhere, just a short time before the close of the Age of Reptiles, there occurred a soundless, violent explosion. It lasted millions of years, but it was an explosion, nevertheless. It marked the emergence of the angiosperms—the flowering plants. Even the great evolutionist, Charles Darwin, called them "an abominable mystery," because they appeared so suddenly and spread so fast.

Flowers changed the face of the planet. Without them, the world we know—even man himself—would never have existed. Francis Thompson, the English poet, once wrote that one could not pluck a flower without troubling a star. Intuitively he had sensed like a naturalist the enormous interlinked complexity of life. Today we know that the appearance of the flowers contained also the equally mystifying emergence of man.

If we were to go back into the Age of Reptiles, its drowned swamps and birdless forests would reveal to us a warmer but, on the whole, a sleepier world than that of today. Here and there, it is true, the serpent heads of bottom-feeding dinosaurs might be upreared in suspicion of their huge flesh-eating compatriots. Tyrannosaurs, enormous bipedal caricatures of men, would stalk mindlessly across the sites of future cities and go their slow way down into the dark of geologic time.

In all that world of living things nothing saw save with the intense concentration of the hunt, nothing moved except with the grave sleepwalking intentness of the instinct-driven brain. Judged by modern standards, it was a world in slow motion, a cold-blooded world whose occupants were most active at noonday but torpid on chill nights, their brains damped by a slower metabolism than any known to even the most primitive of warm-blooded animals today.

A high metabolic rate and the maintenance of a constant body temperature are supreme achievements in the evolution of life. They enable an animal to escape, within broad limits, from the overheating or the chilling of its immediate surroundings, and at the same time to maintain a peak of mental efficiency. Creatures without a high metabolic rate are slaves to weather. Insects in the first frosts of autumn all run down like little clocks. Yet if you pick one up and breath warmly upon it, it will begin to move about once more.

In a sheltered spot such creatures may sleep away the winter, but they are hopelessly immobilized. Though a few warm-blooded mammals, such as the woodchuck of our day, have evolved a way of reducing their metabolic rate in order to undergo winter hibernation, it is a survival mechanism with drawbacks, for it leaves the animal helplessly exposed if enemies discover him during his period of suspended animation. Thus bear or woodchuck, big animal or small, must seek, in this time of descending sleep, a safe refuge in some hidden den or burrow. Hibernation is, therefore, primarily a winter refuge of small, easily concealed animals rather than of large ones.

A high metabolic rate, however, means a heavy intake of energy in order to sustain body warmth and efficiency. It is for this reason that even some of these later warm-blooded mammals existing in our day have learned to descend into a slower, unconscious rate of living during the winter months when food may be difficult to obtain. On a slightly higher plane they are following the procedure of the cold-blooded frog sleeping in the mud at the bottom of a frozen pond.

The agile brain of the warm-blooded birds and mammals demands a high oxygen consumption and food in concentrated forms, or the creatures cannot long sustain themselves. It was the rise of the flowering plants that provided that energy and changed the nature of the living world. Their appearance parallels in a quite surprising manner the rise of the birds and mammals.

Slowly, toward the dawn of the Age of Reptiles, something over two hundred and fifty million years ago, the little naked sperm cells wriggling their way through dew and raindrops had given way to a kind of pollen carried by the wind. Our present-day pine forests represent plants of a pollen-disseminating variety. Once fertilization was no longer dependent on exterior water, the march over drier regions could be extended. Instead of spores simple primitive seeds carrying some nourishment for the young plant had developed, but true flowers were still scores of millions of years away. After a long period of hesitant evolutionary groping, they exploded upon the world with truly revolutionary violence.

The event occurred in Cretaceous times in the close of the Age of Reptiles. Before the coming of the flowering plants our own ancestral stock, the warm-blooded mammals, consisted of a few mousy little creatures hidden in trees and underbrush. A few lizard-like birds with carnivorous teeth flapped awkwardly on ill-aimed flights among archaic shrubbery. None of these insignificant creatures gave evidence of any remarkable talents. The mammals in particular had been around for some millions of years, but had remained well lost in the shadow of the mighty reptiles. Truth to tell, man was still, like the genie in the bottle, encased in the body of a creature about the size of a rat.

As for the birds, their reptilian cousins the Pterodactyls, flew farther and better. There was just one thing about the birds that paralleled the physiology of the mammals. They, too, had evolved warm blood and its accompanying temperature control. Nevertheless, if one had been seen stripped of his feathers, he would still have seemed a slightly uncanny and unsightly lizard.

Neither the birds nor the mammals, however, were quite what they seemed. They were waiting for the Age of Flowers. They were waiting for what flowers, and with them the true encased seed, would bring. Fish-eating, gigantic leather-winged reptiles, twenty-eight feet from wing tip to wing tip, hovered over the coasts that one day would be swarming with gulls.

Inland the monotonous green of the pine and spruce forests with their primitive wooden cone flowers stretched everywhere. No grass hindered the fall of the naked seeds to earth. Great sequoias towered to the skies. The world of that time has a certain appeal but it is a giant's world, a world moving slowly like the reptiles who stalked magnificently among the boles of its trees.

The trees themselves are ancient, slow-growing and immense, like the redwood groves that have survived to our day on the California coast. All is stiff, formal, upright and green, monotonously green. There is no grass as yet; there are no wide plains rolling in the sun, no tiny daisies dotting the meadows underfoot. There is little versatility about this scene; it is, in truth, a giant's world.

A few nights ago it was brought home vividly to me that the world has changed since that far epoch. I was awakened out of sleep by an unknown sound in my living room. Not a small sound—not a creaking timber or a mouse's scurry—but a sharp, rending explosion as though an unwary foot had been put down upon a wine glass. I had come instantly out of sleep and lay tense, unbreathing. I listened for another step. There was none.

Unable to stand the suspense any longer, I turned on the light and passed from room to room glancing uneasily behind chairs and into closets. Nothing seemed disturbed, and I stood puzzled in the center of the living room floor. Then a small button-shaped object upon the rug caught my eye. It was hard and polished and glistening. Scattered over the length of the room were several more shining up at me like wary little eyes. A pine cone that had been lying in a dish had been blown the length of the coffee table. The dish itself could hardly have been the source of the explosion. Beside it I found two ribbon-like strips of a velvety-green. I tried to place the two stips together to make a pod. They twisted resolutely away from each other and would no longer fit.

I relaxed in a chair, then, for I had reached a solution of the midnight disturbance. The twisted strips were wistaria pods that I had brought in a day or two previously and placed in the dish. They had chosen midnight to explode and distribute their multiplying fund of life down the length of the room. A plant, a fixed, rooted thing, immobilized in a single spot, had devised a way of propelling its offspring across open space. Immediately there passed before my eyes the million airy troopers of the milkweed pod and the clutching hooks of the sandburs. Seeds on the coyote's tail, seeds on the hunter's coat, thistle down mounting on the winds—all were somehow triumphing over life's limitations. Yet the ability to do this had not been with them at the beginning. It was the product of endless effort and experiment.

The seeds on my carpet were not going to lie stiffly where they had dropped like their antiquated cousins, the naked seeds on the pine-cone scales. They were travelers. Struck by the thought, I went out next day and collected several other varieties. I line them up now in a row on my desk—so many little capsules of life, winged, hooked or spiked. Every one is an angiosperm, a product of the true flowering plants. Contained in these little boxes is the secret of that far-off Cretaceous explosion of a hundred million years ago that changed the face of the planet. And somewhere in here, I think, as I poke seriously at one particularly resistant seedcase of a wild grass, was once man himself.

When the first simple flower bloomed on some raw upland late in the Dinosaur Age, it was wind pollinated, just like its early pine-cone relatives. It was a very inconspicuous flower because it had not yet evolved the idea of using the surer attraction of birds and insects to achieve the transportation of pollen. It sowed its own pollen and received the pollen of other flowers by the simple vagaries of the wind. Many plants in regions where insect life is scant still follow this principle today. Nevertheless, the true flower—and the seed that it produced—was a profound innovation in the world of life.

In a way, this event parallels, in the plant world, what happened among animals. Consider the relative chance for survival of the exteriorly deposited egg of a fish in contrast with the fertilized egg of a mammal, carefully retained for months in the mother's body until the young animal (or human being) is developed to a point where it may survive. The biological wastage is less—and so it is with the flowering plants. The primitive spore, a single cell fertilized in the beginning by a swimming sperm, did not promote rapid distribution, and the young plant, moreover, had to struggle up from nothing. No one had left it any food except what it could get by its own unaided efforts.

By contrast, the true flowering plants (angiosperm itself means "encased seed") grew a seed in the heart of a flower, a seed whose development was initiated by a fertilizing pollen grain independent of outside moisture. But the seed, unlike the developing spore, is already a fully equipped *embryonic plant* packed in a little enclosed box stuffed full of nutritious food. Moreover, by featherdown attachments, as in dandelion or milkweed seed, it can be wafted upward on gusts and ride the wind for miles; or with hooks it can cling to a bear's or a rabbit's hide; or like some of the berries, it can be covered with a juicy, attractive fruit to lure birds, pass undigested through their intestinal tracts and be voided miles away.

The ramifications of this biological invention were endless. Plants traveled as they had never traveled before. They got into strange environments heretofore never entered by the old spore plants or stiff pine-cone-seed plants. The well-fed, carefully cherished little embryos raised their heads everywhere. Many of the older plants with more primitive reproductive mechanisms began to fade away under this unequal contest. They contracted their range into secluded environments. Some, like the giant redwoods, lingered on as relics; many vanished entirely.

The world of the giants was a dying world. These fantastic little seeds skipping and hopping and flying about the woods and valleys brought with them an amazing adaptability. If our whole lives had not been spent in the midst of it, it would astound us. The old, stiff, sky-reaching wooden world had changed into something that glowed here and there with strange colors, put out queer, unheard-of-fruits and little intricately carved seed cases, and, most important of all, produced concentrated foods in a way that the land had never seen before, or dreamed of back in the fish-eating, leaf-crunching days of the dinosaurs.

That food came from three sources, all produced by the reproductive system of the flowering plants. There were the tantalizing nectars and pollens intended to draw insects for pollenizing purposes, and which are responsible also for that wonderful jeweled creation, the hummingbird. There were the juicy and enticing fruits to attract larger animals, and in which tough-coated seeds were concealed, as in the tomato, for example. Then, as if this were not enough, there was the food in the actual seed itself, the food intended to nourish the embryo. All over the world, like hot corn in a popper, these incredible elaborations of the flowering plants kept exploding. In a movement that was almost instantaneous, geologically speaking, the angiosperms had taken over the world. Grass was beginning to cover the bare earth until, today, there are over six thousand species. All kinds of vines and bushes squirmed and writhed under new trees with flying seeds.

The explosion was having its effect on animal life also. Specialized groups of insects were arising to feed on the new sources of food and, incidentally and unknowingly, to pollinate the plant. The flowers bloomed and bloomed in ever larger and more spectacular varieties. Some were pale unearthly night flowers intended to lure moths in the evening twilight, some among the orchids even took the shape of female spiders in order to attract wandering males, some flamed redly in the light of noon or twinkled modestly in the meadow grasses. Intricate mechanisms splashed pollen on the breasts of hummingbirds, or stamped it on the bellies of black, grumbling bees droning assiduously from blossom to blossom. Honey ran, insects multiplied, and even the descendants of that toothed and ancient lizard-bird had become strangely altered. Equipped with prodding beaks instead of biting teeth they pecked the seeds and gobbled the insects that were really converted nectar.

Across the planet grasslands were now spreading. A slow continental upthrust which had been a part of the early Age of Flowers had cooled the world's climates. The stalking reptiles and the leather-winged black imps of the seashore cliffs had vanished. Only birds roamed the air now, hot-blooded and high-speed metabolic machines.

The mammals, too, had survived and were venturing into new domains, staring about perhaps a bit bewildered at their sudden eminence now that the thunder lizards were gone. Many of them, beginning as small browsers upon leaves in the forest, began to venture out upon this new sunlit world of the grass. Grass has a high silica content and demands a new type of very tough and resistant tooth enamel, but the seeds taken incidentally in the cropping of the grass are highly nutritious. A new world had opened out for the warm-blooded mammals. Great herbivores like the mammoths, horses and bisons appeared. Skulking about them had arisen savage flesh-feeding carnivores like the now extinct dire wolves and the saber-toothed tiger.

Flesh eaters though these creatures were, they were being sustained on nutritious grasses one step removed. Their fierce energy was being maintained on a high, effective level, through hot days and frosty nights, by the concentrated energy of the angiosperms. That energy, thirty per cent or more of the weight of the entire plant among some of the cereal grasses, was being accumulated and concentrated in the rich proteins and fats of the enormous game herds of the grasslands.

On the edge of the forest, a strange, old-fashioned animal still hesitated. His body was the body of a tree dweller, and though tough and knotty by human standards, he was, in terms of that world into which he gazed, a weakling. His teeth, though strong for chewing on the tough fruits of the forest, or for crunching an occasional unwary bird caught with his prehensile hands, were not the tearing sabers of the great cats. He had a passion for lifting himself up to see about, in his restless, roving curiosity. He would run a little stiffly and uncertainly, perhaps, on his hind legs, but only in those rare moments when he ventured out upon the ground. All this was the legacy of his climbing days; he had a hand with flexible fingers and no fine specialized hoofs upon which to gallop like the wind.

If he any idea of competing in that new world, he had better forget it; teeth or hooves, he was much too late for either. He was a ne'er-do-well, an in-betweener. Nature had not done well by him. It was as if she had hesitated and never quite made up her mind. Perhaps as a consequence he had a malicious gleam in his eye, the gleam of an outcast who has been left nothing and knows he is going to have to take what he gets. One day a little band of these odd apes—for apes they were— shambled out upon the grass: the human story had begun.

Apes were to become men, in the inscrutable wisdom of nature, because flowers had produced seeds and fruits in such tremendous quantities that a new and totally different store of energy had become available in concentrated form. Impressive as the slow-moving, dim-brained dinosaurs had been, it is doubtful if their age had supported anything like the diversity of life that now rioted across the planet or flashed in and out among the trees. Down on the grass by a streamside, one of those apes with inquisitive fingers turned over a stone and hefted it vaguely. The group clucked together in a throaty tongue and moved off through the tall grass foraging for seeds and insects. The one still held, sniffed, and hefted the stone he had found. He liked the feel of it in his fingers. The attack on the animal world was about to begin.

If one could run the story of that first human group like a speeded-up motion picture through a million years of time, one might see the stone in the hand change to the flint ax and the torch. All that swarming grassland world with its giant bison and trumpeting mammoths would go down in ruin to feed the insatiable and growing numbers of a carnivore who, like the great cats before him, was taking his energy indirectly from the grass. Later he found fire and it altered the tough meats and drained their energy even faster into a stomach ill adapted for the ferocious turn man's habits had taken.

His limbs grew longer, he strode more purposefully over the grass. The stolen energy that would take man across the continents would fail him at last. The great Ice Age herds were destined to vanish. When they did so, another hand like the hand that grasped the stone by the river long ago would pluck a handful of grass seed and hold it contemplatively.

In that moment, the golden towers of man, his swarming millions, his turning wheels, the vast learning of his packed libraries, would glimmer dimly there in the ancestor of wheat, a few seeds held in a muddy hand. Without the gift of flowers and the infinite diversity of their fruits, man and bird, if they had continued to exist at all, would be today unrecognizable. Archaeopteryx, the lizard-bird, might still be snapping at beetles on a sequoia limb; man might still be a nocturnal insectivore gnawing a roach in the dark. The weight of a petal has changed the face of the world and made it ours.

• DISCUSSION QUESTIONS •

1. What are the basic requirements for life as we know it? To what extent would these same requirements apply elsewhere in the universe? Assuming extraterrestrial life is based on the same organic molecules as life on earth, what are the chances that beings on the other worlds would bear a physical resemblance to earth beings? What other factors would have to be taken into consideration?

2. What is the significance of the Miller-Urey experiments on the origin of life? Why do ethical questions arise when people talk about creating life

in a test tube? What do experiments like these suggest about the responsibility of science, in general, to the preservation of human values? What are the implications of these experiments for life in the universe?

3. How does the notion that Earth has "just the right conditions for life"—moderate temperatures, liquid water, oxygen, and so on—influence our expectations about the types of life forms we might find on other worlds? Is it valid to assume there is any one "perfect set of conditions" for life? Explain your answer.

4. What is the difference between artificial selection and natural selection? In what ways are these two processes alike? Can you think of examples of how primitive peoples may have unknowingly contributed to the survival and/or extinction of certain species of plant and animal life?

5. Does evolution have a purpose? Are human beings the goal toward which all evolution has been purposefully directed? Does evolution imply that humans descended from apes? How easy is it to predict the future course of evolution? If human beings were to become extinct, what types of beings do you think would be most likely to assume a position of dominance on the planet, and why?

• ADDITIONAL ACTIVITIES •

Optional Projects

1. Develop an annotated timeline showing the chronological order in which the various lifeforms appeared following the Cambrian explosion.

2. Interview a botany professor or professional horticulturist to learn how one would go about cultivating a new variety of rose, or some other type of flower. Or interview an animal breeder to find out how one would go about developing a breed of dairy cows that might produce milk with a high cream content. Prepare a written description of your findings, and explain how these procedures illustrate the principles of artificial selection.

3. Construct a diagram showing the basic cycle of exchange that occurs between plants and animals. Write one or two paragraphs explaining why this process is essential to sustaining life on earth.

4. Using other sources, make a list of the oldest known survivors of the evolutionary process. Make another list of species that once flourished on the planet, but are now extinct.

Supplementary Bibliography

Jacob Bronowski, "The Ladder of Creation" in *The Ascent of Man*. Boston: Little, Brown, 1973.
An historical account of the experiences and observations that led to the theory of evolution by natural selection.

J.B.S. Haldane, "On Being the Right Size" in James R. Newman, ed., *The World of Mathematics, Volume II.* New York: Simon & Schuster, 1956.
This lively essay deals with the problems of natural selection and other aspects of evolutionary theory from a mathematical point of view.

Horace Freeland Judson, *The Eighth Day of Creation.* New York: Simon and Schuster, 1979.
A highly readable historical account of the major discoveries of molecular biology—and the people who made them.

G.G. Simpson, *The Meaning of Evolution.* New Haven, Conn.: Yale University Press, 1949.
A good interpretative discussion of Darwin's theory of evolution.

Lewis Thomas, *The Lives of a Cell.* New York: Bantam Books, 1975.
A collection of beautifully written essays on various topics in biology.

James D. Watson, *The Double Helix.* New York: Atheneum, 1968.
A lucid personal account of the events that led to the discovery of the structure of DNA.

Chapter III
THE HARMONY OF WORLDS

• OVERVIEW •

Efforts to describe and interpret the laws of the universe have always been part of the human tradition. In times when there were few other forms of entertainment, watching the skies must indeed have been a favorite pastime. Then, as certain predictable patterns emerged, people discovered how the sky could serve as a kind of calendar by which they could not only mark the passing of time but also plan the course of their daily lives.

Of special interest to the ancients were the movements of the planets, which were thought to be gods—or at least places where the gods resided. If they could understand and predict the movements of the planets, then they could learn how to deal with the ruling forces in their own lives and possibly even foretell the future. It was this obsession with understanding the "moods" of the planets that eventually gave rise to astrology, the basic tenets of which were formulated in the second century A.D. by Claudius Ptolemy. Ptolemy is also credited with naming the stars, establishing rules for predicting eclipses, and developing a mathematical model for predicting the motions of the planets. Ptolemy's model would have worked well except for two basic inaccuracies: he believed that the earth was at the center of the universe and that the planets moved at uniform velocity in circular paths.

It was not until 1543 that Ptolemy's geocentric view of the universe was seriously challenged. In that year a Polish Catholic cleric named Nicholas Copernicus postulated that the sun, not the earth, was at the center of the universe, thus demoting the earth to the status of planet. Although Copernicus' heliocentric model angered many of his contemporaries, it did pave the way a few decades later for the work of Johannes Kepler, who demonstrated that the planets move in elliptical orbits around the sun.

The effort to explain planetary motion was completed by Isaac Newton, who succeeded in deriving Kepler's laws mathematically. He also demonstrated that the same law of gravity that explains the familiar fall of an apple to the ground can also explain why the planets travel in elliptical orbits around the sun. Newton's work culminated in 1687 with the publication of *Principia*, whose appearance marked the beginning of a new era in scientific investigation.

• LEARNING OBJECTIVES •

1. Define and compare astronomy and astrology as these terms are understood today. Describe their historical relationship and the importance of the influence of astrology on the development of astronomy.

2. Compare and contrast the Ptolemaic and Copernican models of the solar system and describe the effect each model had on subsequent generations of astronomers.

3. Describe Kepler's three laws of planetary motion.

4. As briefly as possible, describe Newton's theory of universal gravitation.

5. Explain the relationship between Kepler's laws and Newton's laws.

• KEY TERMS AND NAMES •

Tycho Brahe	Kepler
Copernicus	law of universal gravitation
epicycle	Newton
inverse square law	Ptolemy

• ASSIGNMENT •

Watch COSMOS television series Program 3, "Harmony of the Worlds."

Read Chapter 3, "Harmony of the Worlds," in Carl Sagan's text, *Cosmos*, or other readings assigned by your instructor.

• READINGS •

George O. Abell . . . . **The Age of Astrology**

George Abell, professor of astronomy at the University of California, Los Angeles, traces astrology back to its beginnings in Ancient Greece, and questions whether astrology has a place among the other natural forces and laws that govern the universe.

The sun and moon move through the zodiac in a relatively simple manner. The other planets move in nearly circular orbits around the sun, as does the earth, but we see them from our own moving platform. Thus they have rather erratic-appearing motions, sometimes moving eastward through the zodiac and sometimes (as earth passes one up in moving between it and the sun) backing up and moving westward for a while. From several centuries B.C. until the time of Kepler, in the seventeenth century, a major effort of astronomy was to find a scheme that would describe accurately the apparently perverse motions of the planets.

The reason is that the planets played the roles of gods to the ancients. The Greeks, whose fertile imaginations gave us the beginnings of democracy—the epics of Homer, the stirring speeches of Pericles, the geometry of Euclid, and the philosophy of Plato—blended their mythology, and that of the Babylonians and the Egyptians, with their concept of the majestic regularity of the heavenly motions, albeit complicated with the almost human perversity of the motions of the planets.

PLANETS AND GODS

The Greek gods were immortal, but otherwise they had the same attributes of anger, happiness, jealousy, rage, and pleasure as those of us humans, and these same attributes were assigned to the planets that either were the gods, were their abodes, or at least represented them. Each god, and thus each planet, was a center of force, but how that force prevailed depended on how it was tempered by the effects of other gods.

If the gods themselves were capricious, at least the planets were potentially predictable in their movements. How natural to attempt to understand the whims of the gods by understanding the motions of the planets. Because our own lot in life is unpredictable, it must be purely at the mercy of the gods. But if the gods are the planets, or at least are somehow associated with them, we have only to learn the rules of the motions of the planets to understand the whims of the gods and how they shape our own lives.

As Greek scholars learned more and more about the regularities of the motions of the sun, moon, and planets, therefore, they felt they were learning more and more about the ruling forces in their own lives. How beautifully complete and typically logical of the Greek mind—armed with the geometry of Euclid—to suppose that our lives should be so ordered. The Greeks had the prophetic wisdom to suppose that the motions of the planets are indeed governed by precise laws of nature—transcending even the will of their humanesque gods—and thus, by inference, they presumed that our lives are similarly preprogrammed by the preset motions of the planets. What, then, can determine our individual lots? Only the moment that we happen to enter the world and fall into step with the eternal and predestined movements of the heavens.

Thus the belief developed that each of our lives is preset by the precise configurations of all the planets in the sky at the moment of birth; all the motions of the planets thereafter follow the laws of nature, and hence the influence of the planet-gods must similarly be constrained by their predictable relations with other planet-gods in the years to come. Thus the key to the future of an individual was the map of the heavens, showing where each planet was in the sky as seen from the precise time and place of that person's birth. This is the religion of *natal astrology*, actually believed in by tens of millions of Europeans and Americans today.

THE HOROSCOPE

Of particular importance to a person's future was what was rising when he was born. Perhaps this notion goes back to the time when the earth was believed flat, and that objects in the sky existed only temporarily, dissolving in the west as they set. Consider the effect of a planet just forming as it is about to rise in the east at the moment of a child's birth. Can we imagine the importance of that influence, permeating the atmosphere inhaled in that infant's first breath!? In any case, the ancient astrologers regarded as particularly important what was rising at one's birth. The zodiacal sign on the eastern horizon is still called the *rising sign*, and any sign, planet, or star that is rising or about to rise is said to be in the *ascendancy*. Originally, the word *horoscope* meant the *hour to observe* what was ascending or rising. Later, it meant a map or chart of the heavens, showing the position of each sign and each planet in the sky at some specific time. This is the present meaning of the word. In particular, a *natal* horoscope for an individual is such a chart prepared for the moment of his birth. The first natal horoscope was charted, or *cast*, about the first century B.C.

One thing a horoscope shows is where each planet is in the zodiac, through which it eternally moves. We have seen how the zodiac was divided into 12 equal parts or signs, beginning with the vernal equinox, and proceeding eastward about the sky. Thus a horoscope specifies, in part, the location of each planet according to what part of which sign it occupies. . . .

Also important in astrology is where things are in the sky with respect to the horizon. Thus a horoscope depends not only on the date, which specifies where each planet is among the signs of the zodiac, and on the location on the earth from which the sky is viewed, which specifies where the celestial pole is in the sky, but also on the *time*, which finally fixes the angle through which the celestial sphere has rotated, and thus where each part of it is with respect to the horizon.

Modern astronomers orient the celestial sphere by specifying what is called *sidereal time*, which tells where the vernal equinox is in the sky as seen from the particular place in question on the earth. (Ancient astronomers did likewise.) At 0 hour sidereal time, the vernal equinox is on the meridian; at 6 hours, it is setting. It is as low as it can get in the sky at 12 hours sidereal time, and rises at 6 hours. Since the signs of the zodiac start at the vernal equinox, knowing where it is tells where all the signs and planets are with respect to the horizon.

The ancient astronomers (and astrologers) further specified the matter by dividing the sky into twelve *houses*, each occupying a fixed place with respect to the horizon—that is, with respect to the ground where the individual concerned is born. The *first house* is that part of the sky containing objects that will rise within approximately the next two hours; hence the first house is that part of the sky immediately below the eastern horizon. The second house lies beneath the first, the third beneath the second, and so on, around the lower part of the celestial sphere. The sixth house contains objects that have set within the past couple of hours; the seventh those which will set within the next couple of hours; and so on. Objects that lie in the tenth house will be carried, by the rotation of the celestial sphere, across the meridian during the next two hours. Those in the twelfth house have just risen. Objects in the first house are thus said to be in the ascendancy (or soon will be), and those in the tenth, in *culmination* (they will soon cross the meridian).

Actually the foregoing discussion of houses has been slightly vague, because there has never been agreement among astrologers (even to this day) on the proper way to define the precise boundaries between houses. . . . Although the differences between the various house definitions are technical in nature, they do result in slightly different horoscopes, and can often put one or more of the planets in different houses.

So a natal horoscope is a chart of the sky showing the locations of celestial bodies at the time of a person's birth. The astrologers of antiquity attempted to interpret a person's physical and emotional character, personality, talents, strengths and weaknesses, propensity for various diseases, and the events of his life in terms of his natal horoscope. . . .

Of course, as the person goes on living, the earth goes on turning and the planets go on moving through the zodiac. The astrologer, however, keeping track of these motions and always relating them to the client's natal horoscope, believes he can foretell times of significant events in the subject's life, what times are happy ones for the subject, what ones good for important journeys, and (if the astrologer is confident in himself) even when the subject may suffer calamities or death.

Moreover, each sign of the zodiac is presumed to relate to a given part of the body; thus Aries rules the head, Leo the heart, Cancer the stomach, Scorpio the genitals, and Pisces the feet. Mars in the sign of Aries in a natal horoscope might dispose the poor subject to a tendency toward headaches all his life, and Uranus in Cancer might plague him with stomach cramps. In the Middle Ages most physicians believed in and practiced according to this *medical astrology*, and even today some doctors are reported to seek the advice of astrologers in making diagnoses.

The zodiacal signs were associated with hot and cold, wet and dry, and with the assumed elements: earth, water, air, and fire. The planets were associated with various metals: the sun with gold, the moon with silver, Mercury with quicksilver, and so on. Even nations were thought to be ruled by signs and planets, and not only were individual characteristics of people, such as stature, color of hair and eyes, attributed to details of their horoscopes, but also these characteristics of entire races, according to the signs and planets assigned to them.

There is, of course, far more—far too much even to touch on here. Suffice it to say that in antiquity it was widely believed that the stars ruled not only one's soul, but also all aspects of his life—his physical and emotional characteristics, his occupation, his success, his family, his friends and enemies, his good and bad fortune, up to his death. Astrologers could not claim then, nor can they now, to understand the planets well enough to predict all these factors with complete precision, but they tried. They had amassed an extremely elaborate set of rules to aid them. These rules were not based on centuries of data analysis, nor were they tested in controlled experiments. They were based on what we would call a magical correspondence between the gods, the planets whose names they bore, and the mythological people and creatures for which the zodiacal signs were named. That is to say, the supposed influence of the planets and signs were just those to be expected from the corresponding associations of the gods and animals of the same names.

To verify this last assertion, one need only read the *Tetrabiblos* of Ptolemy, one of the greatest astronomers, and the most important astrologer, of antiquity. The *Tetrabiblos*, written in the second century A.D., is the closest thing that exists to a bible of astrology. There Ptolemy codified the many rules by which horoscopes are interpreted, as well as explained the construction of the horoscope itself. There it can be seen how the effect of Mars in the heart of the Lion (Leo) differs from that when Mars approaches the Lion's tail.

Ptolemy, the scientist, shows through somewhat as well; he must have wondered how it could be that the planets could have these impressive effects, and, at least to me, seems to have been rationalizing the thing in terms of cause and effect—a sort of hardheaded twentieth century attitude. He explains, for example, that the moon, the nearest "planet" to earth, soaks up moisture from the earth, and so has a dampening influence, whereas Mars, just beyond the sun (as assumed at the time), is hot, and has an arid, drying influence. (Actually, the moon is bone dry, and Mars is now known to have considerable water—although presently frozen because of the planet's low temperature.) Also Ptolemy does not attribute *everything* to astrology; he acknowledges that there are three forces affecting man: heredity, environment, and astrology.

In any event, it should now be clear that at least one important reason that the Greeks had for studying astronomy was to understand better the motions of the planets in order to prepare better horoscopes.

The result was that the Greeks advanced astronomy to a point unsurpassed for a millennium and a half. They measured the size of the earth, the size and distance of the moon, the length of the year, and the inequalities in the lengths of the seasons. They kept track of the motions of the planets, and worked out excellent models to predict their motions, and they cataloged the stars, and noted their apparent brightness. . . .

Surely our understanding of the magnificent achievement and universality of Newtonian theory gives us a new perspective of the planet-gods and crystalline spheres of antiquity. As late as the Renaissance virtually all intellectuals believed in astrology. But as the real laws of nature emerged, scientists, with the new realization of the role of the earth as a planet and the grand order that governs the universe, turned away from this ancient religion. Astrology was simply no longer credible in the actual world, any more than are vampires, witchcraft, and the forecasting of events with the entrails of animals. Yet, today hundreds of millions of people in Europe and North America still cling to the ancient belief of astrology.

One reason is probably that astrology claims to tell us something about ourselves—a subject of obvious interest to us all. But so do other superstitions that the modern educated person rejects. I think the main reason that astrology has persisted in our lands is that it is presented (by astrologers) as a science, and most people in our time are just not well enough informed to recognize the difference between science and pseudoscience. As the frontier of knowledge is pushed forward, science has become more and more complex, and scientists themselves have become increasingly specialized. Every new sub-branch of science develops its own jargon, and each of these new languages is incomprehensible to those not in it—even to scientists of other disciplines.

Many modern astrologers, in fact, claim a scientific basis for astrology. I have met some in television discussions and debates, who have claimed that planets exert tidal forces on people. In fact, however, even lunar tides on human beings are completely negligible, and because of their greater distances the planets exert tidal forces on earth that are millions of times smaller yet. For example, the tidal force with which Mars, when at its nearest, tries to distort your body (or the fluids in it) is about 50 million times weaker than is the tidal force exerted on you by this very book, placed 2 m away.

Nor can the light from planets be relevant. Babies are generally born indoors, shielded from the radiation reflected to us and emitted by the planets, and anyway, the light of all the planets combined is minuscule compared to even tiny variations observed in the intensity of sunlight.

One astrologer reminded me of the radio radiation discovered in recent years coming from Jupiter. "Isn't *that* an influence you astronomers didn't know about before?" he asked. It is true; we didn't know of those radio waves from Jupiter until we had built enormous radio telescopes capable of detecting them. Meanwhile, our bodies are continually bathed in radio radiation of the same frequencies from man-made transmitters. Even the radiation we receive from the 100-watt transmitter of a small radio station 100 km away is millions of times stronger than that from Jupiter—no surprise, of course, because we can pick up that station with a pocket transistor radio.

Sometimes astrologers (without understanding the subject) talk about electric and magnetic forces exerted by the planets. Like virtually all bulk matter, however, the planets are electrically neutral. Some do have magnetic fields, but we can detect those fields only with instruments carried to those planets in space probes, not from here on earth. The small permanent magnet in the loudspeaker of a typical portable radio, in comparison, produces an incredibly strong magnetic field in the vicinity of the listener.

To be sure, the sun affects us, and very much so, but in ways understood without invoking ancient gods. And the moon produces tides and reflects sunlight to us. Moonlight can influence the harvester and the hunter, and doubtless can produce psychological effects as well. On the other hand, many of the "well-known facts"—such as the fact that at times of full moon more violent crimes are committed or that more people are admitted to mental hospitals—are not borne out by recent objective investigations. For example, statistical studies of 2497 suicides and 2017 homicides in Texas between 1959 and 1961, of another 2494 homicides in Texas from 1957 to 1970, of 339 suicides in Erie County, New York, and of 4937 mental hospital admissions, all show no correlation with either the phases or the distance of the moon.

In short, there is no way in terms of known laws of nature that the planets' directions in the sky can influence human personality and fortune in the manner predicted by astrology. If the planets were to exert an influence on us, it would have to be through an unknown force—and one with very strange properties: that force would have to emanate from some, but not all, celestial bodies; would have to affect some, but not all, things on earth; and would not have to depend on the distances, masses, or other characteristics of those planets giving rise to it. In other words, it would lack the universality, order, and harmony found for every other force and natural law ever discovered that applies in the real universe.

Charles A. Whitney . . . . Kepler: The First of the Modern Mystics

In the following insightful selection, Harvard astronomer Charles Whitney describes the logic behind Kepler's formulation of the laws of planetary motion. Placing him in an historical context, Whitney demonstrates how Kepler helped bridge the gap between medieval astrology and modern science.

Kepler was one of the last professional astronomers who firmly believed (or admitted believing) in astrology. He cast an elaborate and revealing horoscope for his family, in which he says of his conception and birth: "I have investigated the matter of my conception, which took place in the year 1571, May 16, at 4:37 A.M. . . . My weakness at birth removes suspicion that my mother was already pregnant at the marriage, which was on the 15th of May. . . . Thus I was born premature, at thirty-two weeks, after 224 days, ten hours" (on December 27, 1571).

He was a sickly child, afflicted with myopia, mange, boils, a bad stomach, and a father whom he described as "vicious, inflexible, quarrelsome and doomed to a bad end. Venus and Mars increased his malice. Jupiter . . . made him a pauper but gave him a rich wife. . . .[He] treated my mother extremely ill, went finally into exile and died." Kepler was not much kinder in his description of his mother: "small, thin, swarthy, gossiping and quarrelsome, of a bad disposition." His brother was an epileptic, and Kepler himself was a hypochondriac. Yet he did not sink into self-pity. Like Job, he turned his afflictions to strength, and developed into a man with an incredible capacity for work—though he had little patience with other people.

As a child Kepler had been impressed by Tycho's comet of 1577, and he "was taken by [his] mother to a high place to look at it." He later remarked on the redness of an eclipse of the moon he had seen when he was nine years old. He began his training in a Protestant theological seminary, but before finishing he accepted a job teaching mathematics. A year later, at twenty-three, while drawing at the blackboard during a lecture he was struck by an idea that came to dominate the rest of his life: As he drew an equilateral triangle with one circle inscribed and another circumscribed he realized that the radii of the two circles had nearly the same ratio as the orbits of Jupiter and Saturn. The triangle was the simplest geometrical figure, and Saturn was the outermost planet at the time. What of the remaining planets? Could they be accommodated in such a fashion? He found they could not, but he extended the quest to solid figures. To his delight he realized that there were just five regular solids whose corners would all lie on a circumscribed sphere, and whose faces would all lie tangent to an inscribed sphere. There were just five gaps among the planets—each one corresponding, no doubt, to one of the solids. With some manipulation he found the sequence which gave a tolerable facsimile of the relative distances of the planets, and he published his first book, *Cosmographic Mystery*, with an illustration of the arrangement. He felt the mystery of the universe had been solved; not only had he explained the arrangement of the solar system, he had also discovered why there were just six planets, not "twenty or a hundred." He was hypnotized by this invention and he sought more accurate planetary observations with which to refine the construction.

Tycho Brahe had a goldmine of data, and Kepler determined to "try to wrest his riches from him," because he did not believe that Tycho knew how to use the data—"as is the case with most rich people." Tycho, for his part, knew he needed help if the data were to be properly digested, so he made an overture to Kepler and they collaborated for two years, until Tycho's death. Kepler "inherited" the data and spent decades with them, attempting to determine simple planetary orbits.

Virtually every path and blind alley followed by this "sleepwalker" (Koestler's appellation) is traced in his published books. He found three simple "laws," and they lay like tiny diamonds in the sand of his texts.

Kepler found that each planet moves in an ellipse, a figure which differs from a circle and which cannot be constructed precisely, as Ptolemy and later Copernicus had attempted, by superimposing circular motions—although a close approach is possible if a large number of circles are combined. Kepler thus replaced linked circles with the simple ellipse, but he did not guess why the ellipse appeared in nature.

Kepler also showed that the times required for the planets to complete an orbit were related in a very simple way to the orbital size, and he showed that the planets move most rapidly when they are in that portion of the orbit lying closest to the sun.

In the preface to his greatest work, *The New Astronomy*, published in 1609, Kepler wrote: "What matters to me is not merely to impart to the reader what I have to say, but above all to convey to him the reasons, subterfuges, and lucky hazards which led me to my discoveries."

Kepler claimed to have been motivated by an "affection for the reader" as were Columbus and Magellan, who had provided "grand entertainment" in describing how they had gone astray on their journeys. The urge to confess had evidently been with Kepler since his youth. In his early writing, he had bared himself as did few other men of the Renaissance, and his later books fit this pattern nicely. He was constitutionally incapable of writing a pat, well-organized textbook giving only the fruits of his work.

Kepler's cosmology was an essentially theomorphic one; it centered on the trinitarian concept of God. He said:

In the sphere [of the world] which is the image of God the Creator and the Archetype of the world there are three regions, symbols of the three persons of the Holy Trinity—the center, a symbol of the Father; the surface, of the Son; and the intermediate space, of the Holy Ghost. So, too, just as many principal parts of the world have been made—the different parts in the different regions of the sphere: the sun in the center, the sphere of the fixed stars on the surface, and lastly the planetary system in the region intermediate between the sun and the fixed stars. . . .

The sun is fire, as the Pythagoreans said, or a red-hot stone or mass, as Democritus said—and the sphere of fixed stars is ice, or a crystalline sphere, comparatively speaking.

Thus Kepler retained the ancient crystalline carriers for the stars. But if the stars were confined to a sphere, in consonance with the image of God, it followed that the universe could not be infinite. Kepler, then, was faced with proving the limitation of the starry realm. He met the challenge with a turnabout on Bruno's argument that an infinite universe must be a uniform one without an identifiable center. Kepler said that when we look up at the sky we have the sensation of standing in a central void surrounded by stars. If we are in such a void the universe cannot be infinite.

The problem was to prove we are in a void, and Kepler did this in an ingenious fashion—although modern data would have led him to the contrary conclusion.

He noted that the brightest stars, which are presumably the nearest, have an angular size of about $1/10°$ of arc when viewed with the naked eye. They are about $10°$ apart on the face of the sky, so if we stand on one of them and look about we will see nearby stars whose distances are only about one hundred times as great as their diameters, as is the case for the sun in our sky. Such a sky would be a splendid display of suns—totally different from the view we have on earth. Hence the universe is not uniform and it cannot be infinite.

But Kepler's argument contained an error of fact. A few years later, Galileo found that Kepler had overestimated the apparent diameters of the stars. While the naked eye suggested that the stars covered as much as $1/10°$, Galileo found them to be much smaller in his telescope. In fact, he concluded that their apparent diameter in a perfect telescope might be vanishingly small.

This result destroyed Kepler's argument and dissolved another dilemma that had been introduced by the heliocentric model of Copernicus. If the earth moves about the sun, its motion should be reflected in the stars. Yet even Brahe had failed to detect an apparent yearly motion of the stars; therefore the stars must be extremely far away in comparison to the sun—in fact, they must be several thousand times farther than the sun. But if they were so far, and if they appeared to have a diameter of, say, $1/10°$, it followed from simple geometry that the stars must be individually several thousand times larger than the sun. Galileo's discovery that the stars appear to be mere points of light eliminated these grotesque dimensions and shrank the stars to the dimension of our sun.

Although many scientists would agree with the way history has ranked the parts of their work, this would certainly not have been the case with Kepler. The achievement he rated highest is now considered a curiosity—a relic of his ancient heritage and an example of the aberrations which occured during the transition from medieval to modern science. Had his book *Cosmographic Mystery* been his only achievement, I think Kepler would be virtually unnoticed today, yet he found supreme joy in this realization of Greek geometrical philosophy in the structure of the solar system. To us, his configuration of nesting geometrical solids is more fitting for a garden sculpture than an astronomy book. It has the appearance of crank science, and absolutely no physical foundation for his architecture has come to light—nor does any scientist anticipate that one will.

This is the paradox of Kepler's work; this is what makes it so difficult to classify. We are tempted to class him with the Ancients—the Pythagoreans of Greece, for example—because he placed so much faith in the idea that the world had been cast in a mathematical mold. He felt that the world was *essentially* mathematical: by studying geometry, we study the world. This is an ancient attitude, not a modern one.

Kepler is often classed among the moderns because he was intent on finding a place for observational data in his theories: he fitted his formal constructions to the data. In this, I would concur but go on to say that even this fixation on data cannot guarantee him a place among modern scientists, because there is more to modern science than the mere satisfaction of data and the prediction of events. Modern science seeks to create a simple, yet elegant and comprehensive, description of the world—in short, an "artistic" description. The creative mind in modern science is an artistic mind, and in this sense, we have not come very far from the Ancients. But we have also developed another type: the technologist—the man of numbers and measurement, of tests and machines. This man probably existed among the Ancients as well; perhaps he was the man who constructed elaborate tables to predict the tides; he certainly built the pyramids.

It has become popular to point to the similarity of a good poem and a good physical theory; I cannot disagree with those who hold that they have much in common. Metaphor is the language of much poetry, and a mathematical law or theory is also a metaphor. No one believes that the laws of Kepler actually govern the motion of the planets, nor that they describe those motions precisely. There will always be slight deviations produced by forces too small to be of consequence, and if we wish a very precise description of the motions—for example, in the planning of an interplanetary exploration—we abandon Kepler's laws and use another set of laws, defined by Newton. Even these laws are limited; they apply only to low velocities and to distances not too many times greater than the distance to the nearest galaxy.

But there is one important difference between a poem and a theory. The theory communicates shareable knowledge about the world; the poem communicates a purely personal insight or a mood. The use of a scientific law implies a tacit agreement among scientists; they agree to be charitable toward it. The law will lose validity as soon as scientists wish it to. The validity of a poem, on the other hand, can only be judged by the poet; judgment is his personal responsibility.

The key to the paradox of Kepler's work—that he most highly valued his "garden sculpture" while we most highly value the simple laws that lied buried in his pages of arithmetic—is perhaps to be found in our own attitude. The paradox vanishes if we see the man in the light of his poetic nature, if we admit that Kepler was not a scientist but a poet, striving for personal insight and revelation rather than for shared knowledge. The fact that he dealt with planetary positions rather than the delights and pains of love, for example, may have misled us—the distinction is incidental (although it may reveal something of the man). For Kepler, the observable facts of the solar system were merely the visible signs of a transcending pattern—just as the islands of the South Seas suggest the presence of a mountainous floor beneath the water. As an oceanographer, Kepler would have imagined the undersea mountains rather than the studied islands.

Sir William Dampier . . . . The Newtonian Epoch

Historian of science Dampier provides some background on Newton the man and describes the process that led him to formulate the theory of universal gravitation.

Isaac Newton (1642–1727) was the delicate, posthumous and single child of a small landowner, who farmed his 120 acres. His son was born at Woolsthorpe in Lincolnshire, and educated at Grantham Grammar School. He entered Trinity College, Cambridge, in 1661, where he attended the mathematical lectures of Isaac Barrow. He was elected a Scholar of the College in 1664 and a Fellow in 1665. In 1665 and 1666, driven to Woolsthorpe by an outbreak of plague at Cambridge, he turned his attention to planetary problems. Galileo's researches had shown the need of a cause to keep the planets and their satellites in their orbits and prevent them from moving off in straight lines through space. Galileo had represented this cause as a force, and it remained to show that such a force, or its equivalent, existed.

Newton is said by Voltaire to have grasped the clue while idly watching the fall of an apple in the orchard of his home. He was led to speculate about the cause of the fall, and to wonder how far the apparent attraction of the Earth would extend, whether, indeed, since it was felt in the deepest mines and on the highest hills, it would reach the Moon and explain that body's continual fall towards the Earth away from a straight path. The idea of a force decreasing as the square of the distance increased appears to have been in Newton's mind already, and, in fact, in other men's also. In a memorandum in Newton's handwriting, the following account of these early investigations is given:

> And the same year I began to think of gravity extending to ye orb of the Moon, and having found out how to estimate the force with wch a globe revolving within a sphere presses the surface of the sphere, from Kepler's Rule of the periodic times of the Planets being in a sesquialterate proportion of their distances from the centers of their Orbs I deduced that the forces wch keep the Planets in their Orbs must be reciprocally as the squares of their distances from the centers about wch they revolve: and thereby compared the force requisite to keep the Moon in her Orb with the force of gravity at the surface of the Earth, and found them answer pretty nearly. All this was in the two plague years of 1665 and 1666, for in those days I was in the prime of my age for invention, and minded Mathematics and Philosophy more than at any time since. What Mr Hugens has published since about centrifugal forces I suppose he had before me.

It will be seen that there is no mention here of the story related by his friend Pemberton that Newton put away his calculations because, owing to the use of an inaccurate estimate of the size of the Earth, the force needed to keep the Moon in her orbit did not agree with that of gravity. On the contrary, Newton says that he "found them answer pretty nearly." This has been pointed out by Professor Cajori, who also gives evidence to show that several good enough estimates of the Earth's size were available and likely to be known to Newton in 1666.

A more likely reason for Newton's delay in publishing his calculations was pointed out in 1887 by J. C. Adams and J. W. L. Glaisher. There was one great difficulty in the way of gravitational theory, which Newton at any rate appreciated. The sizes of the Sun and planets are so small compared with the distances between them that, in considering their mutual relations, the whole of each body may fairly be treated, approximately at all events, as concentrated in one place. But the Moon is relatively less distant from the Earth, and it was doubtful if taking either body as a massive point could be justified. Still more, in calculating the mutual forces of the

Earth and the Apple, we have to remember that, as compared with the size of the apple or the distance between the two bodies, the Earth is gigantic. The problem of calculating for the first time the combined attraction of all its parts on a small body near its surface was obviously one of great difficulty. This was probably the chief reason why Newton put aside his work in 1666. Cajori states that Newton also realized the variations of gravity with latitude and the effect of centrifugal force due to the rotation of the Earth, and says that he found their elucidation "more difficult than he was aware of." Newton seems to have returned again to the problem about 1671, but once more took no steps towards publication. Possibly the same considerations deterred him, and moreover he was much worried at that time by the controversies into which his optical experiments had led him, and says "I had for some years past been endeavouring to bend myself from philosophy to other studies." Indeed, he seems to have been more interested in chemistry than in astronomy, and in theology than in any branch of natural science. . . .

But for our immediate purpose his most important results are those on circular motion with which the book ends, though, as has been said before, Newton must have reached the same conclusions in 1666. . . .

Several Fellows of the Royal Society, carrying the matter further, had been discussing in particular whether a planet moving under attraction in accordance with the inverse square relation, as suggested by Kepler's third law, would describe an ellipse in accordance with his first law. Halley, despairing of obtaining a mathematical solution from other sources, went to visit Newton at Trinity College in Cambridge, and found that he had solved the problem two years before, though he had mislaid his notes. However, Newton wrote out another solution and sent it and "much other matter" to Halley in London. Under Halley's stimulus, Newton returned to the subject, and in 1685, overcoming the difficulties of the calculation, he proved that a sphere of gravitating matter attracts bodies outside it as though all its mass were concentrated at the centre. This successful demonstration justified the simplification by which the Sun, the planets, the Earth and the Moon were taken as massive points, and raised the rough approximate calculations to proofs of great accuracy.

This success cleared the way for Newton's original investigation, by which he sought to connect astronomical forces with the Earth's pull on bodies falling to the ground. Using Picart's new measurement of the Earth, he returned to his old question of gravity and the Moon. The Earth could now be taken as having a centre of attraction at the centre of its form, and the verification of his surmise was simple. The distance of the Moon is about 60 radii of the Earth, and the Earth's radius is about 4000 miles. It follows that the Moon falls towards the Earth away from a straight path by about 0.0044 feet in one second. If the inverse square law were true, the same force would be $(60)^2$, or 3600, times as intense on the surface of the Earth, and should there cause a body to fall 3600×0.0044, or about 16 feet in one second. This was in accordance with the facts of contemporary observation, and the proof was complete. Newton had demonstrated that the familiar fall to the ground of an apple or a stone and the majestic sweep of the Moon in her orbit are due to one and the same unknown cause.

His proof that gravity must make a planetary orbit an ellipse meant the rationalization of Kepler's laws, and extended the result he had obtained for the moon to the motions of the planets. The whole intricate movement of the solar system could then be deduced from the one assumption that each particle of matter behaved as though it attracted every other particle with a force proportional to the product of the masses and inversely proportional to the square of the distance between them. The movements so deduced were found to agree accurately with those observed for two centuries. Even comets, with motions hitherto held to be irregular and incalculable, were brought into line; in 1695 Halley wrote that the path of the comet he had seen in 1682 showed that it was controlled by gravity; it returned periodically, and indeed was the same comet as that pictured in the Bayeux tapestry, a portent which was thought to presage disaster to the Saxons in 1066.

The heavenly bodies, to Aristotle divine, incorruptible, and different in kind from our imperfect world, were thus brought into the range of man's enquiry, and were shown to work in one gigantic mathematical harmony, in accordance with the dynamical principles established by the terrestrial experiments and inductions of Galileo and Newton. The publication in 1687 of Newton's *Principia*, the Mathematical Principles of Natural Philosophy, marks perhaps the greatest event in the history of science—certainly the greatest till recent years.

William J. Kaufmann, III . . . . The Foundations of Gravitational Theory

In the following selection, Kaufmann, professor of astronomy at San Diego State University, examines the way ideas concerning the physical laws of the universe have changed historically, beginning with the ancients and concluding with the work of Isaac Newton.

For thousand of years, human beings have looked up into the night sky and has been filled with awe and wonder. Countless stars stretching from horizon to horizon, the silver moon going through its phases, and planets wandering among the constellations of the zodiac inspired people to take up the study of astronomy. But few people are satisfied with endless observations alone. It is not enough to go out night after night and merely record the positions of the moon and planets. If one sees an eclipse of the moon on February 10, 1971, and another lunar eclipse on January 30, 1972, one is naturally prone to ask when the *next* eclipse will occur. It was apparent to ancient peoples that the motions of the sun, moon, and planets among the fixed stars seemed to follow rhythmic cycles. If one could understand these cycles, one could *predict* where various celestial objects would be in the future.

Only recently have we become fully aware of the ingenuity and depth of insight possessed by ancient man in the field of astronomy. The pyramids in Egypt, Stonehenge in England, and the ziggurats of Babylonia are impressive astronomical monuments. In studying these monuments, we realized that for ancient man to have constructed Stonehenge is no less of an achievement than for modern man to have journeyed to the moon.

As far back as 3000 and 4000 years ago, people have devised elaborate systems by which the motion of the sun, moon, and planets could be predicted. The remarkable accuracy of these ancient methods is well known. It has been said that two Chinese astronomers, . ˙˙ and Ho, were executed for failing to predict an eclipse in 2159 B.C. Even today with our advanced techniques, the penalties for making an error in one's computations are considerably less severe!

The methods devised by the ancients for calculating the positions of celestial objects and explaining their motions are truly impressive. Eudoxus proposed a system of concentric crystalline spheres with the earth at the center. The sun, moon, and planets were attached to the spheres, which rotated at various rates with respect to each other. Two centuries later, Hipparchus proposed his famous system whereby the planets were attached to epicycles, which in turn traveled about a deferent centered on the earth. This and similar systems were so successful in predicting planetary positions that today one can turn to Ptolemy's *Almagest* and calculate where the moon, for example, will be tonight. Surprisingly, your calculations will agree fairly well with what you observe.

Why, then, have we moderns rejected these various ancient cosmological models? Why did we become dissatisfied with the idea that the earth is at the center of the universe? Questions such as these are of fundamental importance, because the entire psychological and philosophical orientation of the Western world is involved. But from a much simpler scientific viewpoint, we see that there are at least two reasons for going from a geocentric cosmology to a heliocentric picture of the solar system.

Perhaps the most obvious motivation for our reorientation resulted from increased astronomical knowledge, beginning with Galileo's use of the telescope. Galileo's discoveries of the phases of Venus, mountains on the moon, sunspots, and the Jovian satellites played an important role in the overthrow of the Aristotelian-Ptolemaic systems. In other words, a Copernican cosmology with the sun at the center of the solar system seems far more physically reasonable.

But with the work of philosophers such as Hume and Kant, we realize that through physical science we can never hope to gain insight into the *true* nature of reality. The best we can do is prove what is not true. Therefore, there are probably psychological motivations for the changes in astronomy during the Renaissance.

At work deep in the soul of every scientist are a variety of subconscious or even mystical ideas concerning the nature of reality. For example, it is believed that the laws of nature must be beautiful, harmonious, and simple. If someone were to explain a physical law to you, it is believed that you would ideally find such knowledge aesthetically pleasing. Clearly, the work of astronomers who labored under a geocentric hypothesis was not aesthetically appealing. As the accuracy in the determination of planetary positions increased, more spheres or more epicycles had to be added. As the years went by, these systems became more cumbersome, less simple, and frankly less beautiful.

The first major reinfusion of beauty in theoretical astronomy came with the work of Johannes Kepler in the seventeenth century. Kepler's major contributions dealt with a precise description of how the planets move about the sun. Because his work opened the door to modern physical science, it will perhaps be valuable to review the essence of Kepler's discoveries as stated in his so-called Three Laws.

Up until the time of Kepler, all major ideas concerning the motions of the planets used circles. The possibility that other curves might be necessary was never seriously considered. It was Kepler who first proposed that an ellipse (see Figure 1) and not a circle must be used in describing the orbit of a planet. This idea is stated in his first law as follows:

> Each planet moves about the sun
> in an orbit which is an ellipse with
> the sun at one focus of the ellipse.

Kepler had at his disposal all the astronomical records of Tycho Brahe, and they constituted some of the finest observations available. Based on these observations, Kepler was then able to make a definite statement about how a planet moves along its elliptical orbit. This discovery is formulated in his second law:

> A straight line joining the sun
> and a planet sweeps out equal
> areas in equal time.

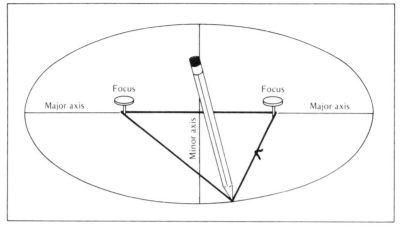

Figure 1. The ellipse. *An ellipse can be drawn very simply using two thumbtacks, a loop of string, and a pencil, as shown in the diagram. The parts of the ellipse are: the two foci (given by the location of the thumbtacks), the major axis, and the minor axis. The major axis is the longest distance across the ellipse and passes through both foci. The minor axis is the shortest distance across the ellipse passing through the center of the ellipse. The semimajor axis refers to one-half of the major axis. Similarly, the semiminor axis is one-half of the minor axis. Note that as the foci get closer and closer, the ellipse looks more and more like a circle.*

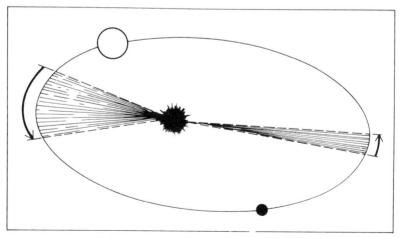

Figure 2. Kepler's first and second laws. *Each planet moves around the sun in an orbit which is an ellipse with the sun at one focus. In addition, a line joining the sun and a planet sweeps out equal areas in equal times.*

Finally, Kepler's third law relates in a quantitative way the orbital period of a planet to the size of its elliptical orbit as follows:

> The squares of the periods of
> planets are in direct proportion
> to the cubes of the semimajor
> axes of their orbits.

The first and second laws are shown schematically in Figure 2, while a graph demonstrating the third law is given in Figure 3.

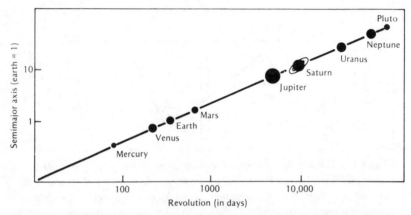

Figure 3. Kepler's third law. *This graph shows a plot of the period of revolution of a planet about the sun against the length of the semimajor axis of the planet's orbit. The fact that the data from all the planets lie along a straight line tells us that there is a very simple relationship between these two quantities. Kepler's third law predicts the exact slope or orientation of this line.*

The planets move through the vast emptiness of space unhampered by many of the extraneous effects that complicate the motion of everyday objects. For example, the planets do not encounter friction or air resistance. Clearly, therefore, the first major advances in discovering the physical laws of the universe were destined to come from astronomy. In the motions of the planets we see the nature of the physical universe revealed in its simplest and purest form.

It was Isaac Newton who possessed the genius to fathom the meaning of Kepler's Three Laws. To accomplish this, Newton had first to invent new mathematical methods, the differential calculus and the integral calculus, which enabled him to deal with variable quantities such as the distances and speeds of the planets about the sun. By applying these new mathematical tools to Kepler's empirical discoveries, Newton concluded that the planets move about the sun under the influence of a force called *gravity*. More precisely, Newton formulated his theory of gravity as follows:

> Two bodies exert a gravitational
> force on each other which is
> proportional to the product of

their masses and inversely proportional
to the square of the
distance between them.

A graph showing the strength of the gravitational field is given in Figure 4.

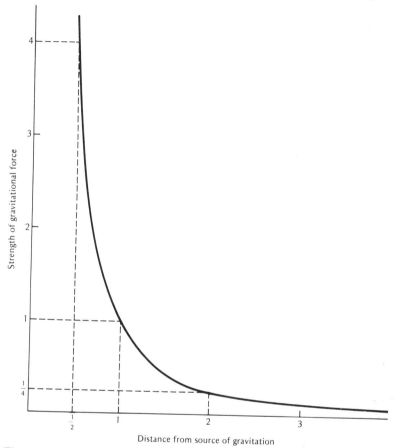

Figure 4.   Newton's law of gravitation. *This graph shows how the gravitational force of a body diminishes with distance from that body. Move twice as far away and the force is only one-quarter as great.*

Every physical object that possesses mass also has a gravitational field. If the mass of the object is doubled, the strength of the field also doubles. In addition, if you are at a certain distance from a massive object, you will experience a certain gravitational force. If you move twice as far away from that object, the strength of the gravitational force will be only one-quarter as great.

Using this law of gravitation and the mathematical methods he developed, Newton then found he was able to derive all of Kepler's laws. In other words, he could explain Kepler's discoveries in terms of an attractive gravitational force that all material bodies (not just planets) must possess. Furthermore, Newton was able to explain and predict a number of phenomena that heretofore had not been understood or known. For example, an ellipse is one member of a family of curves known as *conic sections*. Newton proved that the orbit of an object about the sun could be any one of the conic sections: a circle, an ellipse, a parabola, or a hyperbola. A diagram demonstrating how these curves may be obtained from cutting a circular cone with a plane is shown in Figure 5. The precise orbit of a celestial object about the sun would depend in a very specific fashion on how much energy that object possesses. Objects with little energy (compared to the energy contained in the gravitational field of the sun), such as planets, must orbit the sun in circles or ellipses. Objects with a great deal of energy, such as comets, can orbit the sun in parabolas. These various orbits are shown in Figure 6.

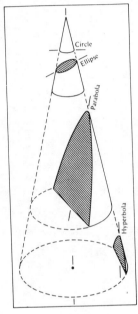

Figure 5. The conic sections. *By slicing up a cone, you can obtain four very important curves. By cutting through the cone perpendicular to the cone's axis, you obviously get a circle. Cutting at a slight angle to the perpendicular direction gives an ellipse. By slicing parallel to the slide of the cone, you obtain a parabola. And, finaliy, cutting parallel to the cone's axis gives a hyperbola.*

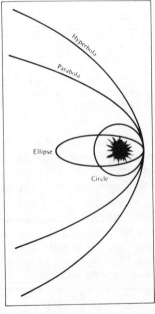

Figure 6. Orbits about the sun. *The circle is the lowest energy orbit. With more energy, a particle can go into an elliptical orbit and get farther away from the sun. With still more energy, a particle can go into a parabolic orbit and escape from the sun, but at an infinite distance from the sun the particle would come to rest. If the particle has a very great deal of energy, the orbit will be a hyperbola. Even infinitely far from the sun, the particle would still be moving away from the sun with a sizable speed.*

Newton's foundation of the first successful theory of gravitation is fundamentally very beautiful. From one simple set of assumptions stated in his universal law of gravitation, he was able to prove the validity of Kepler's laws and explain a number of additional phenomena. In the three hundred years following Newton, the successes of his theory of gravitation mounted steadily. Great mathematicians and physicists such as Gauss, Euler, Lagrange, Laplace, Hamilton, and Jacobi elaborated upon the framework devised by Newton to give us the description of physical reality know as *classical mechanics*. By the turn of the last century, however, a number of troublesome inconsistencies between classical mechanics and electromagnetic theory had become apparent. It was Albert Einstein who resolved these inconsistencies and then forged ahead to formulate a fundamentally new and different theory of gravitation known as the *general theory of relativity*.

• DISCUSSION QUESTIONS •

1. Why have human beings traditionally made such an effort to learn astronomy? To what extent was the survival of early civilizations dependent on an ability to read and interpret the skies? In what ways did our ancestors' systematic observations of the sky contribute to general overall social and intellectual development?

2. What is the historical relationship between astrology and astronomy? How and where did astrology originate? In what ways did the study and practice of astrology influence the development of astronomy as a legitimate science?

3. Can you think of any reasons why the position of the planets at the moment of your birth might influence your personality, your future? Why do you think astrology has traditionally had such a universal appeal? How can you explain its wide popularity in modern times? Develop an argument for or against astrology. On what evidence do you base your views?

4. What were Ptolemy's major contributions to astronomy? Can you describe his model of planetary motions? How did Ptolemy explain the retrograde motion of the planets? On what scientific evidence did he base his conclusions? Why would Ptolemy's scheme make sense to an observer who regarded the earth as the center of the universe?

5. What were Copernicus' two major contributions to our present-day theories of planetary motions? On what scientific evidence did he base his ideas? Contrast Ptolemy's system of the planetary motions with that of Copernicus. In what ways were they similar? How were they different? Why did many people object to Copernicus' heliocentric model of the universe?

6. How many planets were known in Kepler's time? What were they? What did Tycho Brahe's observations of the positions of Mars suggest to Kepler about the motions of the planets? How did Kepler "prove" his three laws

of planetary motion? What observations led Kepler to conclude that the moon was inhabited by intelligent life? In what respects was Kepler more like the ancient astronomers than the modern ones?

7. Can you explain, in simple terms, Newton's law of inertia? What are the basic ideas contained in Newton's theory of gravity? What is the meaning of the word "universal" as applied to Newton's gravitation? How did Newton modify Kepler's third law to deduce the nature of gravitational force? What new mathematical methods did Newton invent?

8. What is the relationship between an object's mass and its gravitational force? How is the gravitational attraction between two bodies related to the distance between them? How does Newton's inverse square law explain the fact that the planets orbit the sun in regular elliptical orbits?

9. Why does Newton's work represent the culmination of the Copernican revolution? How did Newton's ideas build on those of his predecessors? In what respects did his approach differ from theirs?

• ADDITIONAL ACTIVITIES •

Optional Projects

1. Imagine you are living in a time before there was any scientific knowledge of the laws of the universe, before there were telescopes. Watch the sky every night over a period of several weeks, and keep a written account of your observations. Each day note the exact time the sun rises and sets, where on the horizon it sets, and how it changes in appearance as it approaches the horizon. Keep a record of the order in which planets and stars appear following the sunset, and try to locate and identify the constellations. (If you need help, consult the star charts published in many popular astronomy magazines and newspapers.) At regular intervals throughout the evening, check to determine which stars seem to be moving across the sky and which seem to be stationary. Keep a record of the phases of the moon, indicating any changes in brightness and position during the course of a night. Be sure to record any unusual observations and changes in constellations. Upon completing this activity, write a paper describing what you learned about the methods of observation used by early astronomers. On the basis of your own observations, what conclusions could you draw about the nature of planetary motions? About the general predictability of objects in the sky?

2. Conduct an informal survey to find out whether people experience changes in mood or behavior during times of a full moon. Interview law enforcement officers to determine whether there is any real correlation between a full moon and the incidence of violent crimes. Prepare a written report of your findings and conclusions.

3. In a drawing or in words (or both), describe Ptolemy's model of planetary motion.

4. Make simple drawings or sketches illustrating Kepler's three laws, and write a brief description of each.

Supplementary Bibliography

Arthur Beer and Peter Beer, eds. *Kepler: Four Hundred Years, Vistas in Astronomy*, Volume 18. Oxford: Pergamon Press Ltd. 1975.
A collection of papers based on proceedings of conferences held in honor of Kepler.

Arthur Berry, *A Short History of Astronomy*. New York: Dover, 1961.
A good survey of the history of astronomy.

Arthur Koestler, *The Sleepwalkers: A History of Man's Changing Vision of the Universe*. New York: Grosset & Dunlap, 1963.
A history of astronomy from the early Greeks to Newton. Also includes informative biographical material.

E.C. Krupp, ed., *In Search of Ancient Astronomies*. New York: Doubleday, 1978.
This collection of essays on various topics in archaeoastronomy—the study of ancient and prehistoric astronomies—includes a good survey of ancient astronomical monuments.

Frank E. Manuel, *A Portrait of Isaac Newton*. Cambridge, Mass.: Harvard University Press, 1968.
An excellent biography of Newton.

Curtis Wilson, "How Did Kepler Discover His First Two Laws?" *Scientific American*, March 1972.

Chapter IV
HEAVEN AND HELL

• OVERVIEW •

THROUGHOUT TIME, THE diametrically opposed forces of gradualism and catastrophism have shaped our world and all others in the universe. To the trained eye, Earth's history of catastrophe and erosion is obvious. The battered planet shows its scars—meteor craters, volcanic cones, eroded hillsides, footpaths worn in stone, blurred features of monuments being consumed by atmospheric acids. Yet, in spite of those scars, the Earth seems stable and permanent. Healing processes are at work. Grass grows up between the cracks in the concrete, and overhead arches the protective canopy of the sky. Our modern apprehension of catastrophic processes does not have the drama of the terror of the ancients, who feared these so much that they created myths to blunt their dread of the violence of Earth and heaven. Sudden, unusual events—like a meteor streaking white fire across a night sky—were portents of cosmic disaster.

Astronomers now explain what the ancients created myths of. From records left of the solar system's history—craters, rings and moons around planets, asteroid belts and meteor showers, reappearing comets, weather on the planets—they reconstruct the past and draw object lessons for Earth. Beautiful Venus, morning star and evening star, once considered a lush Eden, is actually a hellhole whose runaway greenhouse effect may be an omen of Earth's future if our burning of fossil fuels continues to flood the atmosphere with warming carbon dioxide. The delicate balances of Earth's system can be more subtly yet devastatingly disrupted by human activities than by any storm, volcanic eruption, earthquake, or meteorite impact, no matter how momentarily terrifying. In our solar system is evidence that foreshadows our depressing future if we tinker too much with our own planet.

• LEARNING OBJECTIVES •

1. Describe the minor constituent objects of the solar system—comets, asteroids, meteoroids—and their structure.

2. Describe how cometary material probably produces meteoroids and how meteor showers are related to cometary orbits.

3. Describe the causes and effects of the forces—gradual and catastrophic, internal and external—which alter the physical aspects of planets and other bodies in the solar system.

4. Describe the changes in the surface and atmosphere of Earth that are currently taking place because of human activities and suggest their possible consequences.

5. Describe the surface, atmosphere, and other properties of the planet Venus.

• KEY TERMS AND NAMES •

asteroid	greenhouse effect
Tycho Brahe	Edmond Halley
Giordano Bruno	William Huggins
catastrophism	Johannes Kepler
comet	meteor
crater	Isaac Newton
Galileo Galilei	Pioneer Venus
gamma ray	Soviet Venera expeditions
gradualism	

• ASSIGNMENT •

Watch COSMOS television series Program 4, "Heaven and Hell."

Read Chapter 4, "Heaven and Hell," in Carl Sagan's text, *Cosmos*, or other readings assigned by your instructor.

• READINGS •

Dorothy B. Vitaliano . . . . **The Minoan Eruption of Santorin**

The violent eruptions of Santorin, a volcano in the Cyclades Islands near Crete, in the fifteenth century B.C., *may be one of the forces that caused the collapse of Minoan civilization and the rise of Mycenean civilization. It also probably inspired the Greek myths of Atlantis and several others, as well as a number of Biblical accounts. In this excerpt from her book* Legends of the Earth: Their Geologic Origins, *Dorothy B. Vitaliano of the United States Geological Survey offers an imaginative recreation of the reactions of the inhabitants of Stronghyli (now Thera or Santorini) during the eruptions and shows how the event is recorded in ancient writings.*

A series of mild earthquakes began to be felt by the people of old Stronghyli. At first they were not particularly alarming, for earthquakes had been part of normal existence there as long as anyone could remember. However, the shocks increased in frequency and severity far beyond the usual level of seismicity, and everyone wondered what they might portend. No other islands, including the mother island, were being subjected to any abnormal seismic activity. One or two families, relative newcomers to the colony, packed up their belongings and returned to their former homes. The vast majority offered prayers and sacrifices to their deities and went about their business as normal. Why leave? What part of the Minoan realm was *not* subject to earthquakes? True, Stronghyli was a little more unstable than other areas, but look at the recent shock which had shaken parts of Crete, doing some damage at Knossos and Amnisos.

Before long it became only too apparent that their island was indeed different from its neighbors. High on the flanks of the majestic peak which crowned Stronghyli, goatherds reported that there were places where the ground had become hot and was giving off steam and foul-smelling gases. Could it be that the volcano was not extinct, as they had always believed? As the emissions of vapor and the frequency and severity of the tremors increased, so did their apprehensions. Family after family packed up their valuables and took passage on the first available ship. Among those valuables were their best pieces of pottery decorated in the new style which had just begun to be imported from Crete.

One night eerie flames suddenly flared over one of the spots where hot vapors issued from the ground, from a crack encrusted with an old yellowish deposit. This was taken as a sign from the gods, and a general exodus began the next day. And none too soon. Before all who wished to quit the island had time to do so, the mountaintop burst with a muffled roar. A plume of steam and tephra rose rapidly into the air, and as it ascended it assumed a shape which some compared to a gigantic stone-pine tree, and others to a still more gigantic mushroom. More explosions followed, at intervals of a few minutes. Against the ash-laden eruptive cloud, chunks of rock (looking like black specks as seen from the settlements nestled on the lower slopes) could be seen as they were hurled high into the air, to fall back into the crater or roll down the slope. When darkness fell the scene was even more terrifying. The eruptive cloud was luridly illuminated at its base, reflecting the fires within the mountain, and the ejecta, which appeared dark by day, described fiery parabolas against the blackness of the sky and mountain. The smaller ones faded to black before they hit the ground, but the larger ones landed still aglow and traced a fiery path as they rolled down the slope. Vegetation near the summit was stripped of its leaves, and the red-hot bombs often started fires in the shrubbery.

Now there was panic. No time to take anything but the most valuable and most portable belongings! Jewelry, of course, and metal pots, but only the most precious ceramics. Every available ship, large or small, was pressed into service, and as the refugees reached other ports the call went our for more ships to complete the evacuation. The last people to leave the island were nearly hysterical with fright, for by then the explosions were stronger and more frequent, sizable pumice bombs were falling among them, necessitating that they protect their heads when they left the shelter of their houses, and the rain of ash was so heavy that the sun was dimmed. . . [During the lull following this eruption, looters pillaged the towns and villages.]

Before long the volcano cleared its throat again, and the explosions resumed. Now the tempo of activity quickly accelerated to a climax. In a rapid series of explosions of a magnitude so far unparalleled, whose roar was heard in Crete and on the mainland, Santorin spewed forth countless tons of ash and pumice, nearly all of which fell on the volcano and in the sea in the immediate vicinity. The first of these major explosions was accompanied by a shock strong enough to topple the walls of several buildings (killing one old man as he tried to rush outdoors), and opened cracks in the ground which quickly filled with pumice. All the settlements on

Stronghyli were buried, some completely, some partially. Pumice lumps and fine ash found their way into buildings through every window and door opening. Roofs, weakened by the seismic shocks, caved in under the increasing load, often bringing walls and upper floors down with them. The handful of people who still remained on the island fled toward the beach, but few reached it; most of them lay where they fell in the choking darkness; the others found that the sea offered no sanctuary, for it was so littered with pumice that they could not launch their boats. So perished the last inhabitants of Stronghyli.

On Crete, the effects of the first major outbursts were disconcerting and inconvenient, but not particularly harmful. The thundering roar of the distant explosions was frightening, and even brought down some old mud-brick buildings which were not in good repair. Most awesome was the sight of the huge dark cloud which rose rapidly on the horizon and dimmed the sun, even hiding it completely for a few hours at a time. A rain of very fine ash particles fell from this cloud, getting into eyes, hair, food, and clothing, sifting into all corners of dwellings, and dusting the crops in the fields and the vines and olive trees. To placate the gods, who all too obviously were seriously disturbed about something, the Cretans flocked to their sanctuaries and made the sacrifices and offerings deemed appropriate to the occasion. One of the offerings took the form of burying little cups containing pieces of pumice beneath the threshold of the room set apart for religious purposes. Scattered lumps of pumice had been drifting ashore since the beginning of the very violent phase of the eruption, just a few days before and its source was well known. . . . [Roars from the climax of the eruption were heard in Scandanavia, Africa, and Asia. Volcanic ash drifted as far away as Egypt.]

While Crete and other Aegean Islands received the full force of the various phenomena of the Bronze Age eruption of Santorin, some of its effects must have caused consternation or chaos in more distant parts of the Mediterranean world. Egypt, roughly five hundred miles from Santorin and right in the path of the prevailing northwesterly winds, could hardly have escaped experiencing a series of awe-inspiring manifestations. By analogy with Krakatau we can safely assume that at least lower Egypt was blacked out for a time by the ash cloud accompanying the major paroxysms, and that all Egypt should have heard the noise or felt the shock waves accompanying those tremendous explosions; moreover, any tsunamis could hardly have by-passed the Egyptian coast. Furthermore, Egypt was literate, so it would be very surprising if Egyptian writings contained no mention of unusual phenomena which could be interpreted as direct or indirect effects of the Minoan eruption. It would be even more surprising if the Egyptians who recorded these phenomena realized their connection with such a far-away event, even if they heard about it later.

However, there are not many records at all concerning that particular time in Egyptian history, which fell in the Eighteenth Dynasty. . . . It has been suggested that . . . little of the literature of the time has been preserved because Ikhnaton (Amenhotep IV), the king who tried unsuccessfully to impose a monotheistic religion on Egypt, later ordered all earlier scriptures destroyed in an effort to erase all mention of the names of the ancient gods. There are, however, some later inscriptions and papyri which refer to events which may have taken place in the Eighteenth Dynasty.

Passages like these are encountered in the Hermitage papyrus in Leningrad:

> The sun is veiled and shines not in the sight of man. None can live when the sun is veiled by clouds.
> None knoweth that midday is here . . . his shadow is not discerned. Not dazzled is the sight when he (the sun) is beheld . . . he is in the sky like the moon.

The river is dry, even the river of Egypt.
The south wind shall blow against the north wind.
The Earth is fallen into misery.
This land shall be in perturbation.
I show thee a land upside down: that occurred which never yet had occurred before.

[Other early accounts were similar.] Biblical scholars do not yet agree on the probable date of the Exodus, but one of the possibilities is 1446–1447 B.C. (the other is about 1200 B.C.). This date is based on the statement in I Kings 6:1 that Solomon began to build the temple of Jerusalem in the fourth year of his reign 480 years after the Exodus; Solomon's reign has been fixed with a fair degree of certainty as 970–930 B.C. . . . .Biblical references possibly tied to the eruption include rains of blood (rains laden with pink ash), death of animals (perhaps from toxic ash), and hail (associated with an ash fall).

And there was thick darkness in all the land of Egypt three days: They saw not one another, neither rose any from his place for three days . . ." (Exodus 10:22)

What better explanation could there be than the thick darkness which is certain to have occurred as a result of the Krakatau-like eruption of Santorin? The discrepancy between the Egyptian and biblical versions as to the duration of the blackout can easily be attributed to the fact that both chronicles were compiled hundreds of years after the event. . . .

The plague of darkness is the strongest link to the Santorin eruption; indeed, it is difficult to explain it in any way other than as the effect of an ash cloud. All the other possible links are purely speculative. They constitute an admittedly shaky inverted pyramid of ifs: if the eruption influenced the weather over a wide area (as it well might have, at least to the extent of bringing on more rain than normal) and if as a result there were thunderstorms and hail and enough rain to make things damp in a normally very dry land, then conditions resembling some of the plagues might have been produced. The presence of fluorine in the ash can neither be proved nor disproved, and therefore remains only a possibility. But whenever it occurred with respect to Egyptian history, the Minoan eruption must have been responsible for a series of unusual, largely unpleasant, and even highly alarming manifestations there, which would have seemed to be of supernatural origin. If those manifestations did come when Moses was agitating for the Israelites' release from bondage, they could well have been the reason Pharaoh was finally persuaded to let the people go.

Richard Goody . . . . Climate and the Planets

By exploring Mars and Venus, scientists gain knowledge valuable in studying Earth's atmosphere. Richard Goody, professor of planetary physics at Harvard University, discusses some of the lessons to be learned from the inner planets.

Can ideas gleaned from studies of the inner planets point the way to the solution of an important terrestrial problem? The question is obviously rhetorical since I anticipate that the reader will answer "yes." My personal research interests lie both in the behavior of the earth's atmosphere and in the nature of the other planets of the solar system. Although the planets differ greatly from one another, they also have important fundamental similarities. In so stating I am thinking mainly of the inner planets—Venus, Mars, and Earth. The outer planets, Jupiter, Saturn, Uranus, and Neptune, and the two small, airless bodies, Pluto and Mercury, differ sufficiently from the earth that analogies are few.

In my professional work I have found it interesting and instructive to let my thoughts go back and forth from the immense detail known about our planet to the sparser and very different information available from Mars and Venus. I hope to give a general impression of what this implies by means of a few specific examples.

The terrestrial problem that I have in mind is climate and its variation, a topic that becomes increasingly important as the criticality of global food supplies receives more emphasis and as our capability of understanding our atmosphere increases. We are still in an early research phase. I doubt very much whether there will soon, if ever, be ten-year predictions of the climate or safe and controlled means of changing it. I emphasize the words "safe and controlled" because man, with characteristic haste, is already involved in both deliberate and accidental climate modification without the minimum understanding required to make such tampering safe and controlled. But that is not part of this story.

I can present a picture of climatic change in terms of recent and familiar human experiences, from the pages of written history, from the testimony of archaeological finds, and from many aspects of the geologic record. In recent decades, particularly because of the power of isotopic-dating techniques, these sources of information have coalesced into the beginnings of a consistent picture of significant changes in all meteorological elements, on every time scale from year to year to tens of millions of years.

To look at recent events, a catastrophic drought in the Sahel region of North Africa is now, fortunately, receding; on the other hand, we are experiencing difficulties and discomfort from a series of dry years in the western United States. Before that, in the 1960s, it was the turn of the east coast, which suffered a mini-drought that nearly emptied the reservoirs. And, to make the Great Depression even less bearable, western Kansas and other parts of the Great Plains suffered the dust bowl disasters of the 1930s. All of these events involved decreased rainfall, undoubtedly the most important aspect of climatic change, although temperature is easier to assess objectively.

From about 1890, when the modern thermometer became available, until 1940, amateur scientists helped to establish that, at least in the Northern Hemisphere, the temperature rose about 0.6°C. You may regard that as a very small change but, maintained over many years, it can have important effects. I recollect climbing in Austria and Switzerland in the 1950s with maps based on surveys made in the early part of the century. The glaciers I encountered were not where they were shown on the maps; in some cases the snout was several miles farther back than indicated.

This warming up seems to have been part of a general trend leading out of a cold period in the sixteenth, seventeenth, and eighteenth centuries known as the Little Ice Age, a time when British writings refer to ice fairs on the Thames in London at which oxen were roasted on open fires. Needless to say, this would be inconceivable nowadays. . . . [The Earth has been subject to a continuous series of changes in climate. Some of the evidence for these changes lies in archaeological records of differences in human life patterns over time.]

At this point you may reasonably wonder what Mars and Venus can have to do with the problem of climatic change. As I have already implied, the answer is relatively little, directly, but a great deal indirectly. Curiously enough, although we can now predict weather for a few days ahead, we are very uncertain as to the physical causes leading to the climate in any given epoch. Many important considerations may be involved. For one, the sun's radiation output may change, altering the total amount of heat falling on the earth. This heat provides the driving force for all atmospheric motions and is fundamental to all climate considerations. . . . Other important possibilities are changes in the earth's surface caused by crustal plate motions, variations in the composition of the atmosphere by natural events or by human intervention, changes in atmospheric dust and particles related to volcanic activity, deviations in the ocean currents (which strongly influence coastal climates), waxing and waning of the polar icecaps, factors affecting cloudiness, variations in the earth's orbit around the sun, and fluctuations in atmospheric flow patterns not attributable to external circumstances.

One aspect of the subject of climatic change is that with a single planet the only way to test a theory rigorously is to tinker with the environment and that, as we are increasingly aware, is dangerous. So we fall back on the broader tapestry of the solar system for some help. If we have sufficiently understood our own global atmospheric phenomena, then the same ideas should be applicable to the different circumstances of another atmosphere, and if the theories work out, we may feel confidence in our initial terrestrial conclusions.

Mars, Venus, and Earth offer some important quantitative similarities and differences. The earth's rotation is an essential element in mid-latitude weather. Mars rotates at about the same rare as the earth, but Venus scarcely rotates at all. Atmospheric chemical composition may affect the surface temperature, some aspects of atmospheric motions, and cloud formation. The earth's atmosphere consists principally of oxygen and nitrogen, while the atmospheres of Mars and Venus have carbon dioxide as their principal constituent. Clouds are a crucial element of climate: Mars has only rare condensation clouds; Venus is totally covered by clouds; and the earth is halfway between, with clear and cloudy skies in almost equal amounts. Surface pressure determines the degree of temperature contrast between the equator and the poles. With respect to the earth, Mars has less than a hundredth part of the surface pressure, while Venus has almost one hundred times as much.

This recitation of similarities and differences could continue, but I believe that I have made my point. We will therefore go on to the next stage and describe, by means of examples, a number of areas in which the behaviors of planetary atmospheres are helping to instruct us about the earth.

The first concerns the difference in temperature between the equator and the poles. The question is not why the equator is hotter. This is a matter of gemoetry, which can be determined by looking at a globe, remembering that the sun's rays strike approximately at right angles to the axis of rotation for all three planets. The amount of radiation falling on a given area of a planet's surface varies with the obliquity of the sun's rays. A large amount of solar radiation is absorbed in the tropics but where the sun's rays pass tangentially (somewhere in the polar regions) a minute amount of sunlight warms the surface.

In the simplest case, surface temperature should follow the amount of sunlight. If there is no sunlight, the temperature can sink to absolute zero, $-273°C$ ($-460°F$). Thus, for a planet without atmosphere or oceans, we might expect the temperatures to vary from absolute zero at the poles to a few hundred degrees above absolute zero in the tropics. In fact, the temperature of the earth's surface varies by only 15 percent with respect to its mean value between the equator and the poles or, to put it another way, temperatures in the polar region are 200° or so above the anticipated absolute zero. Our picture must therefore be deficient in some important regard. What has been omitted is that both the atmosphere and the oceans carry heat in large amounts, tending to equalize the temperatures in equatorial and polar regions. That raises the question, What is it that governs the ability of an atmosphere to compensate differences in solar radation by means of atmospheric mixing?

The reason I have asked this question is that it was not asked at all prior to the availability of data from Mars and Venus. These data show that the equator-to-pole temperature contrast on Venus is less than 2 percent, close to that expected for an intensely stirred atmosphere. Mars, on the other hand, has a temperature contrast of 40 percent, well on the way toward the case of an airless body.

There are many factors involved in a complete explanation of these data, but the dramatic differences exhibited encourage a search for the simplest connection between the three planetary atmospheres. The essence of the argument can be captured as follows: The ability of an atmosphere to equalize temperatures by mixing does not depend on the mass of the atmosphere if the velocities involved in the mixing are comparable. On the other hand, the change in temperature that will take place in response to a change in insolation, or received solar radiation, is inversely related to the atmospheric mass. If these two processes conflict, as is the case in the three planets under discussion, the effect of differential solar heating will be less on the planet with the more massive atmosphere. The global temperature contrasts and the surface pressures of Mars, Earth, and Venus are related precisely in the sense that this argument suggests, that is, the larger the surface pressure, the smaller the temperature contrast.

I will now turn to a second example. If we reduce the solar radiation reaching the earth's surface, the surface will cool; a 1 percent decrease in solar radiation could cause the surface temperature to decrease by about 1°C. We have already seen how small temperature changes are associated with major climatic events. A decrease of solar radiation by 10 to 15 percent could cause an ice age.

One way to vary the amount of solar radiation is to reflect some of it back into space from suspended particles. Clouds are a case in point. The loss of heat below a cloud deck, as contrasted to a clear sky overhead, is very evident to any sunbather.

Other particles, solid or liquid, can perform the same function as clouds. A permanent veil of dust in the air, such as that from volcanic eruptions, can lead to a lowering of the surface temperature. Major volcanic explosions, such as Krakatoa in 1883, Pelee in 1902, and Mount Agung in 1963, injected vast amounts of dust into the stratosphere, where it spread over much of the globe, causing spectacular twilight colors for several years. Some believe that increases in volcanic activity could have caused the Pleistocene glaciations. I tend to favor another explanation, but that does not reduce the importance of understanding this phenomenon, particularly since atmospheric dust is also a byproduct of the industrial age and the artificial could eventually exceed the natural variety.

One long-lasting effect of a volcanic eruption comes from the sulfur in the emitted gases. This sulfur goes through a series of reactions and eventually forms sulfate compounds. These compounds collect as a long-lived layer in the lower stratosphere that might have significant climatic results. The sulfate layer exhibits itself as a subtle effect in the twilight, known as the "purple light," when the sun sets some 4° below the horizon. The sulfate layer seems to persist between volcanic events but it then consists primarily of drops of concentrated sulfuric acid. This explanation comes straight from our experience with the clouds of Venus.

It is very difficult to calculate the composition of particles in a cloud without direct *in situ* measurements, and it required a mixture of good fortune and very careful observation to reach the present consensus that the clouds of Venus consist of small drops of concentrated sufuric acid. That discovery was regarded as somewhat bizarre, as was the terrestrial sulfate layer discovered some decades previously.

How did such a strange substance as sulfuric acid come to form a continuous cloud layer? The surface of Venus is very hot; at 700° absolute it should be a visible dull red. This circumstance led investigators to think out from first principles what chemical species might occur if the surface of Venus were similar in composition to that of the earth. One result of this discussion was to predict the existence of an obscure substance, carbonyl sulfide, a figment of the imagination at this stage, for we have as yet no chemical measurements of the lower atmosphere of Venus. Nevertheless, its hypothetical existence fits with the presence of sulfuric acid clouds since there is a predictable scheme of chemical reactions that could lead from carbonyl sulfide to sulfuric acid at the observed cloud levels.

The final chapter in this story was the recent discovery of minute traces of carbonyl sulfide in the earth's atmosphere and the immediate analogy that could be drawn with Venus in order to explain the earth's sulfate layer.

Changing topics again, we may consider the more speculative, but far more dangerous, possibility of a climate catastrophe; that is, that our planet could, perhaps suddenly, change to a completely different condition. . . .[The lack of liquid water on Mars may have been caused by a climatic catastrophe.] There is another and even more disturbing climatic possibility, which planetary research may help to clarify, the so-called runaway greenhouse effect. The question under consideration is whether the surface of the earth could ever become like the surface of Venus, where the temperature is high enough to melt lead and all life, as we know it, is impossible. To answer this we must attempt to understand why Venus is as it it.

The runaway greenhouse phenomenon concerns the effect of atmospheric water vapor and carbon dioxide upon surface temperature. Both gases are transparent to solar radiation and do not interfere with its absorption at the planet's surface. They are not, however, transparent to the thermal infrared radiation emitted by the surface, which in the long run balances the incoming solar radiation. This semi-transparent gaseous screen intercepts some of the outgoing thermal radiation and the surface must become hotter and emit more radiation to balance the incoming solar heat. Thus, the more water vapor or carbon dioxide in the atmosphere, the higher the surface temperature.

Yet another connection between surface temperature and vapor pressure exists, namely, that the pressure of the vapor above a liquid surface increases as the temperature increases. This is why clothes dry more readily when heated and why water will boil if the temperature is high enough. As the temperature rises, therefore, the amount of water vapor above a water surface increases and the greenhouse effect then leads to a higher temperature, hence to a higher vapor pressure, and so on—each boosting the other in turn. Detailed calculations are required to understand whether this chain reaction tends toward a steady condition, as in a nuclear reactor, or toward a runaway condition, as in an atomic bomb.

The answer depends upon how close we are to the sun. It appears that there is a critical distance from the sun, somewhere between that of Earth and that of Venus, that enables us to enjoy a controlled situation while Venus undergoes its present inhospitable runaway condition.

If all this is correct, we may be dangerously close to disaster. Relatively small changes in the amount of our clouds, the nature of our surface, or the chemical composition of our atmosphere could bring us closer to Venus's condition. There is no reason that we know of to take alarm at this circumstance, but every reason to investigate our nearest neighbor with great care. . . .

I have tried to show how ideas can move back and forth between planetary and terrestrial atmospheric problems to the benefit of both subjects. In fact, they are not two subjects, but one. Lest I be misunderstood, I do not suggest that planetary research should be chosen as the main approach to all or any terrestrial climate problems. At best, we gain inspiration from such studies. The required answers to specific questions about climate must also be reachable without the use of space probes. Nevertheless, the knowledge gained from planetary exploration can help us better understand some terrestrial problems and I, for one, greatly appreciate that bonus.

Lewis Thomas . . . . **The World's Biggest Membrane**

The earth's "membrane" (the sky) protects life on Earth as the membrane of a cell protects the life within it. Lewis Thomas, prominent physician and writer, explores this analogy in a chapter from his book, The Lives of a Cell.

Viewed from the distance of the moon, the astonishing thing about the earth, catching the breath, is that it is alive. The photographs show the dry, pounded surface of the moon in the foreground, dead as an old bone. Aloft, floating free beneath the moist, gleaming membrane of bright blue sky, is the rising earth, the only exuberant thing in this part of the cosmos. If you could look long enough, you would see the swirling of the great drifts of white cloud, covering and uncovering the half-hidden masses of land. If you had been looking for a very long, geologic time, you could have seen the continents themselves in motion, drifting apart on their crustal plates, held afloat by the fire beneath. It has the organized, self-contained look of a live creature, full of information, marvelously skilled in handling the sun.

It takes a membrane to make sense out of disorder in biology. You have to be able to catch energy and hold it, storing precisely the needed amount and releasing it in measured shares. A cell does this, and so do the organelles inside. Each assemblage is poised in the flow of solar energy, tapping off energy from metabolic surrogates of the sun. To stay alive, you have to be able to hold out against equilibrium, maintain imbalance, bank against entropy, and you can only transact this business with membranes in our kind of world.

When the earth came alive it began constructing its own membrane, for the general purpose of editing the sun. Originally, in the time of prebiotic elaboration of peptides and nucleotides from inorganic ingredients in the water on the earth, there was nothing to shield out ultraviolet radiation except the water itself. The first thin atmosphere came entirely from the degassing of the earth as it cooled, and there was only a vanishingly small trace of oxygen in it. Theoretically, there could have been some production of oxygen by photo-dissociation of water vapor in ultraviolet light, but not much. This process would have been self-limiting, as Urey showed, since the wave lengths needed for photolysis are the very ones screened out selectively by oxygen; the production of oxygen would have cut off almost as soon as it occurred.

The formation of oxygen had to await the emergency of photosynthetic cells, and these were required to live in an environment with sufficient visible light for photosynthesis but shielded at the same time against lethal ultraviolet. Berkner and

Marshall calculate that the green cells must therefore have been about ten meters below the surface of water, probably in pools and ponds shallow enough to lack strong convection currents (the ocean could not have been the starting place).

You could say that the breathing of oxygen into the atmosphere was the result of evolution, or you could turn it around and say that evolution was the result of oxygen. You can have it either way. Once the photosynthetic cells had appeared, very probably counterparts of today's blue-green algae, the future respiratory mechanism of the earth was set in place. Early on, when the level of oxygen had built up to around 1 percent of today's atmospheric concentration, the anaerobic life of the earth was placed in jeopardy, and the inevitable next stage was the emergence of mutants with oxidative systems and ATP. With this, we were off to an explosive developmental stage in which great varieties of respiring life, including the multicellular forms, became feasible.

Berkner has suggested that there were two such explosions of new life, like vast embryological transformations, both dependent on threshold levels of oxygen. The first, at 1 per cent of the present level, shielded out enough ultraviolet radiation to permit cells to move into the surface layers of lakes, rivers, and oceans. This happened around 600 million years ago, at the beginning of the Paleozoic era, and accounts for the sudden abundance of marine fossils of all kinds in the record of this period. The second burst occurred when oxygen rose to 10 per cent of the present level. At this time, around 400 million years ago, there was a sufficient canopy to allow life out of the water and onto the land. From here on it was clear going, with nothing to restrain the variety of life except the limits of biologic inventiveness.

It is another illustration of our fantastic luck that oxygen filters out the very bands of ultraviolet light that are most devastating for nucleic acids and proteins, while allowing full penetration of the visible light needed for photosynthesis. If it had not been for this semipermeability, we could never have come along.

The earth breathes, in a certain sense. Berkner suggests that there may have been cycles of oxygen production and carbon dioxide consumption, depending on relative abundances of plant and animal life, with the ice ages representing periods of apnea. An overwhelming richness of vegetation may have caused the level of oxygen to rise above today's concentration, with a corresponding depletion of carbon dioxide. Such a drop in carbon dioxide may have impaired the "greenhouse" property of the atmosphere, which holds in the solar heat otherwise lost by radiation from the earth's surface. The fall in temperature would in turn have shut off much of living, and, in a long sigh, the level of oxygen may have dropped by 90 per cent. Berkner speculates that this is what happened to the great reptiles; their size may have been all right for a richly oxygenated atmosphere, but they had the bad luck to run out of air.

Now we are protected against lethal ultraviolet rays by a narrow rim of ozone, thirty miles out. We are safe, well ventilated, and incubated, provided we can avoid technologies that might fiddle with that ozone, or shift the levels of carbon dioxide. Oxygen is not a major worry for us, unless we let fly with enough nuclear explosives to kill off the green cells in the sea; if we do that, of course, we are in for strangling.

It is hard to feel affection for something as totally impersonal as the atmosphere, and yet there it is, as much a part and product of life as wine or bread. Taken all in all, the sky is a miraculous achievement. It works, and for what it is designed to accomplish it is as infallible as anything in nature. I doubt whether any of us could think of a way to improve on it, beyond maybe shifting a local cloud from here to there on occasion. The word "chance" does not serve to account well for structures of such magnificence. There may have been elements of luck in the emergence of chloroplasts, but once these things were on the scene, the evolution of the sky became absolutely ordained. Chance suggests alternative, other possibilities, different solutions. This may be true for gills and swim-bladders and forebrains, matters of detail, but not for the sky. There was simply no other way to go.

We should credit for what it is: for sheer size and perfection of function, it is far and away the grandest product of collaboration in all of nature.

It breathes for us, and it does another thing for our pleasure. Each day, millions of meteorites fall against the outer limits of the membrane and are burned to nothing by the friction. Without this shelter, our surface would long since have become the pounded powder of the moon. Even though our receptors are not sensitive enough to hear it, there is comfort in knowing that the sound is there overhead, like the random noise of rain on the roof at night.

• DISCUSSION QUESTIONS •

1. How do astronomers presently explain the formation of meteors, comets, asteroids, meteorites, and planets?

2. Why are there no rings around the inner planets—Mercury, Venus, Earth, and Mars?

3. What catastrophic forces are at work in the solar system? What evidence is there of catastrophe on the moon? Venus? Jupiter? Why does the evidence seem more obvious on some bodies than on others?

4. What gradual processes have changed the planets?

5. What can be learned from discoveries on Venus about the fragility of Earth's climate?

6. What is the meaning of Lewis Thomas' title, "The Earth's Biggest Membrane"? How does the atmosphere affect life on Earth? What would happen if it were altered?

• ADDITIONAL ACTIVITIES •

Optional Projects

1. Using a chart format, compare theories about comets created by the ancients, Tycho Brahe, Johannes Kepler, Isaac Newton, Edmund Halley, William Huggins, and modern astronomers.

2. Survey your community for evidence of gradual and catastrophic processes causing physical changes in the terrain and atmosphere. Write a report noting locations, causes, effects. Draw conclusions about long-term effects if processes continue unchecked.

3. Imagine you know nothing of modern astronomy and are getting your first look at Jupiter on a television screen. Create a myth to explain one of its features: volcanoes on Io, the Great Red Spot, cracks on Ganymede.

4. Write a report on the effects of slash-and-burn agriculture and excessive burning of fossil fuels on the Earth's atmosphere. Explain how the greenhouse effect can run out of control.

Supplementary Bibliography

Wallace S. Broecker, "The Hazards of Coal Dependence" in *Natural History,* October, 1977.
Discusses the effect of burning fossil fuels on Earth's atmosphere and climate.

Clark R. Chapman, "Craters: Planetary Chronometers," "Uniformitarianism and Catastrophism," and "The Vapors of Venus and Other Gassy Envelopes" in *The Inner Planets.* New York: Charles Scribner's Sons, 1977.
Gives background information on major concepts in this episode.

Stillman Drake, *Discoveries and Opinions of Galileo.* Garden City, New York: Doubleday & Company, Inc., 1957.
A volume of the writings of Galileo, including his discovery of Jupiter's moons and "stars" near Saturn, with commentary by Drake.

Stephen Jay Gould, "Evolution: Explosion, Not Ascent" in *The New York Times,* January 22, 1978.
Presents catastrophism as a philosophy of change, with some discussion of ideological and cultural influences.

William K. Hartmann, "Cratering in the Solar System" in *Scientific American,* January, 1977.
Points out that cratering on bodies in the inner planets and their satellites is a key to learning the history of the solar system.

"Fireball over Siberia" in *Time,* March 3, 1980.
A short explanation of Soviet theories about the Tunguska explosion.

Chapter V
BLUES FOR A RED PLANET

• OVERVIEW •

WHEN MARS WAS was physically inaccessible to us, we peopled it with superior beings, who were benevolent or evil according to our collective states of mind, and we saw reflected in it, as in a giant mirror, our magnified fears and dreams.

Percival Lowell, amateur Bostonian astronomer of the Victorian Age, postulated that the crisscross lines he observed on Mars were gigantic irrigation canals built by clever Martian engineers. Though many of his fellow scientists, including Alfred Russel Wallace, did not agree with his findings—indeed, did not even see what he saw—his ideas captured the imagination of people in the relatively early stages of a romance with technology and astronomy in late 19th Century America. In H.G. Wells' science fiction novel of the same period, *The War of the Worlds*, Martians were portrayed as cold and unsympathetic super-intelligent creatures set on imperial expansion through an invasion of Earth. Orson Welles' 1938 radio version of *The War of the Worlds* terrified Americans, who, weary from the Great Depression and shadowed with the threat of war, were all too ready to believe in a malevolent invasion from space.

Now, when our long technological arm can at last reach Mars, our idea of what a Martian is has radically changed. We look for a microorganism. Our dreams of landing robot-laboratories on the planet were finally fulfilled in 1976, when Viking space probes, after swinging around the sun, settled into orbit around Mars and sent down landers to the surface. In three biology experiments, a lander's mechanical arm scraped up soil, searching for a tiny creature that would give evidence of its existence in a faint exhalation or minute chemical change or almost imperceptible intake of gases. The results? Ambiguous.

Today some scientists have hypothesized that we might eventually "terraform" Mars to change its alien landscape into one more suitable for human habitation.

• LEARNING OBJECTIVES •

1. Describe the topography, climate, and other properties of the planet Mars as best known today.

2. Describe the type of life forms, if any, we believe might develop on Mars, given the conditions we know to exist on that planet.

3. Describe possible social and biological consequences of contact with any form of extraterrestrial life should such contact occur in this generation.

4. Explain why, despite all the Viking project experiments and other observations on Mars, we on Earth still do not know conclusively whether life exists on Mars.

5. Trace the search for life on Mars from the 19th century to the present.

6. List the ethical and engineering considerations involved in terraforming.

• KEY TERMS AND NAMES •

Chryse	Mars Jar
Cydonia	Giovanni Schiaparelli
Robert Goddard	terraforming
Percival Lowell	Konstantin Tsiolovsky
Mariner 9	*Viking 1 and Viking 2*
Mars 3 and *Mars 6*	Alfred Russel Wallace

• ASSIGNMENT •

Watch COSMOS television series Program 5. "Blues for a Red Planet."

Read Chapter 5, "Blues for a Red Planet" in Carl Sagan's text, *Cosmos*, or other readings assigned by your instructor.

• READINGS •

Percival Lowell. . . . . **Mars**

Amateur astronomer Percival Lowell, convinced that lines he saw on Mars represented canals engineered by intelligent beings, presented his findings in Mars, *published in 1895.*

Two lines will be noticed prolonging the twin forks of the Sabaeus Sinus. If we let our look follow down them, we shall mark others then yet others, and so we might proceed from line to line all over the bright areas of the planet. These lines are the famous canals of Mars. With regard to their surprising symmetry, it is only necessary to say that the better they are seen the more symmetrical they look. Of the two first mentioned, the right-hand one is the Gihon, the left-hand one the Hiddekel, and the spot at the limit of the latter is the Lacus Ismenius. From the pearl at the bottom of the Margaritifer Sinus, the Oxia Palus, the Oxus runs nearly north to the Pallas Lacus, while another canal, the Indus, makes off northwest . . .

Unchangeable, apparently, in position, the canals are otherwise among the most changeable features of the Martian disk. From being invisible, they emerge gradually, for some reason inherent in themselves, into conspicuousness. In short, phenomenally at least, they grow. The order of their coming carries with it a presumption of cause, for it synchronizes with the change in the Martian seasons. Their first appearance is a matter of the Martian time of year.

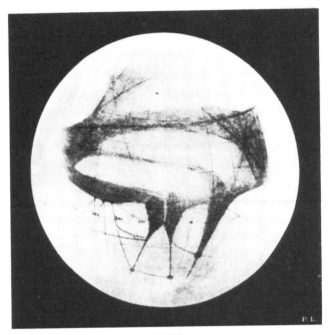

MARS
LONGITUDE 0° ON THE MERIDIAN

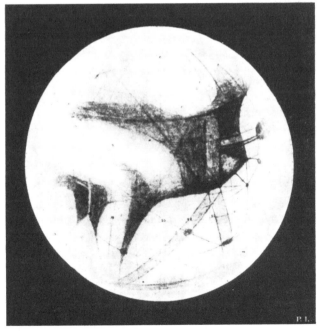

MARS
LONGITUDE 30° ON THE MERIDIAN

To start with, the visible development of the canal system follows the melting of the polar snows. Not until such melting has progressed pretty far do any of the canals, it would seem, become perceptible.

Secondly, when they do appear, it is, in the case of the southern hemisphere, the most southern ones that become visible first. Last June, when the canals were first seen, those about the Lake of the Sun and the Phoenix Lake were easier to make out than any of the others. Now, this region is the part of the reddish-ochre continent, as we may call it, that lies nearest the south pole. It extends into the blue-green regions as far south as 40° of south latitude. Nor do any so-called islands—that is, smaller reddish-ochre areas—stand between it and the pole. It lies first exposed therefore, to any water, descending toward the equator from the melting of the polar cap.

CONCLUSION

To review, now, the chain of reasoning by which we have been led to regard it probable that upon the surface of Mars we see the effects of local intelligence. We find, in the first place, that the broad physical conditions of the planet are not antagonistic to some form of life; secondly, that there is an apparent dearth of water upon the planet's surface, and therefore, if beings of sufficient intelligence inhabited it, they would have to resort to irrigation to support life; thirdly, that there turns out to be a network of markings covering the disk precisely counterparting what a system of irrigation would look like; and, lastly, that there is a set of spots placed where we should expect to find the lands thus artificially fertilized, and behaving as such constructed oases should. All this, of course, may be a set of coincidences, signifying nothing; but the probability points the other way. As to the details of explanation, any we may adopt will undoubtedly be found, on closer acquaintance, to vary from the actual Martian state of things; for any Martian life must differ markedly from our own.

The fundamental fact in the matter is the dearth of water. If we keep this in mind, we shall see that many of the objections that spontaneously arise answer themselves. The supposed herculean task of constructing such canals disappears at once; for, if the canals be dug for irrigation purposes, it is evident that what we see, and call by ellipsis the canal, is not really the canal at all, but the strip of fertilized land bordering it,—the thread of water in the midst of it, the canal itself, being far too small to be perceptible. In the case of an irrigation canal seen at a distance, it is always the strip of verdure, not the canal, that is visible, as we see in looking from afar upon irrigated country on the Earth . . .

Now apply this principle to a possible inhabitant of Mars, and suppose him to be constructed three times as large as a human being in every dimension. If he were on Earth, he would weigh twenty-seven times as much, but on the surface of Mars, since gravity there is only about one third of what it is here, he would weigh but nine times as much. The cross-section of his muscles would be nine times as great. Therefore the ratio of his supporting power to the weight he must support would be the same as ours. Consequently, he would be able to stand with as little fatigue as we. Now consider the work he might be able to do. His muscles, having length, breadth, and thickness, would all be twenty-seven times as strong as ours. He would prove twenty-seven times as strong as we, and could accomplish twenty-seven times as much. But he would further work upon what required, owing to decreased gravity, but one third the effort to overcome. His effective force, therefore, would be eighty-one times as great as man's, whether in digging canals or in other bodily occupation. As gravity on the surface of Mars is really a little more than one third that at the surface of the Earth, the true ratio is not eighty-one, but about fifty; that is a Martian would be, physically, fifty-fold more efficient than man.

As the reader will observe, there is nothing problematical about this deduction whatever. It expresses an abstract ratio of physical capabilities which must exist between the two planets, quite irrespective of whether there be denizens on either, or how other conditions may further affect their forms. As the reader must also note, the deduction refers to the possibility, not to the probability, of such giants; the calculation being introduced simply to show how different from us any Martians may be, not how different they are. . . .

Now, in the special case of Mars, we have before us the spectacle of a world relatively well on in years, a world much older than the Earth. To so much about his age Mars bears evidence on his face. He shows unmistakable signs of being old. Advancing planetary years have left their mark legible there. His continents are all smoothed down; his oceans have all dried up. *Teres atque rotundus*, he is a steady-going body now. . . .

The evidence of handicraft, if such it be, points to a highly intelligent mind behind it. Irrigation, unscientifically conducted, would not give us such truly wonderful mathematical fitness in the several parts to the whole as we there behold. A mind of no mean order would seem to have presided over the system we see,—a mind certainly of considerably more comprehensiveness than that which presides over the various departments of our own public works. Party politics, at all events, have had no part in them; for the system is planet wide. Quite possibly, such Martian folk are possessed of inventions of which we have not dreamed, and with them electrophones and kinetoscopes are things of a bygone past, preserved with veneration in museums as relics of the clumsy contrivances of the simple childhood of the race. Certainly what we see hints at the existence of beings who are in advance of, not behind us, in the journey of life. . . .

Like the savage who fears nothing so much as a strange man, like Crusoe who grows pale at the sight of footprints not his own, the civilized thinker instinctively turns from the thought of mind other than the one he himself knows. To admit into his conception of the cosmos other finite minds as factors has in it something of the weird. Any hypothesis to explain the facts, no matter how improbable or even palpably absurd it be, is better than this. Snow-caps of solid carbonic acid gas, a planet cracked in a positively monomaniacal manner, meteors ploughing tracks across its surface with such mathematical precision that they must have been educated to the performance, and so forth and so on, in hypotheses each more astounding than its predecessor, commend themselves to man, if only by such means he may escape the admission of anything approaching his kind. . . .

We must be just as careful not to run to the other extreme, and draw deductions of purely local outgrowth. To talk of Martian beings is not to mean Martian men. Just as the probabilities point to the one, so do they point away from the other. Even on this Earth man is of the nature of an accident. He is the survival of by no means the highest physical organism. He is not even a high form of mammal. Mind has been his making. For aught we can see, some lizard or batrachian might just as well have popped into his place early in the race, and been now the dominant creature of this Earth. Under different physical conditions, he would have been certain to do so. Amid the surroundings that exist on Mars, surroundings so different from our own, we may be practically sure other organisms have been evolved of which we have no cognizance. What manner of beings they may be we lack the data even to conceive.

For the answers to such problems we must look to the future. That Mars seems to be inhabited is not the last, but the first word on the subject. More important than the mere fact of the existence of living beings there, is the question of what they may be like. Whether we ourselves shall live to learn this cannot, of course, be foretold. One thing, however, we can do, and that speedily: look at things from a standpoint raised above our local point of view; free our minds at least from the shackles that of necessity tether our bodies; recognize the possibility of others in the same light that we do the certainty of ourselves. That we are the sum and substance of the capabilities of the cosmos is something so preposterous as to be exquisitely comic. We pride ourselves upon being men of the world, forgetting that this is but objectionable singularity, unless we are, in some wise, men of more worlds than one. For, after all, we are but a link in a chain. Man is merely this earth's highest production up to date. That he in any sense gauges the possibilities of the universe is humorous. He does not, as we can easily foresee, even gauge those of this planet. He has been steadily bettering from an immemorial past, and will apparently continue to improve through an incalculable future. Still less does he gauge the universe about him. He merely typifies in an imperfect way what is going on elsewhere, and what, to a mathematical certainty, is in some corners of the cosmos indefinitely excelled.

If astronomy teaches anything, it teaches that man is but a detail in the evolution of the universe, and that resemblant though diverse details are inevitably to be expected in the host of orbs around him. He learns that, though he will probably never find his double anywhere, he is destined to discover any number of cousins scattered through space.

Alfred Russel Wallace. . . . . .Is Mars Habitable?

Alfred Russel Wallace, Lowell's contemporary and co-creator with Charles Darwin of the theory of evolution, refuted Lowell's findings in Is Mars Habitable? *(1907)*

This little volume has necessarily touched upon a great variety of subjects in order to deal in a tolerably complete manner with the very extraordinary theories by which Mr. Lowell attempts to explain the unique features of the surface of the planet, which, by long-continued study, he has almost made his own. It may therefore be well to sum up the main points of the arguments against his view, introducing a few other facts and considerations which greatly strengthen my argument.

The one great feature of Mars which led Mr. Lowell to adopt the view of its being inhabited by a race of highly intelligent beings, and, with ever-increasing discovery to uphold this theory to the present time, is undoubtedly that of the so-called 'canals'—their straightness, their enormous length, their great abundance, and their extension over the planet's whole surface from one polar snow-cap to the other. The very immensity of this system, and its constant growth and extension during fifteen years of persistent observation, have so completely taken possession of his mind, that, after a very hasty glance at analogous facts and possibilities, he has declared them to be 'non-natural'—therefore to be works of art—therefore to necessitate the presence of highly intelligent beings who have designed and constructed them. This idea has coloured or governed all his writings on the subject. The innumerable difficulties which it raises have been either ignored, or brushed aside on the flimsiest evidence. As examples, he never even discusses the totally inadequate water-supply for such world-wide irrigation, or the extreme irrationality of constructing so vast a canal-system the waste from which, by evaporation, when exposed to such desert conditions as he himself describes, would use up ten times the probable supply.

Again, he urges the 'purpose' displayed in these 'canals.' Their being *all* so straight, *all* describing great circles of the 'sphere,' all being so evidently arranged (as he thinks) either to carry water to some 'oasis' 2000 miles away, or to reach some arid region far over the equator in the opposite hemisphere! But he never considers the difficulties this implies. Everywhere these canals run for thousands of miles across waterless deserts, forming a system and indicating a purpose, the wonderful perfection of which he is never tired of dwelling upon (but which I myself can nowhere perceive). Yet he never even attempts to explain how the Martians could have lived *before* this great system was planned and executed, or why they did not *first* utilise and render fertile the belt of land adjacent to the limits of the polar snows—why the method of irrigation did not, as with all human arts, begin gradually, at home, with terraces and channels to irrigate the land close to the source of the water. How, with such a desert as he describes three-fourths of Mars to be, did the inhabitants ever get to *know* anything of the equatorial regions and its needs, so as to start right away to supply those needs? All this, to my mind, is quite opposed to the idea of their being works of art, and altogether in favour of their being natural features of a globe as peculiar in origin and internal structure as it is in its surface-features. The explanation I have given, though of course hypothetical, is founded on known cosmical and terrestrial facts, and is, I suggest far more scientific as well as more satisfactory than Mr. Lowell's wholly unsupported speculation. This view I have explained in some detail in the preceding chapter.

Mr. Lowell never even refers to the important question of loss by evaporation in these enormous open canals, or considers the undoubted fact that the only intelligent and practical way to convey a limited quantity of water such great distances would be by a system of water-tight and air-tight tubes laid *under the ground*. The mere attempt to use open canals for such a purpose shows complete ignorance and stupidity in these alleged very superior beings; while it is certain that, long before half of them were completed their failure to be of any use would have led any rational beings to cease constructing them.

He also fails to consider the difficulty, that, if these canals are necessary for existence in Mars, how did the inhabitants ever reach a sufficiently large population with surplus food and leisure enabling them to rise from the low condition of savages to one of civilisation, and ultimately to scientific knowledge? Here again is a dilemma which is hard to overcome. Only a *dense* population with *ample* means of subsistence could possibly have constructed such gigantic works; but, given these two conditions, no adequate motive existed for the conception and execution of them—even if they were likely to be of any use, which I have shown they could not be.

FURTHER CONSIDERATIONS ON THE CLIMATE OF MARS

Recurring now to the question of climate, which is all important, Mr. Lowell never even discusses the essential point—the temperature that must *necessarily* result from an atmospheric envelope one-twelfth (or at most one-seventh) the density of our own; in either case corresponding to an altitude far greater than that of our highest mountains.[1] Surely this phenomenon, everywhere manifested on the earth even under the equator, of a regular decrease of temperature with altitude, the only cause of which is a less dense atmosphere, should have been fairly grappled with, and some attempt made to show why it should not apply to Mars, except the weak remark that on a level surface it will not have the same effect as on exposed mountain heights. But it *does* have the same effect, or very nearly so, on our lofty plateaux often hundreds of miles in extent, in proportion to their altitude. Quito, at 9350 ft. above the sea, has a mean temperature of about 57° F., giving a lowering of 23° from that of Manaos at the mouth of the Rio Negro. This is about a degree for each 400 feet, while the general fall for isolated mountains is about one degree in 340 feet according to Humboldt, who notes the above difference between the rate of cooling for altitude of the plains—or more usually sheltered valleys in which the towns are situated—and the exposed mountain sides. It will be seen that this lower rate would bring the temperature of Mars at the equator down to 20° F. below the freezing point of water from this cause alone. But all enquirers have admitted, that if conditions as to atmosphere were the same as on the earth, its greater distance from the sun would reduce the temperature to −31° F., equal to 63° below the freezing point. It is therefore certain that the combined effect of both causes must bring the temperature of Mars down to at least 70° or 80° below the freezing point.

The cause of this absolute dependence of terrestrial temperatures upon density of the air-envelope is seldom discussed in text-books either of geography or physics, and there seems to be still some uncertainty about it. Some impute it wholly to the thinner air being unable to absorb and retain so much heat as that which is more dense; but if this were the case the soil at great altitudes not having so much of its heat taken up by the air should be warmer than below, since it undoubtedly *receives* more heat owing to the greater transparency of the air above it; but it certainly does not become warmer. The more correct view seems to be that the loss of heat by radiation is increased so much through the rarity of the air above it as to *more* than counterbalance the increased isolation, so that though the surface of the earth at a given altitude may receive 10 per cent more direct sun-heat it loses by direct radiation, combined with diminished air and cloud-radiation, perhaps 20 or 25 per cent more, whence there is a resultant cooling effect of 10 or 15 per cent. This acts by day as well as by night, so that the greater heat received at high altitudes does not warm the soil so much as a less amount of heat with a denser atmosphere. This effect is further intensified by the fact that a less dense cannot absorb and transmit so much heat as a more dense atmosphere.

Here then we have an absolute law of nature to be observed operating everywhere on the earth, and the mode of action of which is fairly well understood. This law is, that reduced atmospheric pressure increases radiation, or loss of heat, *more rapidly* than it increases insolation or gain of heat, so that the result is *always* a considerable *lowering* of temperature. What this lowering is can be seen in the universal fact, that even within the tropics perpetual snow covers the higher mountain summits, while on the high plains of the Andes, at 15,000 or 16,000 feet altitude, where there is very little or no snow, travellers are often frozen to death when delayed by storms; yet at this elevation the atmosphere has much more than double the density of that of Mars!

The error in Mr. Lowell's argument is, that he claims for the scanty atmosphere of Mars that it allows more sun-heat to reach the surface; but he omits to

[1] A four inches barometer is equivalent to a height of 40,000 feet above sea-level with us.

take account of the enormously increased loss of heat by direct radiation, as well as by the diminution of air-radiation, which together necessarily produce a great reduction of temperature.

It is this great principle of the prepotency of radiation over absorption with a diminishing atmosphere that explains the excessively low temperature of the moon's surface, a fact which also serves to indicate a very low temperature for Mars. These two independent arguments—from alpine temperatures and from those of the moon—support and enforce each other, and afford a conclusive proof (as against anything advanced by Mr. Lowell) that the temperature of Mars must be far too low to support animal life.

A third independent argument leading to the same result is Dr. Johnstone Stoney's proof that aequeous vapour cannot exist on Mars; and this fact Mr. Lowell does not attempt to controvert.

To put the whole case in the fewest possible words:

(1) All physicists are agreed that, owing to the distance of Mars from the sun, it would have a mean temperature of about $-35°$ F. ($=456°$ F. abs.) even if it had an atmosphere as dense as ours.

(2) But the very low temperatures on the earth under the equator, at a height where the barometer stands at about three times as high as on Mars, proves, that from scantiness of atmosphere alone Mars cannot possibly have a temperature as high as the freezing point of water; and this proof is supported by Langley's determination of the low *maximum* temperature of the full moon.

The combination of these two results must bring down the temperature of Mars to a degree wholly incompatible with the existence of animal life.

(3) The quite independent proof that water-vapour cannot exist on Mars, and that therefore, the first essential of organic life—water—is non-existent.

The conclusion from these three independent proofs, which enforce each other in the multiple ratio of their respective weights, is therefore irresistible—that animal life, especially in its higher forms, cannot exist on the planet.

Mars, therefore, is not only uninhabited by intelligent beings such as Mr. Lowell postulates, but is absolutely UNINHABITABLE.

George Alexander . . . . Viking Science

The three Viking biology experiments conducted on Mars in 1976 were searches for life's ability to metabolize, not for actual life forms. George Alexander, science writer for the Los Angeles Times, *gives an account of the Viking expedition as a whole—the experiments in biology, chemistry, and meteorology, as well as interpretations of the orbiter pictures, which may provide dating of Mars' "watery episodes."*

Of all the splendors of the night sky, few objects caught the ancients' attention—or impelled their imagination—more than the planet Mars.

It was unmistakably different. It glowed with a steady, reddish hue, quite unlike the hard, brilliant pin-points of white light from the stars. And where those stars seemed to march through the seasons in orderly ranks, Mars wandered, now drawing close to Earth and then receding.

Such color and such movement seemed to ancient peoples to be reflections of supernatural powers. To the Babylonians, Mars was "Nergal," the god of fire, a mighty warrior, and the Greeks and Romans also attributed omens of warfare and strife to the planet. Indeed, it is named for the Roman god of war.

Down through the centuries, Mars continued to fascinate the inhabitants of Earth. And with the advent of the telescope, which enabled people to see something more of the planet than just its color, Mars grew expansively in the fertile soil of the human mind. The indistinct patches and surface features were sharpened and infused with meaning and purpose more in keeping with the terrestrial experience. It seemed certain that Mars was inhabited, just as Earth, and if its plants and creatures were sometimes bizarrely depicted, that was not altogether unreasonable. Mars was populated with the rich products of the human imagination.

And now the human imagination has succeeded in populating Mars with its most complex and remarkable product yet, the Viking spacecraft.

Its form is perhaps as bizarre as any Martian machine ever conceived by a science-fiction writer, for the top and sides of the spacecraft's six-sided box structure are covered with oddly-shaped funnels, covers, tanks, antennas, pedestals, and booms. If the Viking had wheels instead of footpads, if would resemble the overloaded car of some Dust Bowl family of the 1930s, headed west for California.

But Viking is a triumph of function over form. It was designed by National Aeronautics and Space Administration and Martin Marietta Aerospace engineers *not* as some streamlined space yacht, but rather as a sturdy landing barge, a vessel that could beach itself safely upon the rugged Martian shores and, once there, carry out a wide range of scientific investigations. It began doing precisly that on July 20, 1976.

There are eight scientific experiments aboard the Viking lander; a pair of electronic cameras, which have caught not only the color of the Martian surface, but also its rocky texture; a three-part biology "mini-laboratory," designed to detect different facets of life processes, if any exist on Mars, two chemistry labs, one organic and the other inorganic, both of which are meant to reveal the chemical make-up and activity of the planet, a meteorology boom, designed to measure the Martian weather; a seismometer, to record "Marsquakes" if indeed there are such things; an array of permanent magnets, to show the magnetic properties of Martian soil particles; and a grab-bag of physical devices, to demonstrate various aspects about the Martian surface's properties.

The cameras were the first instruments to reveal something about Mars. No sooner had Viking and its precious cargo of experiments settled on the surface than its on-board computer ordered one of the two cameras to take a picture of the immediate landing area.

The tension inside the Vikng mission control center at the Jet Propulsion Laboratory in Pasadena, California, was excruciating as scientists and engineers waited 19 minutes for that first picture to be transmitted over 200 million miles from Mars to Earth. And as the first vertical strips of that initial scene suddenly appeared on television monitors throughout JPL, the tension popped like a cork from a vigorously shaken bottle of champagne, gasps of astonishment, awe, and excitement effervesced from the Viking team members. "Oh!" cried Dr. Thomas Mutch, a Brown University professor of geology and the leader of the Viking lander imaging system team, "Incredible! Incredible!" And cheers broke out in all the mission operations and support rooms at JPL and at the Martin Marietta plant in Denver.

It was indeed a remarkable picture, despite the fact that it was in black-and-white and despite the fact that it revealed an area not much bigger than what a person would see hanging his or her head out a car window and staring straight down.

There were many small rocks in the Martian scene and a soil as seemingly hard-packed as wet sand. And then one of the Viking lander's footpads came into view—a circular metal dish that had stamped Mars with humanity's mark as indelibly as astronaut Neil Armstrong's boot stamped the moon seven years earlier on this very date.

Minutes later, the camera had lifted its gaze and taken a sweeping panorama of the landing area. Dr. Mutch again broke out in a series of "incredibles!" and Viking project scientist Dr. Gerald A. Soffen later said he realized how Lewis and Clark must have felt when they entered the Pacific Northwest.

The panoramic picture disclosed that Viking 1 had come down on a rolling rocky sector of the Martian basin called Chryse Planitia. Parts of the lander intruded in the picture, but rather than detract from the 300-degree breadth of the picture, they gave a reassuringly familiar sense of scale and orientation to the image, as if the human viewer were actually gazing out on the scene from the windowed bridge of a ship.

On July 21, the day after it landed, the Viking camera switched to color and beamed back to Earth the first image to show, vividly, why Mars has long been called "the red planet." The fine-grained material had a reddish-orange tint, more than a little reminiscent of deserts in the southwestern United States and in North Africa. Some rocks were light-gray while others were distinctly dark, with a greenish or even bluish cast to them. And the Martian sky, which at first had appeared to be a pale blue, was eventually determined to be a shade somewhere between a creamy orange and a faint salmon pink—the result of a large number of those super-fine particles of red dust suspended in the wispy Martian atmosphere.

That atmosphere proved to be something of a surprise. When the gas chromatograph mass spectrometer, the organic chemistry experiment, inhaled some Martian air and passed it through its various analytical devices, it found the major constituent was carbon dioxide—accounting for 95% of the planet's gassy envelope. That was not unexpected, but the second principal constituent was nitrogen, to the extent of 2 to 3%. (The remaining gases: argon, 1 or 2%, and oxygen less than 1%).

Nitrogen, of course, is a key ingredient in the biochemical recipe for terrestrial life. If life exists on Mars, or ever started to exist there, in forms comparable to those on Earth, nitrogen would seem to be indispensable—but the presence of this element was, until Viking 1's arrival, only conjectural. Now, however, the chromatograph spectrometer confirmed the tentative finding of a "sniffer" which sampled the atmosphere during the landing process and found traces of nitrogen: the gas is present on the planet. "We learned more about the atmosphere (of Mars) in half an hour from Viking," said Harvard professor Dr. Michael McElroy, "than in 50 years of observations from Earth."

The discovery of nitrogen increased the chances—never very great to begin with—that life might be found on Mars: "The 'stewpot' appears to have been there sometime in its history for biogenesis (the formation of living organisms)," said Dr. Soffen, a biologist, "but whether it took place or not, we don't know."

Long before Viking 1 bore down on Mars, scientists like Dr. Soffen had repeatedly cautioned against fast and easy conclusions about Martian life based on the findings of just one experiment. Life is such a multi-faceted process, they said, that it should make its presence felt not just to one experiment, but to several. They urged that no final judgment about the presence, or absence, of Martian life be made until the findings of all the various biological and chemical experiments were taken into account.

That judgment, however, seemed to fall into the category of easier-said-than-done once those experiments began sending back streams of data about Mars. The planet was revealed to be a strange place where things are never quite what they seem.

That judgment, however, seemed to fall into the category of easier-said-than-done once those experiments were taken into account.

The biology experiments, for example, indicated that there was a great deal of activity in the Martian soil. And while Viking team scientists would not flatly rule out the possibility that there might be organisms in the red soil giving rise to that activity, they were most reluctant to embrace biological agents as the probable cause. They preferred instead to seek a chemical answer to those phenomena.

One instrument, the "gas exchange" experiment, reported an unusually large flow of oxygen from the small soil sample it had been given to work on. It is a basic tenet of biology that living organisms trade in gases—inhaling some and exhaling others. If there were Martian organisms and if they trafficked in different gases, the gas exchange instrument would detect that; it was designed to catch molecular hydrogen, nitrogen, oxygen, methane, and carbon dioxide. The heavy flow of oxygen from the Martian soil sample seemed to be precisely the sort of thing that the experiment was supposed to find.

Similarly, a second experiment—the "labeled release" unit—reported the discovery of a surprisingly high number of radioactive carbon dioxide molecules coming off its soil sample. The radioactive carbon had been provided in a dilute nutrient solution misted over the soil sample, but something in the Martian soil was taking those carbon atoms and combining them with oxygen atoms to form carbon dioxide.

"We believe there is something in the surface, some chemical or physical entity, which is affording the surface material great activity," said Dr. Harold Klein, the leader of the Viking biology team, in announcing those findings July 31. "And it may mimic—let me emphasize that, *may mimic*—biological activity."

But neither landing sat easily on the minds of Viking scientists. It was, said Dr. Soffen, "a case of too much too soon." All terrestrial life forms with which science has any familiarity take time to grow, to reproduce; plotted on a graph, those manifestations of growth would trace out a curve that slopes gently upward at first and jumps markedly only after an interval of time. The Martian curves, however, zoomed upward right away.

"If it is a biological response," said Dr. Klein voicing a reservation shared by many of his colleagues, "it is stronger than anything we have obtained from terrestrial soil (organisms). It would mean that biology on Mars is more highly developed, more intense, than life on Earth."

Reluctant to accept a concept of such advanced life forms in such a seemingly hostile environment, the Viking scientists turned to chemistry for answers to the puzzles posed by the spacecraft. There was good reason for them to do so. From the pictures taken of the planet by both the Viking 1 orbiter and the Mariner 9 reconnaissance spacecraft several years earlier, it was clear that some liquid—most likely water—had once washed down the red Martian slopes.

And unlike the Earth's moon, or the planet Mercury, both of which have never had even the slightest puff of an atmosphere in all the 4½ billion years of their existence, Mars does. A curious atmosphere it is, at that, thick enough to kick up some wild dust storms that scour the planet with the intensity of sand-blasting, and yet thin enough (it has 1% the density of Earth's airy envelope) to allow virtually all solar radiation to strike the planet's iron-rich surface.

Taken together—the past presence of water, the thin atmosphere posing no hindrance to solar ultraviolet rays, and the abundance of iron oxides—Mars seemed to have all the ingredients for a very reactive surface. Indeed Dr. Robert L. Huguenin of the Massachusetts Institute of Technology had previously constructed a theory about the Martian surface that incorporated all of these elements. While the actual chemical details of that theory are perhaps too complex to describe here, Dr. Huguenin nevertheless postulated a mechanism that would strongly oxidize the planet's topmost soil layer and provide a rich vein of oxygen in that soil.

Of course, everything is relative, even on Mars. The amount of oxygen detected by the gas exchange experiment was a lot *relative* to the scant amount of this gas in the total Martian atmosphere (about 0.3%) and *relative* to what scientists had expected to find (it was 15 times more). But in absolute terms, it wasn't much.

As for the radioactive carbon that seemed to be combined with something in the soil inside the labeled release experiment to generate carbon dioxide, there again the answer seemed to be chemistry: one of the nutrients carried to Mars aboard the Viking spacecraft was formate, the salt of formic acid. Chemically, formic acid is a molecule of carbon dioxide with two hydrogen atoms attached; in chemical terms, it is written HCOOH (the "H" being hydrogen, "C" carbon, and "O" oxygen). In a strongly oxidized environment, any chemist would expect the oxidants to pick the hydrogen atoms off the formate molecule like small boys plucking apples off a tree—leaving the carbon dioxide by itself. And since that carbon atom was the radioactive isotope of carbon, carbon-14, that would seem to explain why a sample of Martian soil would, when given a small amount of nutrients that included formate, generate a generous stream of radioactive carbon dioxide.

But even as Viking scientists were arranging for laboratory tests on Earth that would either corroborate or refute these chemical explanations of the oxygen and carbon dioxide findings, Mars pulled another rabbit out of its planetary hat. On August 6, the first data from the "pyrolic release" experiment, the third of the three biology instruments, was received by Earth tracking stations—and it contained quite a surprise.

The pyrolytic instrument indicated that something in its soil sample was pulling carbon dioxide (also radioactively tagged) out of the air in the test chamber and incorporating it into other compounds within that soil. Whether that "something" was biological or chemical in nature was not immediately clear. But a definitive answer was of paramount importance, for this experiment—provided by Dr. Norman Horowitz of the California Institute of Technology—was widely regarded by scientists as the most definitive test for Martian life of the three biology instruments.

The way that the pyrolytic worked was this: A small bit of Martian soil was dropped into a test chamber made to resemble as closely as possible the real Martian environment. A xenon lamp bathed the soil with simulated sunlight. Carbon dioxide and carbon monoxide gases circulated in the air space above the sample.

The catch was that the carbon dioxide and carbon monoxide molecules were tagged with carbon-14 atoms. If there was anything in the Martian soil that takes in carbon compounds, as green plants do on Earth in photosynthesis, the radioactive tag would enable scientists to find it.

The sample was given five days in which to take up as much or as little of the tagged carbon dioxide and carbon monoxide gas molecules as it could. Then the air space was purged and the gases driven off. Once this had been done, the soil was pyrolyzed—heated to a very high temperature—to chase out into the open, like a covey of quail, any carbon 14 atoms that had gone to ground. (Not literally "into the open," but rather into a radiation detector that counted the numbers of radioactive particles striking it.)

The detector had been expected to register as many as 15 counts per minute (cpm) over and above the normal background of 477 cpm, without any inferences deduced about Martian life from that low reading. Instead, the unit reported 573 cpm which, when the background level was subtracted, left a net of 96 particles of radioactive carbon per minute—more than six times the anticipated value.

Drs. Horowitz, Klein, and the other Viking biologists were flabbergasted. "I am tantalized," Harold Klein confessed. "It is a very tantalizing result."

Still, they cautioned that the finding should not be construed as irrefutable proof of the existence of Martian life. "I would emphasize that we have not discovered life on Mars," Dr. Horowitz said, and he repeated the "not" just in case anyone missed the word.

No one knew what to make of the curious pyrolytic release results. If the explanation was chemistry, according to Norman Horowitz, then it had to be a chemical process different from that at work inside the gas exchange and labeled release instruments. The latter appeared to be oxidation, while the former necessarily had to be reduction, the chemical equivalent of a polar opposite. The scientists planned to repeat the experiment just as soon as they could, but this time with a soil sample that had been sterilized. The second experiment would serve as a "control" for the first. If the results from both tests matched, the tantalizing suggestion of Martian organisms would have to be ruled out. And if they didn't agree, then the scientists would have to conclude that there was something in the first run that wasn't present in the second—and that something could be life.

Whichever way the pyrolytic experiment turned out, it would have to be fitted to the findings from two chemistry experiments also aboard the Viking lander—one an organic instrument, the other inorganic.

The inorganic instrument, the X-ray fluorescence spectrometer, began working shortly after the Viking had settled down on the surface of Mars. The instrument in effect used photons to "ring the bell" of the various elements in the soil. The photons excited the elements and caused them to emit characteristic X-rays.

Silicon, iron, calcium, aluminum, and titanium were quite abundant in the sample analyzed by the X-ray spectrometer, and scientists said that the mix was rather like that seen in terrestrial basalts, or lava flows.

The organic instrument, the gas chromatograph mass spectrometer or GCMS, was a little slow getting started. It had reported itself as having been short-changed by the Viking's mechanical arm when that ingenious appendage first scooped up some soil from the Martian surface and distributed it to the various experiments.

Scientists were inclined to disbelieve the report, blaming it on a faulty "level full" sensor inside the instrument rather than on any niggardliness on the part of the arm. So much, in fact, did they disbelieve the report that when problems temporarily disabled the arm's operations, they commanded the GCMS to go ahead anyway and begin its analysis of the soil.

The meteorology experiment was another that "came on" early in the landed phase of the mission and worked well all along. Its sensors recorded an unexpected regularity to Martian weather, according to Dr. Seymour Hess of Florida State University, with light winds out of the East in the late afternoon, shifting to light winds out of the Southeast after midnight. Wind velocities were on the order of 15 miles per hour and temperatures ranged from minus 120 degrees Fahrenheit, just after dawn, to minus 20 degrees Fahrenheit in the early afternoon.

A pressure-sensor, similar in purpose to a terrestrial barometer, recorded a slight but persistent decline in the atmospheric pressure at the site. Dr. Hess interpreted this drop-off as due to the continuing condensation of carbon dioxide onto the southern polar cap. At the moment, it is winter in the southern hemisphere of Mars.

Indeed, the only scientists who were disappointed with the performance of the Viking 1 lander were the seismologists. Their instrument somehow remained "caged," or strapped down, and its usefulness was consequently limited.

The success of the Viking lander, with spectacular pictures from its cameras and strange findings from its biology experiments, tended to overshadow the continuing fine work of the Viking 1 orbiter.

Like the "third man" of the Apollo moon crews, who remained in the command ship and circled the moon while his two partners journeyed down to the lunar surface, the Viking orbiter continued to sail around and around Mars, taking pictures of the surface and other measurements as well.

Those pictures not only provided coverage of possible landing sites for the Viking 2 spacecraft, which entered Martian orbit early in August, but also gave scientists like Dr. Harold Masursky of the U.S. Geological Survey deeper insights into the planet's past.

Perhaps the most striking features that showed up on orbiter pictures were the dry beds of long-ago rivers and streams that left graceful, sinuous channels in the Martian terrain, like the flowing pattern of watered silk.

Dr. Masursky believes there were at least three major times in the planet's past when liquid water coursed down the Martian mountainsides and carved those channels: an "old" period, somewhere around 2½-billion years ago, an "intermediate" period one billion years ago; and a "young" period some 100 million years or more ago.

It would, however, be a mistake to conjure up babbling brooks, serene lakes, majestic oceans, or even April showers in trying to imagine what liquid water on Mars was like. "Mars never had oceans, never had large standing bodies of water," Harold Masursky said. "It's always been desiccated. The episodes of liquid water have been short, lasting maybe a few thousand years during each episode. And those episodes have been scattered over this immensity of time."

Dr. Masursky believes that many of the large channels spotted by the Viking orbiter's cameras were created by geothermal action. That is, a convective current of hot Martian mantle material welled up beneath the outer crust and melted subsurface layers of ice. Liquefied by the heat, the water erupted from the ground as if issuing from some gigantic hot spring and coursed across the "Marsscape."

Such eruptions would have put a relatively large amount of water into a localized region over a short period of time. Some of that water then evaporated into the atmosphere and fell back again to the surface as rain.

"Martian rains were probably like the flash flood that just happened at Big Thompson (a Colorado canyon)," Dr. Masursky said. "A cloudburst would occur over one spot and the rains would fall heavily, eroding the hell out of that particular spot. It was a sporadic process, sporadic in time and place, and that would account for the fact that we see both water-cut channels and craters that somehow avoided being eroded away by that water."

To Dr. Masursky's thinking the most important thing that may come out of Viking's exploration of Mars is the dating of those watery episodes. If those episodes correlate in time with Earth's glacial cycles, he explained, then it almost certainly means that the sun and its radiation are responsible for the long-term, large-scale climatic shifts on both planets.

And if there is no correlation between Martian episodes and terrestrial cycles, he went on, science would have to conclude that each body is driven by its own internal heat engine. "I happen to think that both have occurred," Dr. Masursky said. "There's been heating (of each planet) from without and heating from within. The challenge will be in trying to sort these out."

Indeed, the very essence of the Viking program has been that of challenge—the challenge to conceive and build an electronic mechanical machine that would serve as a surrogate for man's curiosity, the challenge to steer it safely and surely across the vastness of the cosmic ocean over an 11-month journey from Earth to Mars, the challenge to land without mishap on the planet's surface; the challenge of operating in an environment radically different from that whence the machine came; and, finally, the greatest challenge of all—to understand the information sent back by those Vikings, to understand the evolution of Mars and of Earth.

James Oberg . . . . Terraforming

One solution to the problem of overpopulation on our planet in the future might be to colonize other artificial and real bodies in our solar system. Planets and asteroids must be "terraformed"—made more like Earth—if they are to be inhabited by humans. James Oberg, a computer specialist for NASA, discusses the methods and ethical considerations of terraforming.

Philosophers and anthropologists mark the beginnings of human intelligence at the point in dim prehistory when human beings began to deliberately alter their environment, rather than passively accepting physical hardship as a natural occurrence. After that breakthrough, the march from scraped animal hides and campfires to spacesuits and life support systems was only one of technology, not concept.

For several decades, space prophets have forecast reshaping of other worlds to satisfy human physical needs. Massive planetary engineering—*terraforming*—is a long way from lighting a fire to warm a cave, but it's an extension of the same basic theme.

These visionaries suggest that through use of engineering skills and energies of the future we will be able to transform hostile worlds into comfortable human living areas. Even if it's possible to accomplish such feats, critics may ask if they are justifiable. Will this practice of remodeling planets be an important activity of the 21st, 25th or 30th century?

We have already demonstrated our ability to change local— even global—environments on Earth. Meteorologists consider techniques of weather control in an age when human industrial and land clearing activities have already altered natural balances.

The cause and effect of our terrestrial climate is still poorly understood. Rainfall is affected by things such as humidity, aerosols, dust and land reflectivity. All types of wind, from zephyrs to hurricanes, depend on solar energy input, surface waters and landforms—and tornados have some sort of connection with electrostatic and ball lightning phenomena. Sunlight on a surface depends on geological, astronomical and meteorological conditions.

Humans are altering the balance of nature, deliberately or not. Where the causal relationships are unknown, mysterious and sometimes damaging changes can occur.

Considering our state of ignorance about the basic mechanics of our terrestrial climate, it may seem presumptuous to entertain sweeping visions of planetwide engineering. But there is no holding back; the first world to be terraformed by human activity will be Earth itself. Hopefully, our home planet will survive our unwitting experimentation.

Entire continents may someday have their rainfall and wind patterns modified to improve agriculture, extend human comfort and promote industrial convenience. More than weather, even climate itself may be modified for the "better"—once that term can be quantified and agreed on.

Terrestrial climate control and modification techniques will be the first step in learning how to alter the ecologies of entire worlds beyond Earth. With a set of well understood tricks-of-the-trade, and specialized tools developed for use on alien worlds, future planetary engineers will be able to carry out what we can only dream of today:

- evaporate the clouds of Venus, spin up the retrograde planet, cool it, and allow oceans to form;

- make rain fall again on Mars, turning the red skies dark blue and tinging the red rocks with the green of lichens;

- give an atmosphere to Earth's barren moon, as an aid to surface transportation, as an experiment, or as an esthetic monument to "mankind's giant leap";

- dismantle the outer planets, using their hydrogen as rocket fuel and their rocky cores as material for a dozen new Earths;

- collect comets, asteroids and interplanetary dust—raw material for housing billions of our not-so-remote descendants.

These visions of future planetary modifications are breathtaking. But other futurologists disagree with the scenario, the assumptions and the projected outcome. They foresee a different future in which planets as we know them today would no longer be needed for human habitation, except perhaps as natural parks, wildlife sanctuaries and sentimental monuments to human origins.

Initially, in this alternate vision, people would move out into artificial habitats—space colonies—which would spin to produce a simulacrum of gravity, *ersatz gravity*. Within a century or two, anticipated breakthroughs in physics would allow engineers to construct space platforms dozens of miles across using great machines to generate real *artificial gravity*.

Rock and soil from hard planets would be used in thin topsoil layers for esthetic or ecological reasons. These platforms in space, a million or a billion miles from the place Earth once was, would have powers of gravity and tamed stellar energy to last for millions of years. They would become the dwelling places of all but a tiny portion of the human race 1,000 years hence.

Let's look at these futures. Let's examine the proposed techniques of the profession of terraformers, of planetary engineers. Don't look in the "help wanted" ads or in college curriculum guides, since we are a century ahead of our time. But try to imagine . . .

THE SEARCH FOR A LEVER

Planets, without human intervention, seem to go through major climate changes by themselves. Often they seem to have leaped from one stable regime to another, perhaps in centuries or less. On Earth, ice ages are an example; on Mars, the dead river gulleys hint at one another; on Venus, the strangling atmosphere may belie a more hospitable past in which oceans covered much of the planet and were the habitat of living creatures.

Although these changes may have been brought about by tremendous variations in solar output, or by interstellar dustclouds passing through the solar system (blocking a large fraction of sunlight), or by random collisions between solar system objects, many planetologists suspect that the shifts came about by some minor triggering action which modulated the great natural energy flux on each world.

Like Archimedes, who boasted that he could move the world with a lever if given a place to stand (and a long enough lever!), planetary engineers of the future will need to seek the ecological instability—the fulcrum and the lever which, when activated, will move a planetary biosphere—the kind of subtle change that may trigger terrestrial ice ages.

Just as a tiny cap can dislodge a huge teetering boulder, by finding those sensitive points it may be possible with relatively little effort to create planetary alterations such as:

• changing a planet with fast growing organisms whose specially tailored biological processes rapidly shift the former balance;

• "importing" light element volatiles from passing carbonaceous chondrite asteroids or water comets;

• changing the length of a planet's day;

• modifying the *insolation* (incoming sunlight) with giant mirrors or manmade obscuring dustclouds;

• modulating atmospheric transparency—indeed an entire planetary climate—by controlling ocean evaporation with a few well placed oil slicks, or finding ways to control devastating duststorms by trapping particulates on the surface, perhaps with plants.

Other terraforming projects may require less delicate tools—perhaps a brute force approach which might stagger the 20th century mind! Imagine building a planet from space debris, and then dispersing the heat of the new planetary crust melted during "assembly." Perhaps humans will disintegrate Saturn and distill from it the elements needed for human progress. There may come a time when the energies needed to move Neptune's moon Triton into orbit around Venus or Mercury will be available. There could be prospecting expeditions to the giant cloud of comets that circles our sun hundreds of billions of miles beyond sunless wastes beyond Pluto. Or there may be engineering to take an icy world like Ganymede, melt its surface, and then construct a solid surface suitable for comfortable habitation.

A NEW MARS FOR THE OLD MARS

Mars glitters in the human imagination even more brilliantly than it does in the night sky. It has already played a critical role in developing the concept of terraforming and will play an even more important role when terraforming moves from theory to practice.

The idea of terraforming originated from a mistake. At the beginning of this century, Percival Lowell "discovered" canals on Mars. He imagined that they were part of a massive planetwide irrigation system built to save the Martians as their small cold planet dried up. As the harsh conditions on Mars became better known, philosophers had difficulty imagining anything resembling a human being existing under Martian conditions. Lowell rejected this philosophical dead end. His Martian men were attempting to alter the whole ecology of their planet to fit their physical needs; they were conducting planetary engineering.

Lowell, with his vivid imagination, failed to establish the reality of his canals. But he produced something far more important—the concept of terraforming.

Since then, science fiction writers have been playing around with the idea of terraforming Mars. It was not dying Martians but immigrating Earthmen who, in Arthur C. Clarke's *Sands of Mars*, engineered an atmospheric buildup program. Clarke's acclimatized humans could stand outside briefly without oxygen masks—but the humans had to adjust physically to the thin air as, indeed, they have in such places as the high Andes and Tibet on Earth. A quarter century later, author Jerry Pournelle wrote of a project involving the detonation of nuclear bombs inside Martian volcanos to trigger the outgassing of a thicker atmosphere.

During the Viking missions in 1975–76, NASA's Ames Research Center sponsored a special research effort devoted to terraforming Mars. The result of the study was published in the NASA pamphlet, *On the Habitability of Mars: an Approach to Planetary Ecosynthesis*.

What would be required for the creation of a human supporting ecosphere on today's Mars? Compared to even the most hostile environments on Earth, such as the dry Antarctic valleys where the soil can be absolutely sterile, Mars is colder, drier, more airless, and more irradiated by lethal ultraviolet radiation. A human being suddenly turned out unprotected on Mars would gasp his last breath in the near vacuum. His feet would begin to freeze, although there would be little heat loss elsewhere. The ultra-violet flux would begin a sunburn from which he would not live to suffer. Consciousness would fade with lack of oxygen. The corpse could take a million years to disappear, as first all the water sublimed out, and then the mummified flesh and bones were eroded ever so slowly by the soft Martian sandstorm.

There is neither free oxygen nor significant airborne water on Mars; even its air-pressure is only one percent that of Earth. Ordinary Earth plants would be killed within minutes by the ultraviolet light. Yet the NASA study suggested that a tailored form of Earth life might be able to survive unprotected on Mars—even grow and reproduce. That biological tool might provide one lever in the delicate ecological system which could move that entire world closer to where we want it to be.

But first the key ingredients of temperature and air pressure must be considered. If the planet were warmer, the carbon dioxide in the polar caps would evaporate into an atmosphere perhaps 1/10 as thick as that of Earth. If the atmosphere were a lot thicker than it is now, various heating mechanisms would raise planetary temperatures, melt much of the icecaps and permafrost, and create a more benign environment.

The relationship is circular. Each undesirable factor (very cold, and nearly airless) supports the other. How can terraforming break into this closed loop?

To increase the mass of the atmosphere, we might try to vaporize the native gases of the surface layers or the interior, perhaps volatilize the icecaps and permafrost, or possibly import water and frozen gases from off-planet. Consider each of these possibilities, and choose the least impossible!

Perhaps the volcanoes can indeed be set off again as Pournelle imagined, even if they do turn out to be ice volcanos instead of lava volcanos. Perhaps water ice and other frozen gases can be obtained from carbonaceous Deimos, the asteroid belt, or the rings of Saturn as in Isaac Asimov's *The Martian Way*. Brute force methods might indeed be the most cost effective for Mars.

Let's examine an ecological lever: the idea of melting the polar caps. We cannot safely stoke the fires of the sun, but we can imagine doing other useful things. We could increase the amount of sunlight hitting the polar regions; we could decrease the amount of sunlight blocked by the thin atmosphere; we could decrease the amount of sunlight reflected uselessly from the material we are trying to heat.

Nature may follow the first technique (increasing the amount of sunlight on the poles) in the natural precession of the Martian axis and in the orbital motion of the planet over the millenia. Altering planetary orbits, spin rates and axes might be a terraforming trick-of-the-trade in the 25th century, but it will be too much to expect of the first generation of planetary engineers in the next century.

Instead, tools which will soon be in operation in Earth orbit could prove useful on Mars and elsewhere. In the 1980s, space engineers will be building highly reflective (but very thin and light) metalfoil mirrors hundreds of meters on a side, which will circle Earth in geosynchronous orbits (keeping them over the same spot on the equator). From this vantage point, the first space mirrors (space planner Krafft Ehricke calls them *lunettas*) could provide nighttime illumination for rescue, emergencies or military operations. larger mirrors (Ehricke's *solettas*), hundreds of kilometers on a side, could replace an entire state's street lighting—banishing night—at tremendous energy savings; they could also raise local temperatures several degrees, saving a frost threatened crop or perhaps steering a dangerous hurricane out to sea.

Now look at Mars. It receives about 60 percent as much solar energy as does Earth. As on Earth, the amount of sunlight at the poles is always reduced by the low angle of incidence of the sun's rays. To increase the polar energy flux by about 20 percent, we would need to use mirrors—not as large as 20 percent of the area of Mars, as considerably less would be sufficient.

No matter what their size, space mirrors will be capital investments which are not used up, and can be utilized elsewhere on other projects. The orbits of these space mirrors will impose constraints, since they cannot just hover weightlessly over the pole. Nevertheless, their orbits can be designed so that a number of mirrors can contribute to the concentration of sunlight on the icecaps.

There are other ways to terraform Mars. Reducing the opacity of the atmosphere ties in with keeping duststorms down, as it reduces the temperature extremes which lead to high winds, or reduces the amount of dust the high winds will raise. The latter could be accomplished by moistening the soil or by covering it with plant life. These techniques, too, are circular, because you cannot have one (more incoming heat and greater transparency, and therefore less dust to raise) without the other (water in the soil).

As our last alternative (or perhaps another factor to be used in combination with the two processes just outlined), the amount of sunlight absorbed by the polar caps could be increased. The whiter a surface is, the more heat it reflects and the less it absorbs. More than 3/4 the icecaps' sunlight is reflected. If that could be decreased by as little as five percent, the caps would begin to evaporate.

To darken the polar caps, perhaps planetary engineers could spread soot over them. Where could they obtain such material? Viking discovered that this is exactly what Deimos and Phobos are made of: very dark, sooty carbonaceous material. An electromagnetic cannon (mass driver) established on Deimos could shoot buckets of the brittle black powder down onto the polar caps. The material, rich in carbon, nitrogen, hydrogen and oxygen, would be a valuable fertilizer as well, once the caps were reduced.

If some stupendous engineering project manages to vaporize much of the Martian polar caps (at least the carbon dioxide parts: the water ice can follow later), the atmospheric pressure will temporarily be elevated. But what will happen when the destabilizing lever is removed? Will Mars freeze up again?

Many astronomers do not think so. Instead, Martian climate will have been switched from one stable state (today's) to another stable state (an atmosphere 10 to 100 times as thick, and warmer). Two processes can help maintain this change naturally—*advective heating* and the *greenhouse effect*.

On Mars today, the sparse atmosphere is a minor factor in heat transport from the equatorial regions to the poles. The thin air does rush around, raising duststorms, but essentially all the heat which reaches the polar regions does so via direct sunlight. However, once the air is thicker, the atmosphere becomes a significant mechanism of heat transport known as advective heating. The warm southern winds can help prevent the northern polar regions (and, conversely, the northern winds help the southern polar regions) from ever getting as cold as they were before—even in winter when the sunlight fails altogether.

Therefore, the air does not freeze into dry ice in the winter, but stays gaseous. The poles maintain their warmth from the equatorial winds, too warm for the air to freeze out in the winter. Now we are on the happy side of a stable, circular, closed causal chain.

The second factor is the greenhouse effect. Without heating on Earth in winter, gardeners' greenhouses stay warm. How? This physical process is extremely important for planetologists working on a wide variety of worlds.

Essentially, incoming visible light passes through an atmosphere and warms a planetary surface. Some of the energy is sent back toward space as heat in the form of infrared radiation. Certain components of the atmosphere, gases, aerosols and dust, may be transparent to the incoming visible wavelengths, but are not as transparent to the infrared wavelengths trying to go back through. So the radiation is absorbed in the atmosphere, warming it, or is reflected back into the ground, keeping it warmer too. The atmosphere seems to act like a blanket, although the physical process of the greenhouse effect is *not* the same as the insulating process of a blanket.

Earth has a greenhouse effect largely due to water vapor. Without it, Earth's surface temperature would be more than 70 degrees below what it is. Water vapor cools Earth, too. In the form of clouds, it increases the reflectiveness of the atmosphere, sending back much solar radiation before it can heat the ground. Both conflicting processes are at work simultaneously—a challenge to planetary scientists and meteorologists, and a compound problem for terraformers.

The composition of our hypothetical Martian atmosphere will be crucial to the successful exploitation of the greenhouse effect in order to further warm the planet. A hundred-fold increase of carbon dioxide alone (and Viking has shown that there is not enough carbon dioxide in the polar caps to accomplish this) would give a net greenhouse gain of only 15 degrees. If 1/10 of this new atmospheric pressure were due to water vapor, the greenhouse dividend would be more than twice as great.

So thick air leads to greenhouse-preserved warmth, which maintains the thick air, which in turn maintains the warmth. Once again we are on the happy side of a stable new situation, and we've done it with a lever: An orbiting mirror massing a few thousand tons has given Mars the gift of tons of air, and the sun contributed its energy free of charge!

The next step is oxygen generation. Here, original speculation centered on biological levers until Viking showed that adding water to Mars' soil caused it to give off free oxygen. That process needs more study, but it may be an example of a serendipitous discovery, making terraforming not as hard as previously thought.

Meanwhile, consider just the biological tools available. A few hundred pounds of algae sown on a fertile, warm, well-watered Martian landscape could multiply and spread across the planet in a matter of decades at most. While this was happening, the algae could convert much of the atmospheric carbon dioxide to oxygen, locking the carbon up into organic compounds in the soil.

Yet to be considered are implications of the availability of the "new form of life" discovered late in 1977—a primitive type of cell whose metabolism seems almost too ideally suited for the biological processing of the atmospheres of alien worlds. Possibly the most primitive form of life on Earth, these bacteria might be readily modified where needed for use on Mars and elsewhere.

The NASA study on Martian ecosynthesis considered beginning the introduction of biological agents while Mars is still dry, cold and nearly airless. Scientists looked at the characteristics of certain simple plants which might be suitable for bioterraforming Mars: green algae, lichens, moss, and blue-green "algae" (actually a type of bacteria). According to the study, a combination of mats of blue-green algae and lichen might be able to survive today's Martian conditions, but they would grow very slowly and would be active making oxygen for only a few hours a day, even in the most benign season. With 1/4 the Martian surface covered with such biota, starting from present conditions, NASA computer simulations demonstrated that it could take more than 100,000 years to produce the minimum required for breathing. That does not account for the fact that even with sufficient oxygen, the remaining carbon dioxide would still be enough to suffocate a human being trying to breathe the new atmosphere.

In the brute force approach, once there is enough oxygen, you must also remove the excess carbon dioxide. But it requires a great deal of water. On Earth, water has aided the reaction of carbon dioxide with silicates to form carbonates (limestone). Venus, with its thick carbon dioxide atmosphere, and Earth, with very little, began with about the same amount. On Earth, it was converted to limestone, while an equivalent mass of carbon dioxide remains at large in Venus' atmosphere.

Oceans thus play an important role as atmospheric buffers, storing a significant amount of carbon dioxide dissolved in the form of bicarbonates. A large area of open water—perhaps 1/4 of a world's surface—is not simply an esthetic frill. Along with oceanic plankton and the humidifying effects of wind whipped sea foam, it is crucial to atmospheric engineering. So engineering of the Martian climate is imperative, in order to let the oxygenating plants grow on land and in the oceans. Even after this stage is reached, we still won't be done.

What should be sowed on Mars to maintain the atmosphere and create a food chain? The sterile alien desert, even temperate and well-watered, must be transformed into a garden of unearthly Earthliness.

Lichens and blue-green algae are a good bet, the NASA study concluded, even without genetic engineering to bring out their best points (and to suppress any taste they might have to consume oxygen). Lichens can grow on or in stone, excreting acids to dissolve a few hundredths inch of the rock's outer layers. They can even incorporate sand in their outer skins as an ultraviolet shield. Algae could grow below the surface of a layer of sand, where the ultraviolet level has dropped off but where visible light is still strong enough for photosynthesis. Later an ozone layer would form, blocking ultraviolet radiation before it reached the surface. But before that time, the biology would need to fend for itself.

The sand of Mars would become the soils and humus of a new world. The lichens could help break down the rocks. Algae could build up the soil and combine nitrogen into it. Organic matter could begin to accumulate, in compounds of carbon, nitrogen, sulfur, phosphorus, oxygen and hydrogen. This might still be the longest stage, taking up to a century or more.

NASA's study described the next step: "It would be most desirable to prevent such a one-way flow of elements into nonusable, high molecular weight organic compounds by establishing biogeochemical cycles which do not utilize free oxygen (to allow the oxygen to accumulate for breathing and ozone layer formation) . . . .

While not minimizing the enormous complexity of designing a planetwide, efficient, steady state microbial ecology, this task does not seem to be insuperable."

Not insuperable, that is to say, for planetary engineers of the next century or two. Among the other tools of engineering, chemistry, geology and so forth, the tool of biology will be a paramount one.

So one day a human being may stand maskless under the blue Martian sky, and poke a hole into the ground to begin planting a field of pine tree seedlings. With a clean slate, mankind would open a new world. [Oberg describes the hypothetical terraforming of Venus, Mercury, and Earth's moon; the dismantling of Jupiter to make Earthlike planets; terraforming of Galilean moons; an ocean planet; artificial islands; and more.]

Terraforming may never become feasible or desirable. If the planets are left alone, they may forever remain uninhabited except by tourists, scientific expeditions and hermits. But the force of destiny, if such a concept exists, suggests that people move into every ecological and climatic niche which their technology makes available—whether it's hunters in the Arctic or nomads in the deserts. Even today the permanent residents of Antarctica and the ocean depths are preparing to move in.

So if it's at all feasible, some people will move to other planets. They may be a small fraction of the whole population, and they may not have the entire resources of the whole population, but they will want to go. If history is any teacher, the rest of mankind will be happy to see them go, too.

Tailored planets, artificial planetoids, the inhabited human influence stretching out toward the nearest stars—these concepts are exciting ones. They stretch the imagination and challenge our knowledge. Even if they never come to be, they will have been valuable exercises in man's learning to choose what's best for mankind. And if these ideas, or others now unimagined, ever do come to pass, they will make living on Earth a way of life as obsolete as living in trees.

• DISCUSSION QUESTIONS •

1. What might Lowell's "canals" actually have been? Why did Lowell assume that the canals were built by intelligent beings? What was wrong with his assumption? Compare the views of Lowell and Wallace about Lowell's observations of the planet. How do Wallace's arguments hold up today?

2. How have conditions on Mars changed over the millenia? Why is it reasonable to assume that water once existed on the Martian surface? Why is Mars now dry?

3. Why is Mars more likely to support life than other planets in our solar system? What conditions for life does it meet? What conditions make it only marginally likely that life exists there?

4. Do you believe that space exploration is justified? Should we wait to explore space until our earthly problems, like poverty, are solved? Do the directions and peripheral benefits from space exploration—medical breakthroughs, for example—make it all worthwhile? Explore the arguments for and against a space program. Has your exposure to the *Cosmos* series changed your stance? Why?

5. What are the implications of finding life on Mars? Of not finding it? Scientist Wolf Vishniac said that if there were no life on Mars, we would have the classical confrontation of experiment and control. What did he mean by that?

6. Why were the results of the Viking biology experiments considered to be ambiguous by most scientists? What direction might future biology experiments on Mars take?

7. What are the ethical considerations of further exploration of Mars if life is found there?

8. Through what processes might Mars be terraformed? Venus? What are alternative methods of colonizing space (within our solar system)?

• ADDITIONAL ACTIVITIES •

Optional Projects

1. If a telescope is available to you, train it on Mars and sketch what you see. Compare your drawings to those of others in the group, to Lowell's representations and to recent photographs of Mars. Write a short paper about your comparisons and the reasons for the differences between your observations and those of others.

2. You are an intelligent being on a planet in another solar system. You conveniently speak and write English. Write a report to your superiors giving the evidence for your conclusion that Earth, which you have been observing, supports intelligent life.

3. On a map of Mars showing latitude and longitude, mark the parameters of areas in which landing the Viking landers was feasible. List all the considerations which the JPL scientists took into account—elevation, wind speeds, and other Martian characteristics—along with the difficulties each presented.

4. Write a description of each of the three Viking biology experiments and its results.

Supplementary Bibliography

Svante Arrhenius, "The Planet Mars" in Destinies of the Stars. New York: G.P. Putnam's Sons, 1918.
A discussion of the possibility of life on Mars (an anti-Lowell view) by the Swedish physicist and chemist.

M.M. Averner and R.D. MacElroy (Eds.), On the Habitability of Mars: An Approach to Planetary Ecosynthesis. Washington, D.C.: National Aeronautics and Space Administration, 1976 (SP-414)
Points of view on the possibility of finding life on Mars before the Viking mission.

Ray Bradbury, Arthur C. Clarke, Bruce Murray, Carl Sagan, and Walter Sullivan, *Mars and the Mind of Man*. New York: Harper and Row, Publishers, 1973.
A series of essays and panel discussion.

Jonathan Eberhart, "A Sense of Mars" in *Chemistry*, November, 1977.
A short and appreciative description of the Viking expedition.

William Graves Hoyt, *Lowell and Mars*. Tucson: University of Arizona Press, 1976.
Definitive and highly readable account of Lowell's unsuccessful search for life on Mars, and the reactions from his fellow astronomers and the general public.

Viking Imaging Team, *The Martian Landscape*. Washington, D.C.: National Aeronautics and Space Administration, 1978.
A somewhat technical review of the findings resulting from the Viking expedition.

Mark Washburn, *Mars at Last!* New York: G.P. Putnam's Sons, 1977.
A popular account of Martian exploration.

Chapter VI
TRAVELERS' TALES

• OVERVIEW •

SAILING STRANGE SEAS—of the Earth, space, or mind—is adventure that excites the desire to tell tales. In their creaky wooden caravels, early explorers looked over the rail to see sea serpents and strange lands with sheep-bearing trees (they said). Columbus, conjecturing about the shape of the world and the lush lands he was discovering, truly thought he had found the Garden of Eden.

During the European Renaissance and Enlightenment, when the mind was free to speculate and conjecture on previously forbidden ideas, ships roamed the seas even farther and scientists turned their telescopes to the oceans of space to observe planets and satellites never seen before. They wondered if there were inhabitants on those distant worlds, and what they were like. Particularly in the Dutch Republic of the 1600s, masters of intellectual derring-do basked in the sun of society's approval. Their imaginings were magnificent expeditions of the mind.

Today, with the help of robots masterminded by scientists on Earth, we sail the seas of space by proxy. Close-up images of the swirling Great Red Spot, a white volcanic plume rising from Io, and the tumbling potato-shaped moon Amalthea— more fantastic than anything a special effects expert could dream up—appear on our television screens. And the true tales told by the armchair travelers, the scientists—of underground oceans and million-year-old storms and rotten-egg atmospheres—rival any created by those sea captains of long-ago caravels.

• LEARNING OBJECTIVES •

1. Describe how the four large, gaseous planets—Neptune, Uranus, Saturn, and Jupiter—are themselves like miniature solar systems; and, in particular, describe the properties of the satellites Io and Titan.

2. List the major properties of the planet Jupiter, and describe its energetic and active environment.

3. Describe the parallels Dr. Sagan draws between the *Voyager* space program of the 20th century and the exploration programs of the Dutch Republic of the 17th century.

4. Describe the planet Saturn and compare its properties with those of Jupiter.

5. Describe Christiaan Huygens' speculations about life on other planets and how these visions were colored by his environment.

• KEY TERMS AND NAMES •

Amalthea	Jupiter
asthenosphere	lithosphere
Callisto	Neptune
Europa	particulate rings
Galilean satellites	radiation belt
Galileo Galilei	Saturn
Ganymede	solar wind
heliopause	Titan
Christiaan Huygens	Uranus
Io	Voyager 2

• ASSIGNMENT •

Watch COSMOS television series Program 6, "Travelers' Tales."

Read Chapter 6, "Travelers' Tales," in Carl Sagan's text, *Cosmos*, or other readings assigned by your instructor.

• READINGS •

Christiaan Huygens . . . . **The Celestial Worlds Discover'd**

Huygens was lucky enough to live in the Dutch Republic of the 17th century, which was receptive to new ideas. He took full advantage of it. He was an inventor (of the aerial telescope and pendulum clock), a pioneer in the field of optics, and an astronomer of the first rank. In this excerpt from his book The Celestial Worlds Discover'd, *Huygens describes some of his discoveries and conjectures, especially about the kinds of life other planets might support. It was Huygens who first spotted Saturn's ring (as well as Saturn's moon Titan). He imagines days and nights on that distant planet.*

In the Figure 1 you have the Globes of the Planets, and of the Sun, represented to your eyes as plac'd near one another. Where I have observ'd the same Proportion, of their Diameters to that of the Sun, that I publish'd to the World in my Book of *the Appearances of Saturn:* namely, the Diameter of the Ring round *Saturn* is to that of the Sun as 11 is to 37; that of *Saturn* himself about as 5 to 37; that of *Jupiter* as 2 to 11; that of *Mars* as 1 to 166; of the Earth as 1 to 111; and of *Venus* as 1 to 84: to which I shall now add that of *Mercury* observ'd by *Hevelius* in the Year 1661, but calculated by myself, and found to be as 1 to 290. . . .

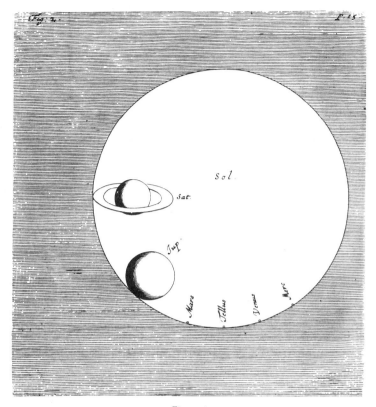

Figure 1

Having thus explain'd the two Schemes, there's no body I suppose but sees, that in the first the Earth is made to be of the same sort with the rest of the Planets. For the very Position of the Circles shows it. And that the other Planets are round like it, and like it receive all the Light they have from the Sun, there's no room (since the Discoveries made by Telescopes) to doubt. Another thing they are like it in is, that they are moved round their own Axis; for since 'tis certain that *Jupiter* and *Saturn* are, who can doubt it of the others? Again, as the Earth has its Moon moving round it, so *Jupiter* and *Saturn* have theirs. Now since in so many things they thus agree, what can be more probable than that in others they agree too; and that the other Planets are as beautiful and as well stock'd with Inhabitants as the Earth? or what shadow of Reason can there be why they should not? . . .

As for what I have said concerning their Propagation, I cannot be so positive; but the other thing, namely, that they have Plants and Animals, I think I have fully proved. And by the same Argument, of their not being inferiour to our Earth, they must have as great a variety of both as we have. What this is, will be best known to him that considers the different ways our Animals make use of in moving from one place to another. Which may be reduc'd, I think, to these; either that they walk upon two feet or four; or like Insects, upon six, nay sometimes hundreds; or that they fly in the Air bearing up, and wonderfully steering themselves with their Wings; or creep upon the Ground without feet; or by a violent Spring in their Bodies, or paddling with their feet, cut themselves away in the Waters. I don't believe, nor can I conceive, that there should be any other way than these mention'd. The Animals then in the Planets must make use of one or more of these, like our amphibious Birds, which can swim in Water as well as walk on Land, or fly in the Air; or like our Crocodiles and Sea-Horses, must be Mongrels, between Land and Water. There can no other method be imagin'd but one of these. For where is it possible for Animals to live, except upon such a solid Body as our Earth, or a fluid one like the Water, or still a more fluid one than that, such as our Air is? The Air I confess may be much thicker and heavier than ours, and so, without any disadvantage to its Transparency, be fitter for the volatile Animals. There may be too many sorts of Fluids ranged over one another in rows as it were. The Sea perhaps may have such a fluid lying on it, which tho ten times lighter than Water, may be a hundred times heavier than Air; whose utmost Extent may not be so large as to cover the higher places of their Earth. But there's no reason to supect or allow them this, since we have no such thing; and if we did, it would be of no advantage to them, for that the former ways of moving would not be hereby at all increas'd: But when we come to meddle with the Shape of these Creatures, and consider the incredible variety that is even in those of the different parts of this Earth, and that *America* has some which are no where else to be found, I must then confess that I think it beyond the force of Imagination to arrive at any knowledge in the matter, or reach probability concerning the figures of these Planetary Animals. . . .

If our Earth can claim preeminence of the fore-mentioned Planets [Mercury and Venus], for having a Moon to attend upon it, (for its Magnitude can make but a small difference) how much superiour must *Jupiter* and *Saturn* be to all four of them, Earth and all? For whether we consider their bulk, in which they far exceed all the others, or the number of Moons that wait upon them, it's very probable that they are the chief, the primary Planets in our System, in comparison with which the other four are nothing, and scarce worth mentioning. For the easier conception of their disparity, I have thought fit to add a Scheme of our Earth, with the Path of the Moon about it, and the Globe of the Moon itself; and the systems of *Jupiter* and *Saturn*, where I have drawn every thing as near the true Proportion as possible. *Jupiter* you see has his four, and *Saturn* his five Moons about him, all plac'd in their Orbits. The *Jovial* we owe to *Galileo*, 'tis well known: and any one may imagine he was in no small rapture at the discovery. The outermost but one, and brightest of *Saturn's*, it chanc'd to be my lot, with a Telescope not above 12 foot long, to have the first sight of in the year 1655. . . .

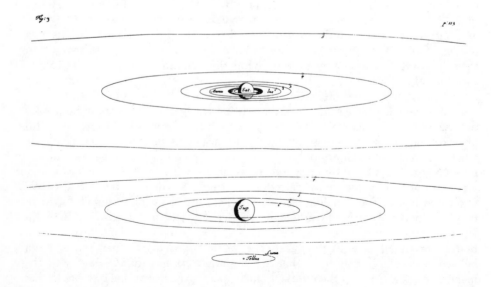

Saturn enjoys all those Pleasures and Advantages in a still higher degree, as well for his five Moons, as for the delightful prospect that the Ring about him affords his Inhabitants night and day. But we will be as kind to them as we have bin to the rest of the Planets, in giving an account of their Astronomy.

And first of all we shall observe what we might have remark'd before, but will be more strange here, that the fix'd Stars appear to them of the same Figure and Magnitude, and with the same degree of Light that they do to us: and this, by reason of their immense distance, of which we shall have occasion to speak by and by. In comparison with which the space that a Bullet shot out of a Cannon could travel in 25 years, would be almost nothing.

Their Astronomers have all the same Signs of the Bear, the Lion, Orion, and the rest, but not turning upon the same Axis with us: for that's different in all the Planets.

As *Jupiter* can see no Planet but *Saturn*, so *Saturn* knows of no Planet but *Jupiter;* which appears to him much as *Venus* doth to us, never removing above 37 degrees from the Sun. The length of their days I cannot determine: But if from the distance and period of his innermost Attendant, and comparing it with the innermost of *Jupiter's,* a Man may venture to give a guess, they are very little different from *Jupiter's,* 10 hours or somewhat less. But whereas in *Jupiter* these are equally divided between Light and Darkness, the *Saturnians* must perceive a more sensible difference than we, especially between Summer and Winter. For our Axis inclines to the place of the Ecliptick but 23 degrees and a half, but there's above 31. Upon this account his Moons must decline very much from the Path that the Sun seems to move in, and his Inhabitants can never have a full Moon but just at the Equinoxes: two of which fall out in 30 of our years. 'Tis this Position of the Axis too that is the cause of those delightful appearances, and wonderful prospects that its Inhabitants enjoy: for the better understanding of which I shall draw a Figure of *Saturn* with his Ring about him: in which the proportion between the Diameters of the Globe and Ring is as 9 to 4. And the empty space between them is of the same breadth with the Ring it self. All Observations conspire to prove that that is of no great thickness, altho if we should allow it six hundred German Miles, I think, considering its Diameter, we should not overdo the matter. . . . [There follows a description of the rings and the eclipses they cause.]

With *Saturn* in this Scheme you have the Globes of the Earth and Moon drawn in their true proportion, to put you in mind again of a thing very fit to be remember'd, how very small our Habitation is when compar'd with that Globe or the Ring about it. And now any one, I suppose, can frame to himself a picture of the Night in *Saturn*, with two Arches of the Ring, and five Moons shining about, and adorning him. This then shall be what I have to say to the primary Planets.

William K. Hartmann . . . . Moons of the Outer Solar System Become Real, Although Weird, Places

The two Voyager flights afforded us spectacular views of the moons of Jupiter, first discovered by Galileo in 1610. Planetary scientist William K. Hartmann presents details about these dramatic moons.

The year 1979 was one of extraordinary and under-appreciated planetary exploration. Eleven years had gone by as we got close-up pictures of the worlds in the inner solar system, from the first detailed lunar photos in 1964, revealing a dusty world blasted by meteorites, to the first surface photos of boulder-strewn Venus in 1975. But in only two days in early March 1979, we added to our gallery shots of four new planet-class bodies: Callisto, Ganymede, Europa and Io. They are the four large satellites of Jupiter, discovered in 1610 by Galileo Galilei and Simon Marius, worlds ranging roughly from the size of our moon to the size of the planet Mercury. For the last 370 years they have been mere points of light in astronomers' telescopes but now, in the pictures sent back across interplanetary space by Voyager 1, they have become real places each with its own weird landscape:

• Callisto, the outermost Galilean moon, heavily cratered and covered with a layer of dark soil, dotted with bright areas where impacts have exposed the bright ice underneath;

• Ganymede, the largest and next inner moon, with some Callistolike cratered patches but also grooved areas of mysterious geological activity;

• Europa, an unprecedented icy billiard ball, broken by a network of fractures hundreds of miles long;

• and Io, innermost of the four Galilean moons and most bizarre of all. Out of its mottled orange-and-white sulfurous surface, the first active extraterrestrial volcanoes discovered in the solar system shoot bluish plumes of debris more than a hundred miles into space.

Voyager 1 did not only reveal the features of the Galilean moons. It also photographed the tiny moonlet Amalthea, a cosmic potato just 90 miles high and 165 miles long, and discovered the millions of tiny "moons" that make up hitherto unseen rings around Jupiter, now the third planet known to have them.

There was more. Voyager 2 flew through the Jovian system in early July, adding new views and showing the changed pattern of volcanic eruptions on Io. On July 20 we celebrated the tenth anniversary of our first landing on our own moon. And in September lonely Pioneer 11, which had flown by Jupiter in 1974, finally reached Saturn and sent back not only new views of those rings but a blurry vision of Titan, the solar system's only moon with a dense atmosphere. This disk appears nearly featureless, confirming Earth-based evidence that Titan is covered by clouds.

All this happened, it seemed to me, with inadequate fanfare. Here a spacecraft was sending back pictures, broken down into numbers for transmission and then reconstructed on their arrival on Earth. Television stations were invited to use the pictures as rapidly as they appeared on the screens of the Jet Propulsion Laboratory in Pasadena—essentially what broadcast people call a live feed—but few stations bothered to carry them. It was as if Renaissance television networks passed up their chance to carry live pictures from the Santa Maria in 1492.

During the second Voyager flight among the alien craters, plains and volcanoes in July, the news media riveted their attention not on Jupiter's satellites but on an artificial satellite, Skylab. Skylab's fall during the week of the Voyager 2 flyby was a serious event, but most news accounts failed to mention that natural meteorites the size of Skylab's components hit the Earth every few years. Skylab showed not only that anthropocentricism is still with us centuries after the Copernican revolution ("I am worried that a truck-sized object dropped at random on the Earth is going to hit me"), but it also blanked out the excitement of Voyager 2's exceptional discoveries.

Front-page news or not, we now have color pictures and memory banks full of data on these new worlds. We can study their environments, identify resources we may be able to use in the future when we arrive in person, and better answer the ultimate questions of how our worlds came to be and how they evolved. All of this comes, of course, on top of the simple thrill of discovery.

Until now, Earth was the only place we could study a living planet, one where the surface is still being worked by a seething interior. And scientists tend to be uncomfortable with a sample of one. Suddenly, we have more and the rush is on to see how such awesome forces work on other bodies.

One unifying concept is emerging as a key to understanding planets with solid surfaces, like the Earth. A planet's landscape is largely determined by the nature of a relatively rigid and solid outer layer known as a lithosphere. Below this lithosphere is usually a hotter, amorphous layer, which may be partially or completely melted, called an asthenosphere. The origin of these two layers is easily understood. Planets usually have sufficient radioactivity to have caused their interiors to heat up and melt. The surface layers cool off rapidly because they are exposed to space and radiate their heat into the black night around them. Hence, the outermost layers crystallize into a solid lithosphere, while the deep layers remain partly melted.

A revolution shook the geological sciences about ten years ago with the culmination of years of controversy about continental drift on Earth. What emerged was the theory of plate tectonics: Earth not only has a relatively thin lithosphere (45 to 60 miles deep), but it also has an active asthenosphere which has split the lithosphere into a number of distinct plates. These are pushed about as they float on the asthenosphere, sometimes separating, sometimes colliding with each other.

Precisely because Earth has a thin lithosphere and active asthenosphere, its surface is young and constantly changing; its ceaseless churning has erased many of the large impact craters that have accumulated on other planets.

At the other extreme is our moon. The lunar surface still carries the scars, long since obliterated on Earth, of the bombardment of meteorites, miles across, that went on during the first half billion years of the solar system. The lunar surface also indicates that in its first 100 million years or so, the moon was covered by a vast ocean of molten magma that rapidly solidified. As this lithosphere formed, it was scarred by the impacts of the giant meteorites, forming the moon's familiar craters. The seismographs left behind by the Apollo astronauts recorded a zone of "moonquakes" about 600 miles down in the moon. This is interpreted as the base of the lunar lithosphere today, 4.5 billion years after the moon formed. So the moon has a dormant, solid lithosphere, active only at its base where some stresses may be built up by a more fluid asthenosphere material. The great thickness of this solid layer explains why the moon's surface has not been broken into plates and is not mobile and does not have ongoing volcanic eruptions or mountain-building activities.

Generalizing as to other planets, we can say a dense crowding of impact craters suggests that a planet's surface has been dormant for at least 3.5 or 4 billion years and, therefore, the lithosphere is thick and unbroken. This applies to the moon, Callisto and most of Mercury. Fault scarps, fracture patterns and so on, such as we see on Mars, Ganymede and Europa, suggest a thinner lithosphere. Active volcanoes, as on Earth and Io, indicate a still thinner lithosphere.

Prior to 1979, these ideas could be tested in the inner solar system only. Because the outer planets, the gas giants, don't have anything like lithospheres, scientists spent much effort estimating what the planet-sized moons of the outer solar system might tell us. Only a few years ago, they were virtually unknown and seemed unknowable. The astronomer's usual ferret, the spectrograph, produced only a few clues from the sunlight reflected by them. In 1944, the Dutch-American astronomer Gerard Kuiper, using infrared dectectors, showed that Titan has an atomosphere. But the rest of the satellites remained unremarkable star-like dots. A 1958 compendium on Jupiter by the aptly named British visual observer, B. M. Peek, devoted only a few pages to the satellites, though noting "light and dusky markings" must exist on them and that they kept the same faces toward Jupiter.

The relative low density of these moons indicated that though they might contain some rock, they also had to have some material of lower density than rock. This was generally assumed to be some kind of ice, such as frozen water or methane, because such materials were common in the early solar system and the sunlight reaching the outer solar system was too weak to burn away ices of these abundant compounds. Thus, while the inner solar system features rocky planets, the outer features icy ones. Sure enough, in the mid-1950s and early 1960s, Kuiper and the Russian astronomer V. I. Moroz applied better infrared equipment and discerned features that indicated ice or frost on Europa and Ganymede.

In 1964, the innermost of the four Galilean moons, Io, began to stand out from the rest. Radio astronomers discovered that at certain frequencies Jupiter's radio noise occurred at times when Io was in certain positions in its orbit *as seen from Earth*. Within a couple of years analysts deduced that Jupiter's strong magnetic field, in which the natural radio signals originate, extends out as far as Io and interacts with that satellite. This causes beams of radio noise to shoot out in certain directions. The revolution of Io around Jupiter acts something like the rotation of a searchlight, causing the beam to sweep Earth and to produce such intermittent radio bursts when Io reaches various positions.

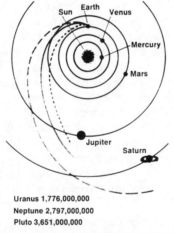

Uranus 1,776,000,000
Neptune 2,797,000,000
Pluto 3,651,000,000

Diagram shows progress of spacecraft to Jupiter and Saturn
(Voyagers solid line, short dashes; Pioneer long dashes).
Distances from sun to outer planets in miles.

A second peculiar observation of Io was published in 1964. Two of Kuiper's graduate students, Alan Binder and Dale Cruikshank, had the unusual idea of looking for thin atmospheres on Galilean satellites by studying their brightnesses as they passed into and out of Jupiter's shadow. They reasoned that the strong temperature drop as the satellites went through the shadow might cause condensation of clouds or frost, so the satellites would be brighter when they emerged from eclipse. Callisto, Ganymede and Europa showed no substantial effect. But several times they watched Io disappear into the shadow normally, then emerge 5 to 12 percent brighter, only to fade back to normal in about 15 minutes. This might have been firm evidence for an atmosphere, except that other observers sought the effect with only mixed results. By the early 1970's, some of the Io eclipses had yielded reported brightenings, while others, observed with high precision, yielded no effect at all.

By 1973, the Pioneer 10 spacecraft established that Io does have a tenuous gas envelope with less than a millionth of Earth's surface pressure, but no atmosphere worthy of the name. The whole affair was temporarily relegated to the rapidly filling file drawer of Io anomalies.

While observers discovered peculiar phenomena, theorists also stayed busy. In 1971 American geochemist John Lewis made the first serious calculations of conditions inside the Galilean satellites. Lewis' basic model was that these satellites, having formed in the cold outer solar system, contained ices as well as some rocky material. Radioactivity melted them, and the denser material sank to form a central rocky core. A cold, thin "lithosphere" or ices would crystallize at the surface. This icy lithosphere floats on a deep asthenosphere of slush.

The density of the Galilean moons increases as we move inward toward Jupiter. During its formation Jupiter radiated considerable heat, forming a kind of weak mini-sun that burned away most of the ices from the inner satellites, just as the sun produced high-density planets in the inner solar system and less dense, icy planets in the outer solar system.

By 1973, improved infrared results supported this general picture. Frost or ice was firmly identified on Europa and Ganymede and weakly indicated on Callisto. Though Callisto has the most ice-rich interior, it apparently has the most soil mixed in its surface layer and the darkest surface of the four. Io, once again, was found to be different, with no surface ice or water in any identifiable form.

Still another Io anomaly appeared in 1972, when observer Robert Brown, then at Harvard, found a faint cloud of sodium atoms surrounding Io. These atoms are being knocked off the surface of Io by the high-energy particles that zip back and forth in Jupiter's magnetic field. Astronomers began to home in on the question of Io's surface. If it isn't ice, what is it? Scientists had long known that Io was reddish-yellow. In 1973 the Arizona observer R. B. Minton took particularly sharp photographs showing dark-reddish polar areas and yellowish-white equatorial regions. These colors suggest sulfur compounds. By the following year, geochemist Fraser Fanale and his associates at Caltech's Jet Propulsion Laboratory speculated that if Io had been strongly heated, the water would have been driven to the surface and evaporated into space, leaving surface deposits like those in the ancient lake-bed salt flats of Earth. In particular, they postulated the presence of both sulfur and sodium-rich compounds such as salt.

But why is Io's water loss so efficient? During 1978 dynamicist S. J. Peale and two colleagues studied the tidal forces exerted by Jupiter on Io and the other satellites. The tidal forces actually stretch the satellites; Jupiter's gravitational field pulls hardest on the satellite closest to it. As such a moon moves around Jupiter, its eccentric orbit carries it closer and then farther away so that these tidal forces are constantly changing. The resulting flexing is always much stronger on the closest satellite, and Peale concluded that it would be strong enough not only to melt Io, but to keep its interior intensely hot. With admirable nerve, Peale's group published their conclusion that Io might display "widespread and recurrent surface volcanism" in the March 2, 1979, issue of *Science*, which appeared during the very week that Voyager I sailed into the Jupiter system.

After its 18-month trip across some 625 million miles of interplanetary space (not to mention our 370-year wait), Voyager gave us our first look at these new moons. The outermost, Callisto, is an old, battered world with many impact craters. The preservation of so many craters means that Callisto's lithosphere has long been dormant. Probably it is thick and, thus, not broken by volcanism and plate-tectonic motion. As early as 1972, planetary astronomer T. V. Johnson and geologist T. R. McGetchin pointed out that glacierlike ice flow on these satellites would probably reduce topographic relief. Indeed, old Callisto craters that were initially as much as a mile deep seem to have flattened out, producing ghostlike ring systems. The dark surface suggests that dirt has been left behind as ice slowly vaporized into space during Callisto's long history. Brilliant aureoles around some of the fresher craters may be impacts that blew away the soil cover and exposed fresh ice. Callisto apparently never mustered enough geological strength to break its lithosphere or obliterate the ancient impact craters.

The next moon in has been more active. Ganymede looks at first most like our own moon, with large dark patches. But these dark areas are not the younger plains, as on our moon. Rather, they are patches of ancient Callisto-like cratered crust, broken by strange bright bands of grooves. The grooves are the younger regions, unlike any large-scale planetary features seen before. They are typically hundreds of miles long. Individually, the grooves appear to be a few miles wide and only a few hundred yards deep.

Some planetary researchers speculate that bands of grooves mark "plates" formed by cracking of the ancient Callisto-like crust. Modest internal heating might have cracked the lithosphere but was inadequate to drive eruptions of water or lava that could resurface the planet. The grooves might be zones of fractures created when the "plates" jostled against one another as they floated on a slushy asthenosphere. Voyager scientists believe that any such activity occurred billions of years ago, judging from the impact craters accumulated in the grooved terrain.

Europa revealed a still different, but related, picture. From a distance, Europa shows not the plate pattern of Ganymede but a nearly featureless, bright disk. Closer inspection shows a relatively uncratered billiard ball, broken by an intricate pattern of fractures more than a thousand miles long. Detailed photos show apparent ridges of new ice squeezed up along the fractures. The surface, with its comparative lack of craters, indicates that Europa's original crust has been resurfaced sometime in the past, but the age and the mechanism are unclear.

Some tidal heating, predicted by Peale's group, may have produced a world with a single lithospheric plate broken by fractures where hot springs of "molten" water occasionally erupted onto the surface. These ideas could explain the high concentration of surface ice and raise the question of whether Europa experiences occasional geyserlike outbursts even today.

Interestingly, the closest terrestrial analogue to the surfaces of Ganymede and Europa are the ice packs of the Arctic Ocean, where thin lithosphere-like ice floats on asthenosphere-like water. High altitude photos of these areas show patterns of fractures resembling those on Ganymede and Europa.

IO, THE WILDEST OF THEM ALL

When the first photographs of Io came in, one Voyager team member quipped that it looked like the cheap mock-ups of planets that we used to laugh at when they appeared outside spaceship portholes in Grade B science-fiction movies. Patches of different colors alternated on the surface with dark spots and fuzzy patches. Chemical studies show that the colors come from sulfurous deposits, just as yellow and white sulfur mottles the eruptive areas of Yellowstone Park.

On Io, no impact craters could be seen, indicating that the surface was quite young. A few days later, Jet Propulsion Laboratory flight engineer Linda Morabito discovered an erupting volcano—an immense, fuzzy, umbrella-shaped plume rising 160 miles above the edge of the planet. Altogether, eight major erupting volcanoes were discovered, of which at least six were still erupting four months later when Voyager 2 flew by. In retrospect, an outburst may have been spotted a year earlier by NASA observer F. C. Witteborn and colleagues, who detected a strong, brief emission of heat from Io. In Hawaii, obeserver W. M. Sinton reported a similar outburst last June. These observations suggest that there may be occasional explosions of molten sulfur even more violent than the normal eruptions seen by the Voyagers.

Scientists are now thinking about a "double lithosphere" for Io. They envision a surface layer of sulfur compounds comprising a thin lithosphere floating on a molten sea, all of which rests on a deeper rock layer, a true lithosphere that in turn floats on a molten silicate magma. The rock subsurface provides the strength to support the mountains seen on Io. The concept resembles Earth's Arctic surface ice floating on the polar ocean, which rests on a rocky sea floor, in turn resting on a partially molten mantle.

An observer on Io would confront a spectacle. The landscape would be dominated by brightly colored deposits and perhaps even flows of molten sulfur. From time to time enormous plumes would be shot out of volcanoes. And although the sky would normally be as black as the sky on our moon, the glow of sodium atoms would sometimes be visible as a ghostly aurora.

If the variety of these Jupiter satellites is not enough, we can turn for one last look at Saturn's large satellite, Titan. Titan has always interested armchair astronauts because its thick atmosphere implies a blue sky, and the thought of Saturn hanging in a blue sky over some strange landscape excited visual imaginations. Observations in the last few years, however, have shown that Titan has a fairly thick cover of reddish clouds. An observer on Titan might have to fly above the clouds to see Saturn at all. To reverse the problem, we probably cannot see below the clouds to determine what the surface of Titan is like. Because the methane-rich Titan atmosphere is something like that postulated for the early Earth and because we now recognize the possiblilty of hot-water asthenospheres, Titan might be one of the solar system's best prospects for warm springs where biological or prebiological chemical evolution might be occurring. All we can say is that cloud-top temperatures are well below minus 300 degrees F. These very cold values are consistent with Titan's enormous distance from the sun and were generally supported by measurements from Pioneer 11 as it flew by at some distance from Titan. To know whether hot springs exist, we'll have to wait at least until Voyager 1's Saturn flyby in November 1980.

Nonetheless, the large satellites of the outer solar system are dramatic worlds with unique landscapes. They may display various stages of plate tectonics and geologic activity. Thjey have craters, soil, exotic chemical compounds, ice, erupting volcanoes and perhaps even hot and cold running water. The new discoveries promise better understanding of the workings of all planets, including our own Earth. And they have given us new Yellowstones, new Grand Canyons hundreds of millions of miles away.

James L. Elliot, Edward Dunham, and Robert L. Millis . . . . Discovering the Rings of Uranus

From an airborne observatory where they planned to record the occultation of a star by Uranus, a group of scientists observed something unexpected. This recording of their conversation and tentative conclusions provide a ring-side seat on a new discovery in astronomy.

On March 10, 1977, NASA's Kuiper Airborne Observatory (KAO) was flying at 41,000 feet over the Indian Ocean. Aboard it, Jim Elliot, Ted Dunham, and Doug Mink were preparing to record photoelectrically the occultation by Uranus of the 9th-magnitude star SAO 158687. Meanwhile, at Perth Observatory in Australia, Bob Millis, Peter Birch, and Dan Trout were waiting for the occultation inside the dome of the 24-inch planetary patrol telescope.

Thirty-five minutes before the Star was expected to be covered by Uranus, the star's light unexpectedly dimmed for a few seconds. Several minutes later, another abrupt dip occurred—then another, and another, and another. At first these events caused concern, puzzlement, and then excitement. But only later was it realized that the sudden dips in the star's intensity were caused by the shadows of the rings of Uranus as they passed over the telescopes.

PEOPLE ABOARD THE KAO

Observing team
  Jim Elliot, principal investigator
  Ted Dunham, data recorder
  Doug Mink, data recorder
NASA team
  Carl Gillespie, mission director 1
  Jim McClenahan, mission director 2
  Don Olson, telescope operator
  Milo Reisner, telescope operator
  Al Meyer, telescope operator
  Tom Matheson, computer (ADAMS) operator
  Don Oishi, telescope technician
  Pete Kuhn, meteorologist
Flight crew
  Rond Gerdes, pilot
  Dave Barth, co-pilot
  Bob Innis, third pilot
  Jack Kroupa, navigator
  Frank Cosik, flight engineer
Guests
  Wilson Hunter, NASA
  Two flight controllers from Perth

As the KAO turns to track Uranus . . . .

Dunham: OK, it's 19:59:50. Now.
Elliot: OK, we're in the turn.
Dunham: 20 00 hours.
Reisner: Long way to go.

Dunham: What's our altitude, currently?
?: 41,000

They watch the wide-field acquistion camera as the KAO nears the heading to track Uranus

Reisner: It's going to be left of the mount.
Mink: That's the moon, off across the top.
Reisner: The moon over Antarctica. On heading.

Setting up for recording data.

Dunham: OK, what we would like to do is some burst modes during this run, and we would like to have 0.1 second integrations. OK? So integrate 10 points.
McClenahan: OK, we're on the heading.
Dunham: . . . and it'll all be channel zero, which is our channel one. And they will all be a hundred seconds.

Uranus is acquired.

Meyer: The object is centered. I have identified it.
Elliot: You see it, Al?
Meyer: Yeah, looking right at it.

Continuous data recording begins.

Elliot: OK, we can say it definitely hasn't occulted yet. The counting rates are right for the star and Uranus.
Dunham: 37, 8, 9, now!
Mink: OK, 20:05:40.

A check that data are being recorded properly.

Elliot: Well, according to the best prediction it should happen about half an hour from now.
Mink: Don't hold your breath.
Elliot: OK. It took about nine minutes to get all set up and situated.
Dunham: OK. The Cipher is still running properly.
Elliot: ADAMS status?
Matheson: Running—luckily.

First secondary occultation appears on the chart record, but is not noticed for almost a minute.

Dunham: What was that? What was that?
Elliot: What?
Dunham: This!
Elliott: I dunno. Was there a tracker glitch?
Meyer: Nothing here.
Dunham: Uh-oh. No. I don't think it's anything here, it's clearly duplicated in both channels.
Elliot: Yeah, I mean, clouds or . . . ?
Meyer: Ask Pete.
Dunham: Pete, what's your water vapor?
Kuhn: Eight point nine.
Dunham: Well, that's pretty low.
McClenahan: What happened?

Elliot: Well, we got a dip in the signal here, which was either due to a loss or momentary glitch in the tracker, or a cloud whipping through.

Dunham: OK, I think somebody should have the responsibility of always watching the focal plane there. I suppose that a lot of people are.

Elliott: But no one caught that one.

McClenahan: Nobody caught that one. I didn't. I wasn't looking.

Elliot: All right, I've moved it a little to the left . . . actually, I didn't mean to do it. Down back to the right. OK.

Gillespie: There was no movement in the focal plane. I was watching it.

Matheson: I was pretty much watching. I didn't see any.

Dunham: OK.

Gillespie: There's nothing the eye could detect, Tom.

Matheson: . . . it was a pretty long period, too.

Elliot: That, you should be able to see, because last night I saw a big glitch that went half way out of the aperture and back, and it was about like that on the plot we got.

More dips.

Dunham: Well, the long haul begins.

Many: Yep.

Mink: Fifteen more minutes.

Dunham: Epsilon Gem was nice, because the predictions were a lot better, because we had a better ephemeris.

Elliot: It happened a little late, didn't it? By the prediction?

Dunham: Yeah, not much, though.

Elliot: Ten seconds, or twenty?

Dunham: OK, I got a deep short spike here. [Delta ring occultation]

Elliot: I wonder if we're getting any clouds?

Dunham: No, Pete said we had . . . microns of water.

Kuhn: There's no clouds; I mean, truthfully, there's nothing up here.

Elliott: Well maybe this is a D ring. The D ring of Uranus. [This comment, which causes general laughter, was prompted by a team joke: If we didn't observe an occultation, we could use the data to put an upper limit on the optical depth of a hypothetical ring around Uranus!]

Dunham: With a normal optical depth of three, right? Another one. [Gamma ring occultation]

Elliot: Yeah, those are real—I guess.

Oishl: Boy, that was a deep one.

Kuhn: Yep. There's no indication of any fog at all.

McClenahan: Doesn't seem to be any bore-sight shifting.

Elliot: Yeah, that's good. I think we're getting real—could be small bodies—the satellite plane is face on, or it could be just small bodies like thin rings.

The team realizes the dips are due to a loss of light from the star rather than Uranus.

Elliot: Maybe it's something to do with Uranus, because they seem to be about the same amplitude on that scale. Normal occultation in twenty minutes.

Mink: Right.

Dunham: Another one! [Beta ring occultation]

Elliot: It's definitely the star being occulted somehow.

Dunham: Well—OK.

Elliot: Yeah, the original thing being that this ratio to this is like that ratio to that.

Dunham: Right I agree.

Elliot: Yeah, well I told you every occultation [mission] comes up with a new surprising thing, and this may be it.

Dunham: OK, its 20:20:20.

Elliot: Wait a minute, Millis wouldn't see the same ones, because if we're 2,000 kilometers . . .

Dunham: Yeah, but if you're seeing similar things . . .
Elliot: Similar things, yeah . . .
Dunham: How close are we to Sutherland?
Elliot: We're north of them.
Dunham: Yeah, but we're a lot closer to them than we are to Millis, right?
Elliot: Right, right. They probably can't see it yet, because it's down at 10° now, it's the pre-occultation time.
Dunham: There's another one! [Alpha ring occultation]

The ring hypothesis is taken more seriously.

Dunham: Channel one will acutally be an acid test, won't it?
Elliot: Yes, I'm very glad we have it. We're always joking about this D ring, but maybe we've *got* one.
Dunham: The watched pot never boils, here, we haven't got one so far.
Elliot: That's OK, we've got enough already.

Just past the nominal immersion time for Uranus.

Elliot: It's going to be late, if it is.
Dunham: Just on the general principle that it can't be on time.
Mink: Right! It's not obviously going to be very early, anyway.
Dunham: 20:47:02.

About five minutes later.

Dunham: These things are starting to look real.
Elliot: Yeah.
Mink: Yeah.
Elliot: We might be starting to occult.
Dunham: Yep.
Kuhn: No clouds at all, just crystal clear.
Dunham: Its right in the middle of the aperture. Yeah, we're starting to get in on it here. OK, the cassette will last until this is over. Yeah, without a doubt, this is the thing.
Elliot: Well, I don't know.
Dunham: OK, I'm starting the burst mode on this, this—they'll run for a hundred seconds. Yeah, Elliot, that's definitely it.
Elliot: Ahhhhhh!! [Loud whoopees and yays]
Dunham: Oh, look at the spikes. Boy, have we got a lot of those!
?: Hey, disappearance.
?: There you go. Boy, you've got more than enough.
McClenahan: Another Ph.D. in the world.

Attention aboard the aircraft was now turning to the occultation by Uranus. The chart recorder had continued its steady tracings well past the predicted immersion time of 20:47 UT. Finally, at 20:52 the occultation began, and the star remained behind the planet for about 25 minutes. During immersion and emersion, many "spikes" or brief flashes of intensity appeared in the light curve, much like the spikes recorded during the occultations of stars by Jupiter and Neptune.

The original flight plan had called for an immediate return to Perth folowing the reappearance of SAO 158687, but we continued tracing Uranus until 22:17:40 UT, when the morning twilight became too bright for the photomultipliers. During this time, several additional secondary occultations were observed.

Dawn in Africa was not due for another five hours. To alert observers there to record data for as long as possible, [a] message . . . was sent. Radioed from the plane, it was received at Perth by Bob Barrow of the KAO crew, who telephoned

Brian Marsden, the editor of the International Astronomical Union *Circulars*, in Cambridge, Massachusetts. He, in turn, contacted someone in Johannesburg, South Africa, who said it was raining but that he would try to reach the South African Astronomical Observatory at Sutherland.

Though not the intention of the KAO group, an IAU *Circular* issued the same day stated that we had observed an occultation by a previously unknown satellite of Uranus. Somewhere in relaying the message, the plural form [of *satellite*] was lost.

AT PERTH OBSERVATORY

Meanwhile, Millis made ready the photometric equipment at Perth Observatory that had been used in 1973 to observe mutual phenomena of Jupiter's satellites. Everything was in good working order except a beamsplitter, so the observations had to be interrupted periodically to recenter the planet in the 28-second-of-arc diaphragm. Assisted by Birch and Trout of the observatory staff, Millis began recording the combined light of Uranus and the star at 4:00 a.m., nearly an hour before the predicted time of disappearance. Again, this early start was prompted by the remaining uncertainty in the predictions.

After 10½ minutes, the signal dropped abruptly by 30 percent at 20:10:33.2 UT. (This was about 70 seconds before a similar event was observed aboard the KAO.) The drop looked quite unlike what was expected for the planetary occultation or for the passage of a cloud (which would have been visible anyway in the moonlit sky). At first, it seemed as if Uranus had drifted partly out of the aperture, but as Millis was preparing to check, the signal suddenly jumped back to the normal level. A quick look revealed Uranus precisely in the center of the field. The dip in the signal had lasted just over eight seconds. During the next 14 minutes, four more drops were observed, all of which were shallower than the first and lasted only about one second each.

The three observers discussed these strange glitches, particularly the first one; Millis suggested that it might have been caused by the occultation of the star by a previously unknown satellite. Observations then continued for the occultation of the planet itself—which never occurred, for the shadow had passed south of Perth. Up to 22:34 UT, when the sky became too bright to continue, no further dips in the signal were observed.

THE RETURN OF THE KAO

Upon leaving the observatory, Millis went to Perth airport to meet the returning KAO. He was afraid that the occultation zone might have been so far south that even the aircraft had been unable to reach it, But when Elliot stepped of the plane, his first words were, "How many satellites did you see?"

After everybody made a cursory examination of the data that morning, the initial interpretation was that several satellites in a "swarm" around Uranus had been observed. The possibility of rings had been discussed but rejected because of the extremely brief duration of most of the drops. Doubts remained, however, for the longest dimming had not been total and there was a large variation in the signal during it.

The weary astronomers' desire to study their data further that day was frustrated by a news conference, a colloquium, and the need for sleep.

Next morning the KAO left for Melbourne, where it would be based for the next few weeks to make infrared observations of southern-hemisphere sky objects. Millis stayed at Perth to make more photometric observations of Uranus, for a determination of the planet's rotation period. The Cornell group returned to the United States, arriving on the night of March 13th.

LATER ANALYSIS

The following evening Elliot checked the time intervals between the secondary occultations—something that could have been done on the morning of the 11th. He and his wife Elaine unrolled the chart record—over 40 feet long—in their small living room. The five secondary events before the occultation of the planet were aligned with the five after—the spacings matched! Uranus must be encircled by narrow rings!

Assuming that the rings lay in the same plane as Uranus' satellites, Dunham calculated the distance of each ring from the center of the planet. The distances for corresponding dips in the light curve before and after the occultation of the planet agreed. In order of increasing distance from Uranus, the rings were named Alpha (α), Beta (β), Gamma (γ), Delta (δ), and Epsilon (ε).

Then Mink, using the same distance scale, plotted light curves for both occultations of each ring. They too matched, except for the ring Epsilon, which may be elliptical, or not lie in the same orbit plane, or be fragments of two rings.

Since Millis was not scheduled to return for several days, the narrow-ring hypothesis cound not be checked against his data. Marsden was telephoned to suggest that he issue an IAU *Circular* with calculated times of the ring occultations for other sites, thus aiding possible observers.

Thin rings seemed fantastic, and Marsden was skeptical. He wanted to verify the ring hypothesiɔ and called Cape Town, where he found that Joe Churms had recorded six secondary occultations, five of which matched the predicted times. By then, Millis had returned, and three of his five events agreed with KAO ones. IAU *Circular* 3051 was issued on March 21st.

The discrepancy between Millis' data and those of the Cornell group was resolved two days later. At the times when rings Alpha and Delta should have been occulted at Perth, he had interrupted the observations to recenter Uranus. Also, in rechecking the Cornell data, some shallow occultations were found that corresponded to events recorded by Millis.

Three weeks later, Bill Hubbard at the University of Arizona reported that Ben Zellner of the Lunar and Planetary Laboratory had recorded three ring occultations from Perth. At this writing five different groups at four observatories have reported occultations of SAO 158687 by the rings.

In contrast to the rings of Saturn, each of which is nearly 20,000 kilometers wide, the rings of Uranus all are extremely narrow, Alpha through Delta being less than 10 kilometers in width. Though the rings of Uranus are too faint to be detected visually, perhaps photographs taken in the light of a deep methane band could reveal them. The 2.4-meter Space Telescope should be capable of separating the main components. However, the finest details of the rings are likely to be recorded only by a space probe to Uranus, since the narrowest rings are less than 0.001 second of arc wide as seen from Earth.

AN HISTORICAL FOOTNOTE

William Herschel, who discovered Uranus on March 31, 1781, thought in 1787 and 1789 that he saw two stubby rings around it at right angles to each other. However, further observations convinced him by 1798 that "it has no ring in the least resembling that, or rather those, of Saturn" *(Philosophical Transactions for 1798)*. The newly detected Uranian rings would have been far too difficult for Herschel's telescopes.

• DISCUSSION QUESTIONS •

1. What characteristics of the Dutch Republic of the 1600s made it a particularly good place for scientists to work? Why might a more repressive society have frowned upon the investigations of Leeuwenhoek and Huygens?

2. What are some specific advances in our understanding of particulate rings around planets? How are these related to the state of technology at the time they were made?

3. Why is Jupiter considered a star that "failed"? What does the planet consist of? What is the origin of its moons? What discoveries were made by Voyager 2? What remains to be explained about the jovian system?

4. What makes Jupiter a radio source?

5. What features of Jupiter and Saturn can never be duplicated on earth? Why?

6. How might discoveries about Jupiter and Saturn help in solving questions about Earth?

• ADDITIONAL ACTIVITIES •

Optional Projects

1. Develop a method of demonstrating comparisons of time-speed-distance between early voyages by explorers and space probes such as Voyager 2.

2. Observe the planets with the naked eye or a telescope (if available) for several nights in a row. Pretend you know nothing of modern astronomy. Write a short paper about your observations. (To locate planets, see star charts in astronomy magazines.)

3. Sketch the path followed by Voyager 2 through the solar system. Indicate which forces are propelling Voyager at crucial spots along the path.

Supplementary Bibliography

Gregory Benford, "Atmospheric Titan" in *Natural History*, April, 1974.
Why the study of Titan may solve many riddles about Earth, particularly concerning its early history.

Galileo Galilei, *Discoveries and Opinions of Galileo* (translated and with introduction and notes by Stillman Drake). Garden City, New York: Doubleday & Company, Inc., 1957.
Contains Galileo's writings about the satellites of Jupiter and Saturn.

Rick Gore, "What Voyager Saw: Jupiters Dazzling Realm" in *National Geographic*, January, 1980.
An account of Linda Morabito's discovery of a volcano on Io, along with other findings about Jupiter by Voyagers 1 and 2, with color photographs.

John R. Hale, *Age of Exploration*. New York: Time-Life Books, 1974.
The story of exploration by Europeans between 1420 and 1620.

Stephen P. Maran, "Rings Around Uranus" in *Natural History*, August/September, 1977.
Describes the discovery of the rings of Uranus, along with background concerning the event.

Samuel Eliot Morison, *The European Discovery of America*, (2 vols.). New York: Oxford University Press, 1974.
Detailed and entertaining accounts of early voyages to the New World, including those of Columbus and the Dutch.

Joseph Needham, *Science and Civilization in China*, Volume 1, Part 3. Cambridge University Press, 1971.
Tells the story of the Cheng-Ho voyages during the 1400s, when Chinese exploration was at its peak.

Chapter VII

THE BACKBONE
OF NIGHT

• OVERVIEW •

For thousands of years people lived in what they believed to be a lawless and inscrutable universe, governed by mysterious supernatural forces and capricious gods. In this chaotic and unpredictable world, where events seemed to occur without rhyme or reason, it is not surprising that people relied on myth, superstitions, and religious explanations to abide nature's mysteries.

Then, around 600 B.C. on an isolated Greek island in Ionia, a new breed of thinkers emerged. In contrast to their predecessors, the Ionians believed that the universe *was* knowable, arguing that nature exhibited certain regularities that bespoke an internal order. If nature itself obeyed a set of laws, then it was possible to describe and understand them and perhaps even predict how they might behave in the future. These revolutionary ideas, which represented a radical departure from the tradition of mysticism that had prevailed up to that time, marked the beginning of a new awakening in scientific thought, characterized by the fundamental notion that the universe is harmonious—and therefore accessible to human beings through observation and reason. Ionia became the birthplace of science.

The scientific methods developed in Ionia some 2,500 years ago helped lay the groundwork for science as we know it today. The tradition of open inquiry and careful observation that enabled the Ionians to make seminal discoveries in physics, biology, geography, medicine, mathematics, and astronomy has had a profound and lasting impact on the development of modern science.

• LEARNING OBJECTIVES •

1. Identify the following three Ionian thinkers and list the contributions to human understanding associated with each: Democritus, Aristarchus, and Pythagoras.

2. Describe the special place in human history that Sagan accords the Ionians and identify the factors that made Ionia the center of the "new awakening."

3. Describe the conflict between Pythagorean thought and the methods of the earlier Ionians, and describe the effect of Pythagorean thought on Ionian science.

4. Compare the approach to scientific inquiry of the Ionians, Democritus, Aristarchus, and Pythagoras, with the approaches of Kepler, Newton, and Huygens, concentrating on the relative importance of experimental fact, theoretical hypothesis, and religious belief.

• KEY TERMS AND NAMES •

Anaxagoras	Democritus
Anaximander	Empedocles
Aristarchus	Parmenides
Cosmos	Pythagoras
Chaos	Thales

• ASSIGNMENT •

Watch COSMOS television series Program 7, "The Backbone of Night."

Read Chapter 7, "The Backbone of Night" in Carl Sagan's text, *Cosmos*, or other readings assigned by your instructor.

• READINGS •

Benjamin Farrington . . . . Greek Science

Historian of science Benjamin Farrington describes, in this short essay, the world of Ionia during the sixth and fifth centuries B.C.

The sixth and fifth centuries [B.C.], the period known as that of Pre-Socratic philosophy or as the Heroic Age of Science, are characterized not only by a development of abstract thought. They were also a time of great technical progress, and what is new and characteristic in their progress is derived from the techniques. Technical development was the magic wand which was changing the old form of society based mainly on the land into a new form of society based largely on manufacture. Technical progress was calling into existence a new class of manufacturers and merchants which quickly assumed political control in the cities. In the first decade of the sixth century, Solon, who represented the new class, attempted to modernize Athens, the old Athens torn with the strife between landlord and peasant. In order to acheive this, Solon, we are told by Plutarch, "invested the crafts with honor." He turned the attention of the citizens to arts and crafts, and made a law that a son need not support his father in old age unless his father had taught him a trade." "At that time," says Plutarch, "work was no disgrace, nor did the possession of a trade imply social inferiority." The men then honored were men like Anacharsis the Scythian, whose titles to glory were that he had improved the anchor and invented the bellows and the potter's wheel. Or men like Glaucos of Chios, the inventer of the soldering iron; or Theodorus of Samos, who was credited with a long list of technical inventions—the level, the square, the lathe, the rule, the key, and the method of casting bronze. These navigational and industrial achievements were appreciated by the merchants of Miletus, among others. Their growing prosperity depended on manufacture for export. It was among them that Thales applied his skill in mathematics and geometry to the improvement of the art of navigation. It was for them that Anaximander made the first map of the world. It was there that the world began to be thought of as a machine. The temper of the age was such that honor was still given to the technician. The Greek word for wisdom, *sophia*, still meant at this time technical skill, not abstract speculation. Or rather the distinction between the two was not forced, for the best speculation was based on technical skill. The author of *Ancient Medicine* knows no higher title than *technician*. It was in this context that the natural philosophy of the Old Ionians was born. To represent it as wholly absorbed in speculation on the heavens to the neglect of human interests is false.

But the ripest product of this new outlook is still to be mentioned. In the free cities of Old Ionia the conquest of nature through technique gave birth to the ambition of extending the domain of reason over the whole of nature, including life and man. There was definite and conscious movement of rational thought over the whole sphere of existence. There was a propaganda of enlightenment, as many pages in the Hippocratic writings show. "It seems to me," says one writer, dealing with the mysterious affliction epilepsy, "that the disease is no more divine than any other. It has a natural cause, just as other diseases have. Men think it divine merely because they do not understand it. But if they called everything divine which they do not understand, why, there would be no end of divine things." These are truly classical words. They mark the advent of a new epoch in human culture. In their gentle irony they pronounce final judgement on a past age, on the period of mythological explanation. True, their point of view has not yet prevailed everywhere on earth. The battle is still joined and the issue doubtful. Miracles are still the basis of the world-view of large sections even of civilized mankind. Christendom has not yet made up its mind to accept accept a strictly naturalistic history of Christianity, or even, for that matter, of Joan of Arc. But the old Ionian formulation remains to do its silent work in the mind of civilized man. "Men think it divine merely because they do not understand it. But if they called everything divine which they do not understand, why, there would be no end of divine things." The identification of the divine with the not-yet-explained was the shrewdest of blows for reason and nature.

Sir William Dampier . . . . The Ionians

In this selection, historian of science William Dampier surveys the major accomplishments of the early Greek scientists.

The first European school of thought to break away definitely from mythological traditions was that of the Ionian nature philosophers of Asia Minor, of whom

Thales of Miletus (c. 580 B.C.), statesman, engineer, mathematician and astronomer, is the earliest known to us. The importance of this Milesian School of
philosophy lies in the fact that, for the first time, it assumes that the whole universe
is natural, and potentially explicable by ordinary knowledge and rational inquiry.
The supernatural, as fashioned by mythology, simply vanishes. The idea of a cycle
of change appears, a cycle from air, earth and water through the bodies of plants
and animals to air, earth and water again. Thales observed that the food of plants
and animals is moist, and revived the old theory that water or moisture is the
essence of all things. This idea of a primary element tended to encourage philosophical scepticism; for if wood and iron are essentially the same as water, then the
evidence of the senses must be untrustworthy.

Traditional anecdotes of Thales have been handed down by Aristotle and
Plutarch. He is said to have visited Egypt, and, from empirical rules for land
surveying, originated the science of deductive geometry on the lines afterwards
developed by others and systematized by Euclid. He is also said to have predicted
an eclipse, either that of 610 or that of 585 B.C., probably making use of Babylonian
tables. He taught that the Earth was a flat disc floating on water.

Anaximander (610–545 B.C.), who followed him, seems to have been the first
Greek to make a map of the known world. He was also the first to recognize that
the heavens revolve round the pole star, and to draw the conclusion that the visible
dome of the sky is half of a complete sphere, at the centre of which is the Earth.
Until Thales and Anaximander propounded this new theory, the Earth had been
imagined as a floor with a solid base of limitless depth. It was now represented as a
finite flattened cylinder, originally surrounded by envelopes of water, air and fire,
and floating within the celestial sphere. It was thought that the Sun and stars, shat-
tered fragments of the original fiery envelope, were attached to celestial circles, and
with them revolved about the Earth, the centre of all things. The Sun passed
underground at night, and not round the rim of the world, as it was supposed to do
in the older systems.

In Anaximander's cosmogony, worlds were supposed to arise by division of
opposites from the primordial stuff of chaos in a way which pushes back to the
beginning the operation of ordinary forces such as we see at work in nature every
day. This developed further a rational mechanistic philosophy.

In the realm of practical arts, we hear by tradition of shadowy figures like that
of Anacharsis (c. 592), who is said to have invented the potter's wheel; Glaucus
(c. 550), who first learnt to solder iron; and Theodorus (c. 530), who devised the
level, the lathe and the set-square. Anaximander is said to have introduced from
Babylon the style or gnomon. This was a rod placed upright on horizontal ground
and used as a sun-dial; it also served to determine the meridian, and the time of
year when the Sun's altitude at noon was greatest. But the many slaves reduced the
incentive to invent machines.

In organic nature Anaximander taught that the first animals arose from sea
slime, and men from the bellies of fish. Primary matter he believed to be eternal,
but all created things, even the heavenly bodies, were doomed to destruction and to
return to the undivided unity of universal being.

Anaximenes (died c. 526) departed further from Orphic mysticism, and held
the primary world stuff or element to be air, which becomes fire when rarefied, and
first water and then earth when condensed. In the air the Earth and planets float;
the Moon shines by reflecting light from the sun.

As against the rationalizing tendency of the Ionian philosophers, Pythagoras
(born at Samos but moved to Southern Italy about 530 B.C.) and his followers

showed a mystical attitude of mind derived directly from Orphism, accompanied by a readiness to observe and experiment. "Pythagoras of Samos," says Heraclitus, "has practised research and enquiry more than all other men, and has made up his wisdom out of polymathy and out of bad arts."

Pythagoras and his school gave up the idea of one single element, and held matter to be composed of earth, water, air and fire, which were supposed to be derived by the combination in pairs of four underlying qualities, hot and cold, wet and dry; water, for instance, being cold and wet, while fire was hot and dry. They carried further the deductive science of geometry, and arranged in logical order something like the first two books of Euclid. The forty-seventh proposition of the first book of Euclid is called the Theorem of Pythagoras. The "rule of the cord" for laying out a right angle may have been discovered empirically both in Egypt and in India, but it is likely that Pythagoras gave the first deductive proof that the square on the hypotenuse of a right-angled triangle is equal to the sum of the squares on the other two sides.

The Pythagoreans also were the first to bring into prominence the abstract idea of number. To us the concept of number is familiar; we are accustomed to deal with an abstract three or five, irrespective of fingers, apples or days, and it is difficult for us to realize the great step made both in practical mathematics and in philosophy when the essential *fiveness* of groups of quite different things was first seen. In practical mathematics that discovery made arithmetic possible; in philosophy it led to the belief that number lies at the base of the real world. "The Pythagoreans," says Aristotle, "seem to have looked upon number as the principle and, so to speak, the matter of which existences consist." Such ideas of definite, indivisible units as fundamental entities seemed inconsistent with another great Pythagorean discovery, the existence of incommensurable quantities, but they were greatly strengthened when the Pythagoreans experimented with sound, and proved that the lengths of string which gave a note, its fifth and its octave were in the ratios of 6:4:3. The theory of the Universe was sought in this scheme of related numbers, which were held to refer to indivisible units of space. It was also thought that the distance of the planets from the Earth must conform to a musical progression, and ring forth "the music of the spheres." Ten was the perfect number (for $10 = 1+2+3+4$), so the moving luminaries of the heavens must be ten also. But as only nine were visible, it was argued that there must be an invisible "counter-earth". At a later date Aristotle very rightly criticized this juggling with facts.

Nevertheless the Pythagoreans made a real advance in cosmogony, our knowledge of which is chiefly derived from the works of Philolaus, who wrote about the middle of the fifth century. They recognized the Earth as a sphere, and eventually realized that the apparent rotation of the heavens could be explained, and explained more simply, by supposing a moving earth. The Earth was thought to revolve, not on its own axis, but, balanced by the counter-earth, round a point fixed in space, as would a stone at the end of a string, and to present its inhabited outer face successively to each part of the surrounding sky. At the fixed point was a central fire, the Altar of the Universe, never seen by man. This idea gave rise in later years to the mistaken belief that the Pythagoreans had devised a heliocentric theory of the Universe, and had thus anticipated Aristarchus and Copernicus.

The mystic view of nature, clearly seen in their doctrine of numbers, shows also in the Pythagoreans' notion of the fundamental importance of contrasted principles—love and hatred, good and evil, light and darkness—a notion which often recurred in Greek thought, that facts about things can be deduced from the meaning of words. The mystic view again appeared in the writings of Alcmaeon the physician, in the idea that man the microcosm is a miniature of the Universe the macrocosm; his body reflects the structure of the world, and his soul is a harmony of number. The Pythagorean School held a philosophy of form as contrasted with the Ionian philosophy of matter. Early in the fifth century it divided; one wing became a religious brotherhood, and the other developed the doctrine of number on quasi-scientific lines.

The essence of Pythagorean philosophy, including the theory that ultimate reality is to be found in numbers and their relations, will be traced in this book through Plato's doctrine of ideas to the Neo-Platonists and Saint Augustine. Under his influence it helped to form that Platonic background of mediaeval thought which survived as an alternative to the scholastic system derived from Aristotle. Even in Scholasticism, the Pythagorean idea of numbered order in geometry, arithmetic, music and astronomy made those four subjects the *quadrivium* of mediaeval instruction. After the Renaissance, the idea of the importance of number was taken up by Copernicus and Kepler, who laid chief stress on the mathematical harmony and simplicity of the heliocentric hypothesis as the best evidence of its truth. In our own day, Aston with his integral atomic weights, Moseley with his atomic numbers, Planck with his quantum theory, and Einstein with his claim that physical facts such as gravitation are exhibitions of local space-time properties, are reviving ideas that, in older, cruder forms, appear in Pythagorean philosophy.

If astronomical phenomena are the more striking, and therefore the first to arrest attention, the problem of the nature of matter cries equally to thoughtful minds for an explanation. The origin of chemistry is to be sought in arts that are as old as mankind, and especially in the discovery and use of fire. Cooking, the fermenting of grape juice, the smelting of metals, the making of stoneware, are prehistoric achievements. The Egyptians were skilled in dyeing, in tempering iron, in making glass and enamel, and in the use of metallic compounds as mordants, pigments and cosmetics, while as far back as fifteen hundred years before Christ, the people of Tyre produced the famous Tyrian purple dye from shellfish.

As in geometry, so in the problem of matter, the Greeks seem to have been the first to theorize. They ignored the vast amount of knowledge which must have been available in what they regarded as base mechanic arts, and reasoned only on what was obvious to every Greek gentleman. We find the Ionian philosophers tracing the changes of substances from earth and water to the bodies of plants and animals, and back again to earth and water. They began to realize the conception of the indestructibility of matter, and, from Thales onwards, despite the obvious superficial differences in bodies, speculated on the possibility of a single "element," water, air or fire, as a common basis of all things.

At the beginning of the fifth century philosophy passed into controversy, and attacks were made both on the Ionians and the Pythagoreans from two sides. All concerned showed the characteristic Greek love of theorizing from first principles and dogmatizing about phenomena.

Heraclitus (c. 502), poet and philosopher, expressed contempt for the materialist tendency of Anaximander and Anaximenes. To him the primary element or reality was the aethereal fire, a kind of sour stuff, of which all is made and to which all returns. The perpetual alternation of opposites in this world—sleeping and waking, death and life—makes the ceaseless rhythm of the ever-living fire. All things move in order, and all are in a state of flux— παντα ϱει. Truth can only be found within, a reflection of the universal Logos or reason.

Another type of critical philosophy was also reached *a priori* by the philosophers of Elea in Southern Italy, of whom the chief was Parmenides, who flourished about the year 480.

Entranced by the operations of the human mind, Parmenides pushed to an extreme the characteristic Greek assumption that what is inconceivable is impossible, even if the senses tell us that it has, in fact, happened. He argued thus: Creation is impossible because something cannot be conceived to arise from nothing, or being from non-being, indeed non-being cannot be. Conversely, destruction is impossible because something cannot vanish into nothing. Even change is impossible, because a thing cannot arise from another thing which is in essence unlike itself. Thus the appearances of change, of diversity and multiplicity, of time and space, which we see or think we see in nature, are but false impressions of sense, which thought proves to be self-contradictory. Hence, sense cannot lead to truth, which can be found by thought alone. Sense perceptions are unreal, non-being; thought alone is real, true being. Interpreted in other terms, to touch reality we must eliminate all differences in bodies, and thus get left with a single uniform essence. This is the only reality, one, eternal and unchangeable, limited only by itself, evenly extended and therefore spherical. In the apparent world of phenomena, the unreal but still observed Universe is a series of concentric shells of fire and earth; though all this is but "opinion" and not necessarily "truth".

Some of these ideas were carried further by Zeno of Elea, a younger contemporary of Parmenides, who opposed the Pythagorean doctrine that all things are made of integral numbers and thought he had discredited multiplicity by his famous series of paradoxes. A manifold must be divisible to infinity and therefore must itself be infinite, but, in trying to build it up again, no number of infinitely small parts can make a finite whole. The swift Achilles, pursuing a tortoise, reaches the spot whence the tortoise started; the tortoise has now moved on to a further spot; when Achilles arrives there, the tortoise has once more advanced—and so on to infinity, but Achilles never catches the tortoise.

Parmenides seems to dispute about the meaning accidentally assigned to words, meanings always arbitrary and often changing, and Zeno's paradoxes rest on misconceptions about the nature of infinitesimals and the relations of time and space cleared up by modern mathematicians. But Zeno certainly proved that the idea of division without limit into infinitesimal units as then understood was inconsistent with experience. The discrepancy would only be resolved completely when different kinds of infinity, not equivalent to each other, were distinguished in the nineteenth century.

Nevertheless, the Eleatic philosophy is important to us in two ways. In the first place, by discrediting the senses, it helped the atomists to seek reality in things imperceptible to the senses, and to explain what afterwards came to be called the secondary or separable qualities of bodies, such as hotness or colour, as mere sense perceptions. Secondly, the search for a single unity, representing the underlying reality in all things, while it aided the physicists in their search for a single chemical element, led the philosophers to separate substance (ουσια) from qualities or accidents (νους). Put in final form by Aristotle, this idea of the nature of matter dominated mediaeval thought.

Anaxagoras was another Ionian philosopher, born near Smyrna about 500 B.C., who took the more materialist Ionian ideas of philosophy with him to Athens forty years later. To Anaxagoras matter was a crowd of different entities each with different qualities or accidents as the senses suggest. However far division is carried the parts contain things like the whole, though differences may arise from different proportions in the ingredients. Motion was originally started by Mind ($\pi\alpha\theta\eta$), a subtle fluid causing rotation which spreads and so makes and orders the world. The heavenly bodies are matter of the same nature as the Earth; the Sun is not the God Helios, but an ignited stone; the Moon has hills and valleys. Besides these speculations Anaxagoras made some real advance in exact knowledge. He dissected animals, gained some insight into the anatomy of the brain, and discovered that fishes breathe through their gills.

We see other ideas of matter in the famous hypothesis of four elements, held by the Pythagoreans and worked out in a more definite form by the Sicilian philosopher Empedocles (450 B.C.), who taught that the "roots" or elements were earth, water, air and fire—a solid, a liquid, a gas, and a type of matter still rarer than the gaseous. These four elements were combined throughout the Universe in different proportions under the influence of the two contrasted divine powers, one attractive and one repulsive, which the ordinary eye sees working among men as love and hatred, ideas which recall the conceptions of Pythagoras. By the various combinations of the four elements all the many types of matter are formed, just as a painter makes all shades and tints by combining four pigments.

Parmenides had argued against the existence of empty space, which men thought they perceived in air. Anaxagoras and Empedocles demonstrated the corporeal nature of air, and, by experiments with a water-clock, the latter showed that water can only enter a vessel as air escapes. This discovery proved air to be distinct both from empty space and from vapour.

The idea that all things are made of four elements seems to have been derived from a natural misinterpretation of the action of fire. When burned, it was thought, a substance must be resolved into its elements; combustible matter is complex, while the small quantity of ash left by burning it is simple. For instance, when green wood is burnt, the *fire* is seen by its own light, the smoke vanishes into *air*, from the ends of the wood *water* boils off, and the ashes are clearly of the nature of *earth*.

Other theories based on this conception of fire followed in later times. It was the first great guiding idea of chemistry. Marsh says: "The fire theories are: the Greek theory of the four elements, the alchemical theory of the composition of metals, the iatrochemical theory of the hypostatical principles and the phlogiston theory," which was developed during the eighteenth century. The rise and fall of these theories will be traced in the later chapters of this book.

Empedocles thought that, by imagining his four elements united in different proportions, he could explain all the endless kinds of different substances known to man. Leucippus and Democritus carried this simplification further, and developed into a theory of atoms the older and alternative hypothesis of a single element.

The ground on which the atomic theory of the Greeks was founded was very different from the definite experimental facts known to Dalton, Avogadro and Cannizzaro when they formulated the atomic and molecular theories of today. The modern chemists had before them exact quantitative measurements of the proportions in which chemical elements combined by weight and by volume. These limited and definite facts led irresistibly to the idea of atoms and molecules, and gave to them at once relative atomic and molecular weights. The theory thus formulated was found to conform with all the rest of the many isolated or interconnected facts and relations which had become the common heritage of science, to be supported by other successive experiences, and to serve as a useful guide in the study and even in the prediction of new phenomena. Although, like every other scientific generalization, it had philosophic meaning, it was not deduced from, or even necessarily bound up with, any complete philosophic theory of the Universe. It was a humbler but more useful affair.

The Greeks had neither definite observed facts to suggest an exact and limited theory in the first place, nor the power of testing by experiment the consequences of the theory when framed. The Greek theory was founded on and incorporated in a cosmic scheme of philosophy, and it remained a doctrine, like the metaphysical systems in ancient and modern times, dependent on the mental attitude of its originators and their followers, and liable to be upset and replaced from the very foundations by a new system of a rival philosopher. And this indeed is what happened.

The Ionian philosophers reasoned from the general knowledge of their time in the light of the prevalent metaphysical ideas. When matter is divided and subdivided, do its properties remain unchanged? Is earth always earth, and water water, however far the process is carried? In other words, are the properties of bodies ultimate facts of which no further explanation can be given, or can we represent them in terms of simpler conceptions, and thus push the limits of ignorance one step further back?

It is this attempt at a rational explanation, in what seemed simpler terms, that makes the efforts of the Greeks to solve the problem of matter important in the history of scientific thought. According to the ideas that preceded their attempt, and followed the fall of the atomic philosophy, the qualities of substances were thought to be of their essence; the sweetness of sugar, and the colour of leaves, were as much a reality as the sugar and leaves themselves, and not to be explained by reference to other facts, or as varieties of human sensation.

It is of interest to trace the origins of the Greek atomic theory. Thales took water, Anaximenes air, and Heraclitus fire, as primary elements. Anaximenes' element, air, suffered condensation and rarefaction with its essence unchanged. Heraclitus' theory of endless flux suggested the idea of invisible moving particles, realized in the evaporation of water and in the diffusion of scent. This led back to the Pythagorean doctrine of integral monads, conforming to the laws of number, as the ultimate reality. The conception of vacant space empty of matter was also held by the Pythagoreans, though they confused it with air. It was atacked by Parmenides, but it was revived by the atomists owing to the difficulty of explaining how particles could move in a fully packed space or plenum. Air was now known to be corporeal, and thus to the atomists empty space became a real vacuum.

Such were the trains of thought which suggested the theory that matter consists of ultimate particles scattered in a void, a theory which explained all the relevant facts then known—evaporation, condensation, motion, and the growth of new material. It is true that the fundamental problem remained, and was emphasized by other Greek philosophers. Were the atoms themselves infinitely divisible? The atomist evaded the logical pitfall, and held that atoms were physically indivisible because there was no void within them.

The earliest atomists whose fame has reached us are Leucippus, a shadowy figure of the fifth century who is said to have founded the school of Abdera in Thrace, and Democritus, who was born at Abdera in 460 B.C. Their views are known to us by references in the works of later writers such as Aristotle, and by the work of Epicurus (341-270), who adopted and taught the theory of atoms at Athens as part of a complete philosophy of ethics, psychology and physics, set forth again two centuries later in the poem of the Roman Lucretius.

Leucippus laid down the basal idea of atomism and also the principle of causation—"Nothing happens without a cause, but everything with a cause and by necessity." He and Democritus carried further the attempt of the Ionian philosophers to explain the properties of matter in terms of simpler elements. They saw that to admit the qualities of bodies as fundamental and inexplicable would stop all further enquiry. In contra-distinction to this view, Democritus taught: "According to convention there is a sweet and a bitter, and a hot and a cold, and according to convention there is colour. In truth there are atoms and a void." Thus, although he opposed Protagoras, who held the relativist view that "man is the measure of all things," so that, for instance, honey may be sweet to me but bitter to you, Democritus saw that reality could not be reached through the senses alone.

The atoms of Democritus were uncaused, existent from eternity, and never annihilated—"strong in solid singleness." They were many in size and shape, but identical in substance. Thus difference in properties is due to differences in size, shape, position and movement of particles of the same ultimate nature. In stone or iron the atoms can only throb or oscillate, in air or fire they rebound at greater distances.

Moving in all directions through infinite space, the atoms strike against each other, producing lateral movements and vortices, thus bringing similar atoms together to form elements and starting the formation of innumerable worlds, which grow, decay and ultimately perish, only those systems surviving which are fitted to their environment. Here we see a faint forecast of the nebular hypothesis, and of the Darwinian theory of natural selection.

In the original form of the theory there is no idea of an absolute up or down, levity or heaviness. Moreover motion persists unless opposed. To Aristotle these sound ideas were incredible, and later on the theory seems to have been modified to meet his criticism. The truth had to be rediscovered by Galileo. In astronomy the atomists were reactionary, picturing the Earth as flat; but in other respects they were in advance of their contemporaries and their successors.

Democritus' teaching, as transmitted to us by Lucretius, effects a wonderful simplification in the mental picture of nature previously held. In fact, the picture is too simple. The atomists passed unconsciously over difficulties which, after the lapse of twenty-four centuries, are still unsolved. Fearlessly they applied the theory to problems of life and consciousness which still defy explanation in mechanical terms. Confidently they believed they had left no mysteries, blind to the great mystery underlying and surrounding all existence, a mystery none the less profound today than when the atomic theory was first formulated.

Lucretius . . . . Movements and Shapes of Atoms

Lucretius, a Roman poet who lived from 98 to 55 B.C., devoted his entire life to an exposition of the teachings and philosophies of Democritus and Epicurus. In the following excerpts from The Nature of the Universe, *Lucretius describes how all material substances in the world are joined together by atoms.*

I will explain *the motion by which the generative bodies of matter give birth to various things*, and, after they are born, dissolve them once more; the force that compels them to do this; and the power of movement through the boundless void with which they are endowed. It is for you to devote yourself attentively to my words.

Be sure that matter does not stick together in a solid mass. For we see that everything grows less and seems to melt away with the lapse of time and withdraw its old age from our eyes. And yet we see no diminution in the sum of things. This is because the bodies that are shed by one thing lessen it by their departure but enlarge another by their coming; here they bring decay, there full bloom, but they do not linger there. So the sum of things is perpetually renewed. Mortals live by mutual interchange. One race increases by another's decrease. The generations of living things pass in swift succession and like runners hand on the torch of life.

If you think that the atoms can stop and by their stopping generate new motions in things, you are wandering far from the path of truth. Since the atoms are moving freely thought the void, they must all be kept in motion either by their own weight or on occasion by the impact of another atom. For it must often happen that two of them in their course knock together and immediately bounce apart in opposite directions, a natural consequence of their hardness and solidity and the absence of anything behind to stop them.

As a further indication that all particles of matter are on the move, remember that the universe is bottomless: there is no place where the atoms could come to rest. As I have already shown by various arguments and proved conclusively, space is without end or limit and spreads out immeasurably in all directions alike.

It clearly follows that no rest is given to the atoms in their course through the depths of space. Driven along in an incessant but variable movement, some of them bounce far apart after a collision while others recoil only a short distance from the impact. From those that do not recoil far, being driven into a closer union and held there by the entanglement of their own interlocking shapes, are composed firmly rooted rock, the stubborn strength of steel and the like. Those other that move freely through larger tracts of space, springing far apart and carried far by the rebound— these provide for us thin air and blazing sunlight. Besides these, there are many other atoms at large in empty space which have been thrown out of compound bodies and have nowhere even been granted admittance so as to bring their motions into harmony.

This process, as I might point out, is illustrated by an image of it that is continually taking place before our very eyes. Observe what happens when sunbeams are admitted into a building and shed light on its shadowy places. You will see a multitude of tiny particles mingling in a multitude of ways in the empty space within the light of the beam, as though contending in everlasting conflict, rushing into battle rank upon rank with never a moment's pause in a rapid sequence of unions and disunions. From this you may picture what it is for the atoms to be perpetually tossed about in the illimitable void. To some extent a small thing may afford an illustration and an imperfect image of great things. Besides, there is a further reason why you should give your mind to these particles that are seen dancing in a sunbeam: their dancing is an actual indication of underlying movements of matter that are hidden from our sight. There you will see many particles under the impact of invisible blows changing their course and driven back upon their tracks, this way and that, in all directions. You must understand that they all derive this restlessness from the atoms. It originates with the atoms, which move of themselves. Then those small compound bodies that are least removed from the impetus of the atoms are set in motion by the impact of their invisible blows and in turn cannon against slightly larger bodies. So the movement mounts up from the atoms and gradually emerges to the level of our senses, so that those bodies are in motion that we see in sunbeams, moved by blows that remain invisible.

And now, Memmius, as to the rate at which the atoms move, you may gauge this readily from these few indications. First, when dawn sprays the earth with new-born light and the birds, flitting through pathless thickets, fill the neighbourhood according to their kind with liquid notes that glide through the thin air, it is plain and palpable for all to see how suddenly the sun at the moment of his rising drenches and clothes the world with his radiance. But the heat and the bright light which the sun emits do not travel through empty space. Therefore they are forced to move more slowly, cleaving their way as it were through waves of air. Ant the atoms that compose this radiance do not travel as isolated individuals but linked and massed together. Thus their pace is retarded by one dragging back another as well as by external obstacles. But, when separate atoms are travelling in solitary solidity through empty space, they encounter no obstruction from without and move as single units on the course on which they have embarked. Obviously therefore they must far outstrip the sunlight in speed of movement and traverse an extent of space many times as great in the time it takes for the sun's rays to flash across the sky. No wonder that men cannot follow the individual atoms, so as to discern the agency by which everything is brought about.

Now, I should judge, is the place to insert a demonstration that *no material thing can be uplifted or travel upwards by its own power.* Do not be misled by the particles that compose flame. The fact that all weights taken by themselves tend downwards does not prevent lusty crops and trees from being born with an upward thrust and from growing and increasing upwards. Similarly, when fires leap up to the house-tops and devour beams and rafters with rapid flame, it must not be supposed that they do this of their own accord with no force to fling them up. Their behaviour is like that of blood released from our body when it spouts forth and springs aloft in a gory fountain. Observe also with what force beams and rafters are heaved up by water. The more we have shoved them down into the depths, many of us struggling strenuously together to push them under, the more eagerly the water spews and ejects them back again, so that more than half their bulk shoots up above the surface. And yet, I should judge, we have no doubt that all these, taken by themselves, would move downwards through empty space. It must be just the same with flames: under pressure they can shoot up through the gusty air, although their weight, taken by itself, strives to tug them down. Observe how the nocturnal torches of the sky in their lofty flight draw in their wake long trails of flame in whatever direction nature has set their course. See how stars and meteors fall upon the earth. The sun from the summit of the sky scatters heat in all directions and sows the fields with light. The sun's radiance therefore tends also towards earth. Note again how the lightning flies through the rain-storms aslant. The fires that break out of the clouds rush together, now this way, now that; often enough the fiery force falls upon the earth.

In this connexion there is another fact that I want you to grasp. *When the atoms are travelling straight down through empty space by their own weight, at quite indeterminate times and places they swerve ever so little from their course,* just so much that you can call it a change of direction. If it were not for this swerve, everything would fall downwards like rain-drops through the abyss of space. No collision would take place and no impact of atom on atom would be created. Thus nature would never have created anything.

If anyone supposes that heavier atoms on a straight course through empty space could outstrip lighter ones and fall on them from above, thus causing impacts that might give rise to generative motions, he is going far astray from the path of truth. The reason why objects falling through water or this air vary in speed according to their weight is simply that the matter composing water or air cannot obstruct all objects equally, but is forced to give way more speedily to heavier ones. But empty space can offer no resistance to any object in any quarter at any time, so as not to yield free passage as its own nature demands. Therefore, through undisturbed vacuum all bodies must travel at equal speed though impelled by unequal weights. The heavier will never be able to fall on the lighter from above or generate of themselves impacts leading to that variety of motions out of which nature can produce things. We are thus forced back to the conclusion that the atoms swerve a little—but only a very little, or we shall be caught imagining slantwise movements, and the facts will prove us wrong. For we see plainly and palpably that weights, when they come tumbling down, have no power of their own to move aslant, so far as meets the eye. But who can possibly perceive that they do not diverge in the very least from a vertical course?

Again, if all movement is always interconnected, the new arising from the old in a determinate order—if the atoms never swerve so as to originate some new movement that will snap the bonds of fate, the everlasting sequence of cause and effect—what is the source of the free will possessed by living things throughout the earth? What, I repeat, is the source of that will-power snatched from the fates, whereby we follow the path along which we are severally led by pleasure, swerving from our course at no set time or place but at the bidding of our own hearts? There is no doubt that on these occasions the will of the individual originates the movements that trickle through his limbs. Observe, when the starting barriers are flung back how the race-horses in the eagerness of their strength cannot break away as suddenly as their hearts desire. For the whole supply of matter must first be mobilized throughout every member of the body: only then, when it is mustered in a continuous array, can it respond to the prompting of the heart. So you may see that the beginning of movement is generated by the heart; starting from the voluntary action of the mind, it is then transmitted throughout the body and the limbs. Quite different is our experience when we are shoved along by a blow inflicted with compulsive force by someone else. In that case it is obvious that all the matter of our body is set going and pushed along involuntarily, till a check is imposed through the limbs by the will. Do you see the difference? Although many men are driven by an external force and often constrained involuntarily to advance or to rush headlong, yet there is within the human breast something that can fight against this force and resist it. At its command the supply of matter is forced to take a new course through our limbs and joints or is checked in its course and brought once more to a halt. So also in the atoms you must recognize the same possibility: besides weight and impact there must be a third cause of movement, the source of this inborn power of ours, since we see that nothing can come out of nothing. For the weight of an atom prevents its movements from being completely determined by the impact of other atoms. But the fact that the mind itself has no internal necessity to determine its every act and compel it to suffer in helpless passivity—this is due to the slight swerve of the atoms at no determinate time or place.

The supply of matter in the universe was never more tightly packed than it is now, or more widely spaced out. For nothing is ever added to it or subtracted from it. It follows that the movement of atoms to-day is no different from what it was in bygone ages and always will be. So the things that have regularly come into being will continue to come into being in the same manner; they will be and grow and flourish so far as each is allowed by the laws of nature. The sum of things cannot be changed by any force. For there is no place into which any kind of matter might escape out of the universe or out of which some newly risen force could break into the universe and transform the whole nature of things and reverse their movements.

In this connexion there is one fact that need occasion no surprise. *Although all the atoms are in motion, their totality appears to stand totally motionless*, except for such movements as particular objects may make with their own bodies. This is because the atoms all lie far below the range of our senses. Since they are themselves invisible, their movements also must elude observation. Indeed, even visible objects, when set at a distance, often disguise their movements. Often on a hillside fleecy sheep, as they crop their lush pasture, creep slowly onward, lured this way or that by grass that sparkles with fresh dew, while the full-fed lambs gaily frisk and butt. And yet, when we gaze from a distance, we see only a blur—a white patch stationary on the green hillside. Take another example. Mighty legions, waging mimic war, are thronging the plain with their manoeuvres. The dazzling sheen flashes to the sky and all around the earth is ablaze with bronze. Down below there sounds the tramp of a myriad marching feet. A noise of shouting strikes upon the hills and reverberates to the celestial vault. Wheeling horsemen gallop hot-foot across the midst of the plain, till it quakes under the fury of their charge. And yet there is a vantage-ground high among the hills from which all these appear immobile—a blaze of light stationary upon the plain. . . .

Give your mind now to the true reasoning I have to unfold. A new fact is battling strenuously for access to your ears. A new aspect of the universe is striving to reveal itself. But no fact is so simple that it is not harder to believe than to doubt at the first presentation. Equally, there is nothing so mighty or so marvellous that the wonder it evokes does not tend to diminish in time. Take first the pure and undimmed lustre of the sky and all that it enshrines: the stars that roam across its surface, the moon and the surpassing splendour of the sunlight. If all these sights were now displayed to mortal view for the first time by a swift unforeseen revelation, what miracle could be recounted greater than this? What would men before the revelation have been less prone to conceive as possible? Nothing, surely. So marvellous would have been that sight—a sight which no one now, you will admit, thinks worthy of an upward glance into the luminous regions of the sky. So has satiety blunted the appetite of our eyes. Desist, therefore, from thrusting out reasoning from your mind because of its disconcerting novelty. Weigh it, rather, with discerning judgment. Then, if it seems to you true, give in. If it is false, gird yourself to oppose it. For the mind wants to discover by reasoning what exists in the infinity of space that lies out there, beyond the ramparts of this world—that region into which the intellect longs to peer and into which the free projection of the mind does actually extend its flight.

Here, then, is my first point. In all dimensions alike, on this side or that, upward or downward through the universe, there is no end. This I have shown, and indeed the fact proclaims itself aloud and the nature of space makes it crystal clear. Granted, then, that empty space extends without limit in every direction and that seeds innumerable in number are rushing on countless courses through an unfathomable universe under the impulse of perpetual motion, *it is in the highest degree unlikely that this earth and sky is the only one to have been created* and that all those particles of matter outside are accomplishing nothing. This follows from the fact that our world has been made by nature through the spontaneous and casual collision and multifarious, accidental, random and purposeless congregation and coalescence of atoms whose suddenly formed combinations could serve on each occasion as the starting-point of substantial fabrics—earth and sea and sky and the races of living creatures. On every ground, therefore, you must admit that there exist elsewhere other congeries of matter similar to this one which the ether clasps in ardent embrace.

When there is plenty of matter in readiness, when space is available and no cause or circumstance impedes, then surely things must be wrought and effected. You have a store of atoms that could not be reckoned in full by the whole succession of living creatures. You have the same natural force to congregate them in any place precisely as they have been congregated here. You are bound therefore to acknowledge that in other regions there are other earths and various tribes of men and breeds of beasts.

Add to this the fact that nothing in the universe is the only one of its kind, unique and solitary in its birth and growth; everything is a member of a species comprising many individuals. Turn your mind first to the animals. You will find the rule apply to the brutes that prowl the mountains, to the children of men, the voiceless scaly fish and all the forms of flying things. So you must admit that sky, earth, sun, moon, sea and the rest are not solitary, but rather numberless. For a firmly established limit is set to their lives also and their bodies also are a product of birth, no less than that of any creature that flourishes here according to its kind.

Bear this well in mind, and you will immediately perceive that *nature is free and uncontrolled by proud masters* and runs the universe by herself without the aid of gods. For who—by the sacred hearts of the gods who pass their unruffled lives, their placid aeon, in calm and peace!—who can rule the sum total of the measureless? Who can hold in coercive hand the strong reins of the unfathomable? Who can spin all the firmaments alike and foment with the fires of ether all the fruitful earths? Who can be in all places at all times, ready to darken the clear sky with clouds and rock it with a thunderclap—to launch bolts that may often wreck his own temples, or retire and spend his fury letting fly at deserts with that missile which often passes by the guilty and slays the innocent and blameless?

After the natal season of the world, the birthday of sea and lands and the uprising of the sun, many atoms had been added from without, many seeds contributed on every side by bombardment from the universe at large. From these the sea and land could gather increase; the dome of heaven could gain more room and lift its rafters high above the earth, and the air could climb upwards. For to each are allotted its own atoms from every quarter under the impact of blows. They all rejoin their own kind: water goes to water, earth swells with earthy matter; fire is forged by fires, ether by ether. At length everything is brought to its utmost limit of growth by nature, the creatress and perfectress. This is reached when what is poured into its vital veins is no more than what flows and drains away. Here the growing-time of everything must halt. Here nature checks the increase of her own strength. The things you see growing merrily in stature and climbing step by step the stairs of maturity—these are gaining more atoms that they lose. The food is easily introduced into all their veins; and they themselves are not so widely expanded as to shed much matter and squander more than their age absorbs as nourishment. It must, of course, be conceded that many particles ebb and drain away from things. But more particles must accrue, until they have touched the topmost peak of growth. Thereafter the strength and vigour of maturity is gradually broken, and age slides down the path of decay. Obviously the bulkier anything is and the more expanded when it begins to wane, the more particles it sheds and gives off from every surface. The food is not easily distributed through all its veins, or supplied in sufficient quantities to make good the copious effluences it exudes. For everything must be restored and renewed by food, and by food buttressed and sustained. And the process is doomed to failure, because the veins do not admit enough and nature does not supply all that is needed. It is natural, therefore, that everything should perish when it is thinned out by the ebbing of matter and succumbs to blows from without. The food supply is no longer adequate for its aged frame, and the deadly bombardment of particles from without never pauses in the work of dissolution and subdual.

In this way the ramparts of the great world also will be breached and collapse in crumbling ruin about us. Already it is far past its prime. The earth, which generated every living species and once brought forth from its womb the bodies of huge beasts, has now scarcely strength to generate animalcules. For I assume that the races of mortal creatures were not let down into the fields from heaven by a golden cord, nor generated from the sea of the rock-beating surf, but born of the same earth that now provides their nurture. The same earth in her prime spontaneously generated for mortals smiling crops and lusty vines, sweet fruits and gladsome pastures, which now can scarcely be made to grow by our toil. We wear down the oxen and wear out the strength of husbandmen, and the ploughshare is scarcely a match for fields that grudge their fruits and multiply our toil. Already the ploughman of ripe years shakes his head with many a sigh that his heavy labours have gone for nothing; and, when he compares the present with the past, he often cries up his father's luck and grumbles that past generations, when men were old-fashioned and god-fearing, supported life easily enough on their small farms, though one man's holding was then far less than now. In the same despondent vein, the cultivator of old and wilted vines decries the trend of the times and rails at heaven. He does not realize that everything is gradually decaying and nearing its end, worn out by old age.

• DISCUSSION QUESTIONS •

1. What is the historical significance of the Ionians? Why are they sometimes called "natural philosophers"? What political, economic, and geographic factors made it possible for Ionia to become the center of the "new awakening"?

2. Who was Thales of Miletus and when did he live? What method did he devise to measure the height of a pyramid? Cite an example of how this same method is used today. How did Thales explain the formation of the earth? What was revolutionary in Thales' approach to studying nature?

3. How did Anaximander determine the length of the year and the seasons? What were his other significant contributions to science? What observation led him to conclude that humans arose from other animals? How did he explain the origin of life?

4. What were Democritus' views on the origin of life? What is the origin and meaning of the word "atom"? How did Democritus explain the nature and movement of atoms? How accurate were his ideas?

5. What major contributions are associated with Anaxagoras? Which of his observations about the moon, the sun, and the stars were accurate? Why was he eventually imprisoned because of these ideas?

6. Who was Pythagoras and when did he live? What was unique about the Pythagorean method? How was it possible for the Pythagoreans to be mathematicians and mystics at the same time?

7. How were the philosophies and methods of the Pythagoreans different from those of earlier Ionians? In what ways did the Pythagoreans advance the cause of science? What negative effects did Pythagorean thought have on later generations of scientific thinkers?

8. What reasoning led the Pythagoreans to conclude that the planets moved in circular paths and at constant speeds around the earth? How did the Pythagorean tradition influence Kepler's work?

9. What circumstances can explain the fact that the experimental method, born in Ionia in the sixth century B.C., was abandoned for some 2,000 years?

10. Who was Aristarchus and why is he a significant figure in the history of astronomy? On what observations did he base his conclusions about the structure of the universe? What is the relationship between Aristarchus and Copernicus?

• ADDITIONAL ACTIVITIES •

Optional Projects

1. Write a short paper explaining how the ancients determined the length of the year and the seasons by 1) observing the points on the horizon where the sun sets and rises each day; and 2) observing the length of the shadow cast by a stick placed perpendicular to the ground. (Consult other sources if necessary.)

2. Develop a chronological chart or timeline showing the most important figures in early Greek astronomy and listing their major accomplishments.

3. Make a list of words and expressions still used in everyday language that reflect historical misconceptions about astronomical phenomena (for example, sunrise, sunset, moonlight). Can you think of replacements for these words and expressions? Does our continued usage of obsolescent terms suggest something about people's reluctance to give up the earth-centered view of the universe, or do we retain these words for other reasons? In a short paper, explore and answer these questions.

4. Construct a timeline showing the influence of ideas formulated by Ionian scientists on scientists of later generations.

Supplementary Bibliography

G. de Santillana, *Origins of Scientific Thought*. Chicago: University of Chicago Press, 1961.
Traces the origins and history of scientific thought.

J.L.E. Dreyer, *A History of Astronomy from Thales to Kepler*. New York: Diver, 1953.
A chronological and somewhat technical account.

Benjamin Farrington, *Greek Science*. New York: Penguin Books, 1944.
One of the definitive surveys of Greek science from Thales to Aristotle.

George Sarton, *A History of Science*. New York: W.W. Norton, 1970.
An erudite and comprehensive survey of ancient science through the Golden Age of Greece. Of special interest are Chapters 7 and 8, titled "Ionian Science in the Sixth Century" and "Pythagoras," respectively.

Erwin Schroedinger, *Nature and the Greeks*. Cambridge, Eng.: Cambridge University Press, 1954.
Explores the development of science in Ancient Greece.

Chapter VIII
TRAVELS IN SPACE AND TIME

• OVERVIEW •

THERE IS AN absolute speed limit in the universe—300,000 kilometers per second, the speed of light—which is described by Einstein in his special theory of relativity. This fact does not significantly affect us in our world, where speeds are considerably less than the speed of light. However, if we should perfect the capability of traveling near the speed of light, we will see a highly altered world. If we were to travel away from the earth near the speed of light, our field of vision would increase; we would perceive the objects rushing past us as severely contracted. Special relativity tells us that time and space are inextricably bound together. When the speed of light is approached, events perceived to be occurring simultaneously by a person at rest appear to us to be happening at different times. What happens is that our time, compared with the time passing on earth, slows down.

This slowing down of time—time dilation—may make interstellar exploration feasible on human timescales, at least for those aboard the spaceship. The price we pay is the tremendous energy expenditure required to accelerate our ship near the speed of light.

The most sophisticated space vehicles launched to date travel at 1/10,000th the speed of light. Designs already have been proposed for spacecraft that may one day visit the stars and travel near the speed of light. But the development of such relativistic space vehicles presents engineering problems that have yet to be solved.

• LEARNING OBJECTIVES •

1. Explain the paradoxes that might arise if one could allow the speed at which light travels to change.

2. Discuss the concept of simultaneity in relativity and explain why we are "looking back in time" when we look at the stars.

3. Describe and explain some of the phenomena that occur as one approaches the speed of light, focusing especially on what happens to length, time, mass, and wavelength (color).

4. Describe the "twin paradox" as exemplified in Goldsmith's "When Time Slows Down," and explain how it can be resolved.

137

5. Summarize briefly your understanding of the theory of special relativity.

6. Describe how the principles of relativity affect possible modes of space travel, and describe some of the existing plans for human space travel.

• KEY TERMS AND NAMES •

aberration of starlight
Albert Einstein
Doppler effect
principle of covariance

special theory of relativity
time dilation
twin paradox

• ASSIGNMENT •

Watch COSMOS television series Program 8, "Journeys in Space and Time."

Read Chapter 8, "Journeys in Space and Time," in Carl Sagan's text, *Cosmos*, or other readings assigned by your instructor.

• READINGS •

Jeremy Bernstein . . . . **Einstein: The Early Years**

In this excerpt from one of the best biographies written to date, Jeremy Bernstein gives us a glimpse into the childhood and early life of Albert Einstein. Bernstein is professor of physics at Stevens Institute of Technology in New Jersey.

There was no precedent in Einstein's family history for any special scientific or intellectual achievement. As far back as he himself was able to trace the lineage on both his maternal and paternal sides, it consisted of typical merchants and artisans of German and, more generally, European Jewish life. Einstein's father, Hermann, was a rather happy-go-lucky, not very successful business man. When Einstein was a year old his father moved the family from Ulm to Munich, where he went into business with a brother with whom they shared a "double-house." The brother, Jakob, had some engineering training and took care of the technical side of the business: the manufacture of electrical equipment. From his mother, Pauline, Einstein acquired an early taste for classical music. She played the piano and he began taking violin lessons at the age of six. There were no visible signs of any special precocity in the very young Einstein. He was a dreamy child who disliked sports and games, talked with some difficulty (his parents were worried that he might be abnormal because it took him until he was three before he began to talk), and was dubbed *Pater Langweil*—"Father Bore"—by his nurse. A year after the family moved to Munich, Einstein's sister, Maja, was born. She was the only other child of the Einsteins.

Perhaps because of his solitary introspective childhood, Einstein appears to have retained a particularly vivid memory of it throughout his life. In a very real sense his feelings about the mysterious order that seems to underline the apparent chaos of natural events—the discovery that nature appears to present itself as a mathematical puzzle with remarkably simple and elegant solutions—were formed in his childhood. When he was in his early forties, in a conversation with the Berlin literary critic Alexander Moszkowski (they were discussing Newton's religious faith) he remarked:

> In every true searcher of Nature there is a kind of religious reverence; for he finds it impossible to imagine that he is the first to have thought out the exceedingly delicate threads that connect his perceptions. The aspect of knowledge which had not yet been laid bare gives the investigator a feeling akin to that experienced by a child who seeks to grasp the masterly way in which elders manipulate things.[1]

Although consistently agnostic with respect to any belief in a God preoccupied with the working out of human destiny, Einstein made throughout his life constant and amiable references to "God," whom he often called "the Old One." In this sense "God" stood for the rational connections, the laws, governing the behavior of the universe: both the fact that such laws seem to exist and that they are, at least to some degree, comprehensible by us. . . .

The two most vivid scientific impressions that Einstein preserved from his childhood were his discoveries of the behavior of the compass—the fact that by some mysterious attraction the compass needle always was made to point in a given direction—and, some time later, of the Pythagorean theorem of Euclidean geometry. These two revelations are almot perfect illustrations of the complementary aspects of scientific phenomena. The behavior of the compass needle is a striking empirical fact which one might take, if so disposed, as evidence for the existence of magic. It requires a vast tradition of scientific experience even to imagine that such a phenomenon might have an explanation or, if one prefers a less loaded word than "explanation," a description in terms of generally applicable physical laws. On the other hand, the truths of Euclidean geometry appear as somehow self-evident, and it takes an equally vast tradition of scientific experience to discover how they fit in with the kind of empirical phenomenon illustrated by the compass. In any event, throughout his life Einstein made reference to the sense of "wonder" that the compass produced in him. When he was sixty-seven he attempted to explain this genesis of his scientific ideas:

> A wonder of such nature I experienced as a child of 4 or 5 years, when my father showed me a compass. That this needle behaved in such a determined way did not at all fit into the nature of events, which could find a place in the unconscious world of concepts (effect connected with direct "touch"). I can still remember—or at least I believe I can remember—that this experience made a deep and lasting impression upon me. Something deeply hidden had to be behind things. What man sees before him from infancy causes no reaction of this kind; he is not surprised over the falling of bodies, concerning wind and rain, nor concerning the moon or about the fact that the moon does not fall down, nor concerning the differences between living and non-living matter.[2]

Both in his elementary school and at the Luitpold Gymnasium in Munich Einstein was exposed to a certain amount of formal religious training. He was the only Jewish student in his Catholic elementary school and had received and, in fact, rather enjoyed the same instruction in Catholicism that the other students had.

[1] Alexander Moszkowski, *Conversations with Einstein*, p. 46.
[2] Paul Arthur Schilpp, ed., *Albert Einstein: Philosopher-Scientist*, p. 9.

He had no sense of anti-Semitism and no particular attachment to Jewish rituals either. His family was entirely areligious, although they maintained their own version of the ancient Sabbath custom of inviting a poor Jew to share a meal with them. In the case of the Einsteins this took place on Thursday noon, when the family shared its meal with a poor Jewish student from Russia. This student, Max Talmey, introduced young Albert to some books on popular science which he read avidly.[3] At the same time in the Gymnasium in Munich he began to receive, as was habitual at the time for Jewish students, special instruction in the Old Testament. For a while, somewhat to the amusement of his family, he developed almost fundamentalist views of the Bible. Very quickly these came into conflict with his studies in science. As he wrote in his "obituary":

> Through the reading of popular scientific books I soon reached [a] conviction that much in the stories of the Bible could not be true. The consequence was a positively fanatic [orgy of] freethinking coupled with the impression that youth is intentionally being deceived by the state through lies: it was a crushing impression. Suspicion against every kind of authority grew out of this experience, a sceptical attitude towards the convictions which were alive in any specific social environment—an attitude which has never again left me, even though later on, because of a better insight into the causal connections, it lost some of its original poignancy.[4]

About this time his engineer uncle began giving Einstein informal lessons in algebra and geometry. Among other things, he told Einstein about Pythagorean theorem, which, after considerable work, Einstein was able to prove. However, he had not realized the intricate logical framework of Euclidean geometry until he received a textbook from his uncle. . . .

Apart from the work he did on his own Einstein hated the Gymnasium. He despised the rote learning and once remarked, "The teachers in the elementary school appeared to me like sergeants, and the Gymnasium teachers like lieutenants."[5] At age fifteen his life was sharply altered when his father's business in Munich failed and the family migrated to Pavia, near Milan, in Italy. Einstein was left behind to live with a family while attending the Luitpold Gymnasium, but after six months he could no longer stand living alone in Munich and the rigid discipline of school and, as Philipp Frank describes it, manufactured a plan that would enable him to drop our for a while. He got a physician to give him a certificate stating that because of a nervous breakdown it was essential that he leave school and join his parents in Italy. Then he obtained another certificate from his mathematics teacher stating that his knowledge of mathematics was sufficiently advanced so that he could present himself for study at the university without the Gymnasium diploma.

> His departure from the gymnasium was ultimately much easier than he had anticipated. One day his teacher summoned him and told him that it would be desirable if he were to leave the school. Astonished at the turn of events, young Einstein asked what offense he was guilty of. The teacher replied "Your presence in the class destroys the respect [for me] of the students." Evidently Einsteins's inner aversion to the constant drill had somehow manifested itself in his behaviour toward his teachers and fellow students.[6]

---

[3] Talmey later wrote a book entitled *The Relativity Theory Simplified and the Formative Period of Its Inventor.*

[4] Schlipp, *op. cit.,* p. 9.

[5] Cited Philipp Frank, *Einstein: His Life and Times,* p.11.

[6] *Ibid.,* p. 15.

Liberated from the Gymnasium, Einstein joined his parents in Milan. One of his first acts was to renounce his German citizenship. As he was a minor, this had to be arranged by his father. Einstein had decided to become a Swiss citizen, which was only possible at the age of twenty-one. Hence he remained stateless from the age of fifteen to twenty-one, which was, apparently, not much of a problem in those days. Like many high-school dropouts before and since, Einstein decided to spend his time in part wandering around on foot. Unlike most dropouts he also engaged in a program of mathematical self-study. This was an extraordinarily happy period in his life and was only interrupted after a year when his father's business failed again and it became clear that Einstein would have to do something to support himself.

His father, apparently, felt that electrical engineering would be a suitable career. So it was decided that Einstein should go to Zurich, where, at the Swiss Federal Polytechnic School, there was the most celebrated center for the study of science in central Europe outside of Germany. This was something he had thought of doing even when he was in Munich, but in 1895 he failed the general entrance examination for the Polytechnic. Still, he had done so well on that part of the examination dealing with mathematics that the director of the Polytechnic suggested that he obtain a diploma at a Swiss cantonal high school and then reapply. Einstein enrolled in a school in Aarau which was run in a progressive fashion and gave the students an opportunity for independent work; above all, it had laboratories with good equipment which students could use to teach themselves science. After a year Einstein reapplied for entrance at the Polytechnic and, armed with a diploma, was accepted without further examination. It was in Zurich, when Einstein was sixteen, that he decided to abandon the study of pure mathematics which he had been teaching himself and to take up physics. In his "obituary" Einstein describes why he made this choice:

> I saw that mathematics was split up into numerous specialties, each of which could easily absorb the short lifetime granted to us. Consequently I saw myself in the position of Buridan's ass which was unable to decide upon any specific bundle of hay. This was obviously due to the fact that my intuition was not strong enough in the field of mathematics in order to differentiate clearly the fundamentally important, that which is really basic, from the rest of the more or less dispensable erudition. Beyond this, however, my interest in the knowledge of nature was also unqualifiedly stronger; and it was not clear to me as a student that the approach to a more profound knowledge of the basic principles of physics is tied up with the most intricate mathematical methods. This dawned upon me only gradually after years of independent scientific work. True enough, physics also was divided into separate fields, each of which was capable of devouring a short lifetime of work without having satisfied the hunger for deeper knowledge. The mass of insufficiently connected experimental data was overwhelming here also. In this field, however, I soon learned to scent out that which was able to lead to fundamentals and to turn aside from everything else, from the multitude of things which clutter up the mind and divert it from the essential.[7]

It was also at this time, Einstein writes in his "obituary," that he began to realize that the foundations of the physics he was learning, mostly by independent study of the original texts, were fundamentally flawed. It took the next ten years, until 1905, before he was able to sort things out sufficiently in his own mind to be able to write his first paper on the theory of relativity.

----

[7] *Ibid.*, pg. 15.

Lincoln Barnett. . . . . Special Theory of Relativity

Lincoln Barnett describes how Einstein arrived at the special theory of relativity. Barnett was a contemporary and acquaintance of Einstein, who wrote the foreword to the book from which the following selection was excerpted.

Among those who pondered the enigma of the Michelson-Morley experiment [explained in the Goldsmith selection in this chapter] was a young patent office examiner in Berne, named Albert Einstein. In 1905, when he was just twenty-six years old, he published a short paper suggesting an answer to the riddle in terms that opened up a new world of physical thought. He began by rejecting the ether theory and with it the whole idea of space as a fixed system or framework, absolutely at rest, within which it is possilbe to distinguish absolute from relative motion. The one indisputable fact established by the Michelson-Morley experiment was that the velocity of light is unaffected by the motion of the earth. Einstein seized on this as a revelation of universal law. If the velocity of light is constant regardless of the earth's motion, he reasoned, it must be constant regardless of the motion of any sun, moon, star, meteor, or other system moving anywhere in the universe. From this he drew a broader generalization, and asserted that the laws of nature are the same for all uniformly moving systems. This simple statement is the essence of Einstein's Special Theory of Relativity. It incorporates the Galilean Relativity Principle which stated that mechanical laws are the same for all uniformly moving systems. But its phrasing is more comprehensive; for Einstein was thinking not only of mechanical laws but of the laws governing light and other electro-magnetic phenomena. So he lumped them together in one fundamental postulate: all the phenomena of nature, all the laws of nature, are the same for all systems that move uniformly relative to one another.

On the surface there is nothing very startling in this declaration. It simply reiterates the scientist's faith in the universal harmony of natural law. It also advises the scientist to stop looking for any absolute, stationary frame of reference in the universe. The universe is a restless place: stars, nebulae, galaxies, and all the vast gravitational systems of outer space are incessantly in motion. But their movements can be described only with respect to each other, for in space there are no directions and no boundaries. It is futile moreover for the scientist to try to discover the "true" velocity of any system by using light as a measuring rod, for the velocity of light is constant throughout the universe and is unaffected either by the motion of its source or the motion of the receiver. Nature offers no absolute standards of comparison; and space is—as another great German mathematician Leibnitz, clearly saw two centuries before Einstein—simply "the order or relation of things among themselves." Without things occupying it, it is nothing.

Along with absolute space, Einstein discarded the concept of absolute time—of a steady, unvarying, inexorable universal time flow, streaming from the infinite past to the infinite future. Much of the obscurity that has surrounded the Theory of Relativity stems from man's reluctance to recognize that sense of time, like sense of color, is a form of perception. Just as there is no such thing as color without an eye to discern it, so an instant or an hour or a day is nothing without an event to mark it. And just as space is simply a possible order of material objects, so time is simply a possible order of events. The subjectivity of time is best explained in Einstein's own words. "The experiences of an individual," he says, "appear to us arranged in a series of events; in this series the single events which we remember appear to be ordered according to the criterion of 'earlier' and 'later.' There exists, therefore, for the individual, an I-time, or subjective time. This in itself is not measurable. I can, indeed, associate numbers with the events, in such a way that a greater number is associated with the later event than with an earlier one. This association I can define by means of a clock by comparing the order of events furnished by the clock with the order of the given series of events. We understand by a clock something which provides a series of events which can be counted."

By referring our own experiences to a clock (or a calendar) we make time an objective concept. Yet the time intervals provided by a clock or a calendar are by no means absolute quantities imposed on the entire universe by divine edict. All the clocks ever used by man have been geared to our solar system. What we call an hour is actually a measurement in space—an arc of 15 degrees in the apparent daily rotation of the celestial sphere. And what we call a year is simply a measure of the earth's progress in its orbit around the sun. An inhabitant of Mercury, however, would have very different notions of time. For Mercury makes its trip around the sun in 88 of our days, and in that same period rotates just once on its axis. So on Mercury a year and a day amount to the same thing. But it is when science ranges beyond the neighborhood of the sun that all our terrestrial ideas of time become meaningless. For Relativity tells us there is no such thing as a fixed interval of time independent of the system to which it is referred. There is indeed no such thing as simultaneity, there is no such thing as "now," independent of a system of reference. For example a man in New York may telephone a friend in London, and although it is 7:00 P.M. in New York and midnight in London, we may say they are talking "at the same time." But that is because they are both residents of the same planet, and their clocks are geared to the same astronomical system. A more complicated situation arises if we try to ascertain, for example, what is happening on the star Arcturus "right now." Arcturus is 38 light years away. A light year is the distance light travels in one year, or roughly six trillion miles. If we should try to communicate with Arcturus by radio "right now" it would take 38 years for our message to reach its destination and another 38 years for us to receive a reply.* And when we look at Arcturus and say that we see it "now" we are actually seeing a ghost—an image projected on our optic nerves by light rays that left their source in 1910. Whether Arcturus even exists "now" nature forbids us to know until 1986.

Despite such reflections it is difficult for earthbound man to accept the idea that *this very instant* which he calls "now" cannot apply to the universe as a whole. Yet in the Special Theory of Relativity Einstein proves by an unanswerable sequence of example and deduction that it is nonsense to think of events taking place simultaneously in unrelated systems. His argument unfolds along the following lines.

To begin with one must realize that the scientist, whose task it is to describe physical events in objective terms, cannot use subjective words like "this," "here," and "now." For him concepts of space and time take on physical significance only when the relations between events and systems are defined. And it is constantly necessary for him, in dealing with matters involving complex forms of motion (as in celestial mechanics, electrodynamics, etc.) to relate the magnitudes found in one system with those occurring in another. The mathematical laws which define these relationships are known as laws of transformation. The simplest transformation may be illustrated by a man promenading on the deck of a ship: if he walks forward along the deck at the rate of 3 miles an hour and the ship moves through the sea at the rate of 12 miles an hour, then the man's velocity with respect to the sea is

---

* Radio waves travel at the same speed as light waves.

15 miles an hour; if he walks aft his velocity relative to the sea is of course 9 miles an hour. Or as a variation one may imagine an alarm bell ringing at a railway crossing. The sound waves produced by the bell spread away through the surrounding air at the rate of 400 yards a second. A railroad train speeds toward the crossing at the rate of 20 yards a second. Hence the velocity of the sound relative to the train is 420 yards a second so long as the train is approaching the alarm bell and 380 yards a second as soon as the train passes the bell. This simple addition of velocities rests on obvious common sense, and has indeed been applied to problems of compound motion since the time of Galileo. Serious difficulties arise, however, when it is used in connection with light.

In his original paper on Relativity Einstein emphasized these difficulties with another railway incident. Again there is a crossing, marked this time by a signal light which flashes its beam down the track at 186,284 miles a second—the constant velocity of light, denoted in physics by the symbol c. A train steams toward the signal light at a given velocity v. So by the addition of velocities one concludes that the velocity of the light beam relative to the train is c plus v when the train moves toward the signal light, and c minus v as soon as the train passes the light. But this result conflicts with the findings of the Michelson-Morley experiment which demonstrated that the velocity of light is unaffected either by the motion of the source or the motion of the receiver. This curious fact has also been confirmed by studies of double stars which revolve around a common center of gravity. Careful analysis of these moving systems has shown that the light from the approaching star in each pair reaches earth at precisely the same velocity as the light from the receding star. Since the velocity of light is a universal constant it cannot in Einstein's railway problem be affected by the velocity of the train. Even if we imagine that the train is racing toward the signal light at a speed of 10,000 miles a second, the principle of the constancy of the velocity of light tells us that an observer aboard the train will still clock the speed of the oncoming light beam at precisely 186,284 miles a second, no more, no less.

The dilemma presented by this situation involves much more than a Sunday morning newspaper puzzle. On the contrary it poses a deep enigma of nature. Einstein saw that the problem lay in the irreconcilable conflict between his belief in (1) the constancy of the velocity of light, and (2) the principle of the addition of velocities. Although the latter appears to rest on the stern logic of mathematics (i.e., that two plus two makes four), Einstein recognized in the former a fundamental law of nature. He concluded, therefore, that a new transformation rule must be found to enable the scientist to describe the relations between moving systems in such a way that the results satisfy the known facts about light.

Einstein found what he wanted in a series of equations developed by the great Dutch physicist, H. A. Lorentz, in connection with a specific theory of his own. Although its original application is of interest now chiefly to scientific historians, the Lorentz transformation lives on as part of the mathematical framework of Relativity. To understand what it says, however, it is first necessary to perceive the flaws in the old principle of the addition of velocities. These flaws Einstein pointed out by means of still another railway anecdote. Once again he envisaged a straight length of track, this time with an observer sitting on an embankment beside it. A thunderstorm breaks, and two bolts of lightning strike the track simultaneously at separate points, A and B. Now, asks Einstein, what do we mean by "simultaneously"? To pin down this definition he assumes that the observer is sitting precisely half way between A and B, and that he is equipped with an arrangement of mirrors which enable him to see A and B at the same time without moving his eyes. Then if

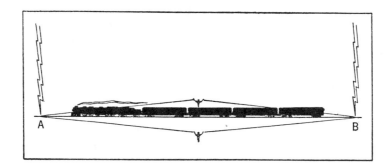

the lightning flashes are reflected in the observer's mirrors at precisely the same instant, the two flashes may be regarded as simultaneous. Now a train roars down the track, and a second observer is sitting precariously perched atop one of the cars with a mirror apparatus just like the one on the embankment. It happens that this moving observer finds himself directly opposite the observer on the embankment at the precise instant the lightning bolts hit A and B. The question is: will the lightning flashes appear simultaneous to him? The answer is: they will not. For if his train is moving away from lightning bolt B and toward lightning bolt A, then it is obvious that B will be reflected in his mirrors a fraction of a second later than A. Lest there be any doubt about this, one may imagine temporarily that the train is moving at the impossible rate of 186,284 miles a second, the velocity of light. In that event flash B will never be reflected in the mirrors because it can never overtake the train, just as the sound from a gun can never overtake a bullet traveling with supersonic speed. So the observer on the train will assert that only one lightning bolt struck the track. And whatever the speed of the train may be the moving observer will always insist that the lightning flash ahead of him has struck the track first. Hence the lightning flashes which are simultaneous relative to the stationary observer are *not* simultaneous relative to the observer on the train.

The paradox of the lightning flashes thus dramatizes one of the subtlest and most difficult concepts in Einstein's philosophy: the relativity of simultaneity. It shows that man cannot assume that his subjective sense of "now" applies to all parts of the universe. For, Einstein points out, "every reference body (or coordinate system) has its own particular time; unless we are told the reference body to which the statement of time refers, there is no meaning in a statement of the time of an event." The fallacy in the old principle of the addition of velocities lies therefore in its tacit assumption that the duration of an event is independent of the state of motion of the system of reference. In the case of the man pacing the deck of a ship, for example, it was assumed that if he walked three miles in one hour as timed by a clock on the moving ship, his rate would be just the same timed by a stationary clock anchored somehow in the sea. It was further assumed that the distance he traversed in one hour would have the same value whether it was measured relative to the deck of the ship (the moving system) or relative to the sea (the stationary system). This constitutes a second fallacy in the addition of velocities—for distance, like time, is a relative concept, and there is no such thing as a space interval independent of the state of motion of the system of reference.

Einstein asserted, therefore, that the scientist who wishes to describe the phenomena of nature in terms that are consistent for all systems throughout the universe must regard measurements of time and distance as variable quantities. The equations comprising the Lorentz transformations do just that. They preserve the velocity of light as a universal constant, but modify all measurements of time and distance according to the velocity of each system of reference.*

So although Lorentz had originally developed his equations to meet a specific problem, Einstein made them the basis of a tremendous generalization, and to the edifice of Relativity added another axiom: the laws of nature preserve their uniformity in all systems when related by the Lorentz transformation. Stated thus, in the abstract language of mathematics the significance of this axiom can scarcely be apparent to the layman. But in physics an equation is never a pure abstraction; it is simply a kind of shorthand expression which the scientist finds convenient to describe the phenomena of nature. Sometimes it is also a Rosetta Stone in which the theoretical physicist can decipher secret realms of knowledge. And so by deduction from the message written in the equations of the Lorentz transformation, Einstein discovered a number of new and extraordinary truths about the physical universe.

Donald Goldsmith . . . . **When Time Slows Down**

Donald Goldsmith elucidates Einstein's theory of relativity, and explains why a person who makes a long journey at nearly the speed of light would return to earth with an age far less than that of a twin who remained behind. Goldsmith is a professor of astronomy at the University of California, Berkeley.

INTRODUCTION

Einsteins's theory of relativity predicts that as one travels closer and closer to the speed of light, time passes more and more slowly. That is, if we could watch a

* The Lorentz transformation relates distances and times observed on moving systems with those observed on systems relatively at rest. Suppose, for example, that a system, or reference body, is moving in a certain direction, then *according to the old principle of the addition of velocities*, a distance or length x', measured with respect to the moving system along the direction of motion, is related to length x, measured with respect to a relatively stationary system, by the equation $x' = x \pm vt$, where v is the velocity of the moving system and t is the time. Dimensions $y' = z'$, measured with respect to the moving system at right angles to each other (i.e., height and breadth), are related to dimensions y and z on the relatively stationary system by $y' = y$, and $z' = z$. And finally a time interval t', clocked with respect to the moving system is related to time interval t, clocked with respect to the relatively stationary system, by $t' = t$. In other words, distances and times are not affected, *in classical physics*, by the velocity of the system in question. *But it is this presupposition which leads to the paradox of the lightning flashes.* The Lorentz transformation reduces the distances and times observed on moving systems to the conditions of the stationary observer, keeping the velocity of light c a constant for all observers. Here are the equations of the Lorentz transformation which have supplanted the older and evidently inadequate relationships cited above:

$$x' = \sqrt{\frac{x - vt}{1 - (v^2/c^2)}}$$
$$y'' = y$$
$$z' = z$$
$$t' = \sqrt{\frac{t - (v/c^2)x}{1 - (v^2/c^2)}}$$

It will be noted that, as in the old transformation law, dimensions y' and z' are unaffected by motion. It will also be seen that if the velocity of the moving system v is small relative to the velocity of light c, then the equations of the Lorentz transformation reduce themselves to the relations of the old principle of the addition of velocities. But as the magnitude of v approaches that of c, then the values of x' and t' are radically changed.

clock moving by us at nearly the speed of light, we would observe that clock takes longer to tick off an hour than does our own stationary clock. Since we have inherited an intuitive belief that time unfolds at the same rate everywhere, such a prediction at first puzzles many people. Only by appeals to reason, experiment, repetition, and authority have astronomers and physicists been able to convince themselves, and other interested parties, that we really do observe that fast-moving clocks keep time more slowly than stationary clocks.

Amazing though it may seem, a person who makes a long journey at nearly the speed of light would return to earth with an age far less that that of a twin who remained behind on earth. The basis behind this is the experimental result—elevated into a universal rule by Einstein's theory—that no matter how a source of light may be moving with respect to an observer, the observer will always find that light arrives at the same speed. This speed is denoted by "c," and is equal to just under 300,000 kilometers per second. (Astronomical distances are often measured in *light years*, the distance light travels in a year, or even in light seconds, the distance light travels in one second.)

THE SPEED OF LIGHT

During the 1880s, Albert Michelson and Edward Morley made observations of the light coming to us from distant stars—at times when the earth's motion in its solar orbit was directed toward the stars and at times when the motion was directed away from the stars. Despite the fact that Michelson and Morley's equipment was sensitive enough to measure the change in the speed of the star's light that would be expected from adding (or subtracting) the earth's orbital speed of 30 kilometers per second to (or from) the 300,000 km/sec speed of light, *no* such change was observed. Michelson was puzzled, Morley was puzzled, and so was everyone else in Cleveland (where the experiment was done), and throughout the world, who dared to think about what these results meant. Something was wrong with the obvious concept that light emitted from a moving source should travel at its usual speed in a vacuum, c, plus or minus the contribution from the motion of the source.

Physicists have rarely died from a lack of understanding, however, and eventually they came to believe what they could not previously understand: no matter how a source of light may be moving with respect to an observer, that observer receiving the light will always find that the light arrives at the same speed c, not that speed plus or minus some contribution from the source's motion (Figure 1). Though it may seem a long jump to pass from one set of observations related to the earth's motion all the way to a general conclusion about the behavior of light, this leap appears natural once we accept the principles that the earth occupies an average position in space and that the laws of physics should be the same everywhere. We could hardly believe that some demon was rigging the show to fool two profesors in Ohio (or succeeding generations of physicists who repeated their experiments with an ever-greater accuracy and still found no change in the speed of light from a moving source.)

THE THEORY OF RELATIVITY

In 1905, Albert Einstein pointed the way out of the disagreement of the observed facts with intuition. Einstein said that it was time for us to shed our belief in an absolute motionless space in which velocities would add and subtract from one another as we feel they should. Any belief in an absolute frame of time, where all accurate clocks would appear to run at the same rate should also be disregarded. Instead, Einstein proposed that we start from what we observe: the measured speed of light is the same no matter what the velocity of the observer relative to the light source. Einstein drew on the mathematical formulation that preceded 1905 (but which failed to admit that the universe might truly live up to the implications of this formulation). In his epochal paper "On the Electrodynamics of Moving Bodies" he showed that if an observer watches a physical system (of particles, bicycles, or whatever) move by at a constant speed, the observer will notice that *lengths* in the

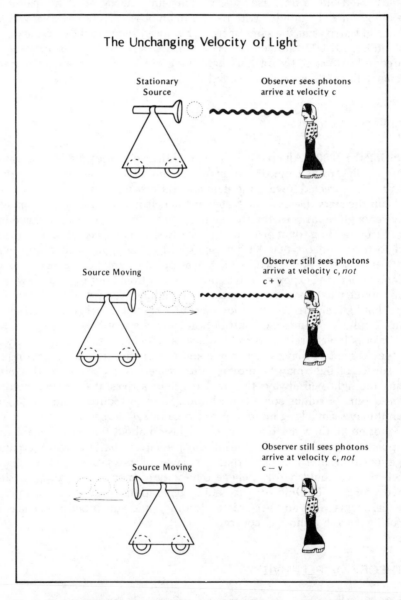

Figure 1. Photons are always found traveling at velocity c (186,000 miles/sec) through empty space regardless of how fast the source of photons is moving.

moving system *decrease*, *time* in the moving system goes *more slowly*, and *inertial masses* (resistance to acceleration) *increase*, all in relation to what an observer finds for a physical system that is at rest with respect to the observer. Furthermore, the amount of the change in the lengths, the time, and the inertial masses increases as the velocity of the system relative to the observer increases. All of this works in just such a way that any observer measuring light produced by the system will always find that the light arrives at the same speed, c, fulfilling the results of the Michelson-Morley experiment. This was the point of Einstein's exposition: to fit the facts known from observation into a theoretical and mathematical framework that could be systematically generalized to apply to a wide range of possible situations.

The "special theory of relativity" that Einstein devised in 1905 predicts what an observer will see if a system moves by at a *constant* speed. (The general theory of relativity deals with cases of accelerating or decelerating motion.) In particular, the theory predicts that time in the system moving at a velocity, v, relative to the observer and time in the observer's own system (zero velocity relative to the observer) obey the following relation:

Time in moving system =

$$\left\{ \sqrt{1 - \left(\frac{v}{c}\right)} \right\} \times \text{Time in observer's system}$$

Because no object can move faster than light another keystone of relativity theory, and never yet contradicted by observation—the ratio $\frac{v}{c}$ is always between zero and one, and so is $\left(\frac{v}{c}\right)^2$. Then $1 - \left(\frac{v}{c}\right)^2$ always has a value between one (for v = o), and zero (for v = c). The square root of $1 - \left(\frac{v}{c}\right)^2$ likewise varies from one (if v = o) down to zero (if v = c), and thus a given time observed in the moving system is always less than (or equal to) the time in the observer's own system.

To take a definite example, suppose that we could propel a subatomic particle at 99½% the speed of light ($\frac{v}{c}$ = .995). We would observe that time in the particle's system passes ten times more slowly than time in our own frame of reference. If we observe that such a subatomic particle has a lifetime of one one-thousandth of a second before it turns into other kinds of particles, we shall observe that its lifetime becomes one one-hundredth of a second when it moves at 99½% the speed of light relative to us. Particle accelerator laboratories like the Stanford Linear Accelerator Center routinely perform such experiments and the results of these tests have verified the predictions of the special theory of relativity millions of times over.

Suppose that we now aim higher than the world of tiny particles and imagine that we could propel a space vehicle at 99½% the speed of light towards the star Aldebaran, 32 light years away. Since the best rockets we have today can reach speeds of only 1/10% of the speed of the light, there clearly are energy problems to be overcome before this example becomes reality. However, if a spaceship did travel to Aldebaran at 99½% the speed of light, it would arrive there 32 years and two months later, *as measured in our time*. But for people aboard the speaceship—the moving system—time would run ten times more slowly than on earth, and we would observe that during the journey they would age not thirty-two and some years, but just about 3 1/5 years! If the space travelers returned home immediately after they arrived at the same speed as they went to Aldebaran, they would not have aged 64 years and four months (the elapsed time on earth), but only about 6 2/5 years, and would in some cases find themselves younger than their grandchildren.

THE TWIN PARADOX

At this point, many a would-be believer in relativity theory has paused to object: Wait a minute! If the rules of the theory hold good for any observer, why don't the space travelers observe us on earth to be aging more slowly than they are? They can claim the earth is moving with respect to the spaceship and thus return to find us on earth younger than they are. This question is often restated as the "twin paradox": if one twin stays home while the other rides the rocket, which is really the younger when they meet again?

The answer is that the traveling twin really comes home younger than the twin who stayed behind. There are vasious ways to demonstrate this result:

(1) By assertion. This method, beloved of politicians and many teachers, reminds the reader that calculations too difficult to be reproduced here have shown conclusively that the twin who travels ages less than the twin who stays on earth.

(2) By experiment. The best test of all would be to send someone to Aldebaran and back at 99½ % the speed of light. Proposals for government funding offering far smaller rewards have often been submitted, but none of them would cost as much as this one. We might think that we could use particle accelerators to send particles with a known lifetime down the tubes at 99½ % the speed of light, turn them around, and bring them back for comparison with stationary particles. In fact, although this experiment has been done in its essential form, though not precisely as described above, there is something unsatisfying about results on the subatomic level to convince ourselves that things really work the same way on a human scale. Still, the experimental results are in, they confirm the prediction made above.

(3) By reasoning. Although we may rightly suspect our intuition about physical reality, we should trust our powers of reason. If we believe the results of the special theory of relativity outlined above, we can proceed to draw conclusions from them: the theory all stands together or all falls together, and so far it has stood the test of experiment. So let us consider the twin aboard the spaceship and the twin at home, and see whether we can answer with certainty the question of who ends up younger when they meet again.

A SPACE JOURNEY

We might first pause to agree that if the twins are not together, comparing their ages becomes very difficult because we cannot pass information instantaneously from one place to another. A twin on earth signalling to a twin on Aldebaran must wait at least 64 years for a message to go to Aldebaran and return, since nothing can move faster than light. Einstein's research helped to illuminate how our intuition glides over the problem of determining whether or not two events that occur at different places are truly "simultaneous." He showed that the key intervals (separations) to concentrate on are neither intervals of distance nor intervals of time, but rather invervals of "spacetime," defined by the relation:

(intervals of spacetime) =
$[c^2(\text{time interval})^2 - (\text{space interval})^2]$

Although two different observers moving at different (but constant) speeds relative to some system may measure different space intervals and different time intervals between two events that occur in that system, the two observers will measure the same spacetime interval between the two events. Fascinating as spacetime intervals are, we can see that the twin problem is in danger of slipping out of the agile grasp of our minds unless we concentrate on the simple question of two twins who start side by side and end up side by side once the journey is over. This means that the spacetime interval questions can be set aside in favor of a direct approach to the time interval, since the twins are not separated in space from either twin's point of view when the journey starts and when it ends. *The key distinction between the traveling twin and twin at home is that the former must reverse direction in order to come home again.*

Suppose that each twin decides to send signals to the other that will let the other twin know how fast time is passing.[1] The twins do this by each wearing a beacon that flashes once each second—each second, that is, of time as determined in their own frames of reference. We can use the observed rates of flashing as a way of measuring how fast time seems to be passing. The same purpose would be served by measuring pulse rates or tree ring growth rates. If we observe a beacon flashing more rapidly than once per second, this corresponds to an observation that time seems to be passing more rapidly than in our own reference frame, and if we observe a rate slower than once per second, this means we are observing time to be passing more slowly than it does for us. Now the twin blasts off from earth and travels to Aldebaran at 99½% the speed of light. How often does the twin who stays behind receive a flash from the traveling twin? The answer is not once per second, but about once every twenty seconds. There are two reasons for the increase in the time interval between flashes. First, since the spaceship moves at 99½% the speed of light relative to the earth, by Einstein's theory, events on the spaceship seem to occur ten times more slowly than they do on earth. Also, the twin in space is constantly receding from the twin on earth, so each flash has farther to travel than the preceding one. The spaceship recedes from earth by almost ten light seconds for every ten seconds of earth time, and this adds almost another ten seconds (of increased travel time) to the ten-second interval established by the spaceship's motion relative to the earth. Hence the interval between flashes observed on earth from the twin on the spaceship is almost twenty seconds. (Figure 2)

What does the twin on the way to Aldebaran find for the time interval between flashes from the earth? The answer is also almost twenty seconds, and for the same reasons: the earth seems to be receding from the spaceship at 99½% the speed of light, so events seem to unfold ten times more slowly on earth than aboard the spaceship. Also, each successive flash must travel ten light seconds further, and so the once-per-second flashes emitted on earth are spaced by intervals of almost twenty seconds when they are observed aboard the spaceship. (Figure 2)

[1] This discussion follows the example of N. David Mermin in Chapter 16 of his book Space and Time in Special Relativity (New York: McGraw Hill, Inc., 1968). This is probably the best book written to explain special relativity theory to the lay reader, and I could not hope to improve on Mermin's explanation of the twin paradox and its resolution.

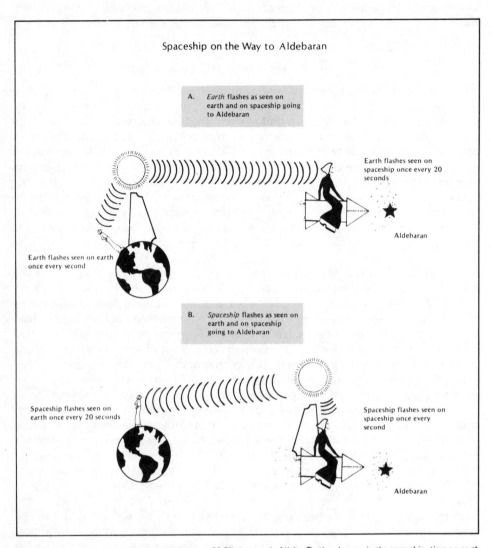

Spaceship on the Way to Aldebaran

A. *Earth* flashes as seen on earth and on spaceship going to Aldebaran

Earth flashes seen on spaceship once every 20 seconds

Aldebaran

Earth flashes seen on earth once every second

B. *Spaceship* flashes as seen on earth and on spaceship going to Aldebaran

Spaceship flashes seen on earth once every 20 seconds

Spaceship flashes seen on spaceship once every second

Aldebaran

Figure 2. *A spaceship is on its way to Aldebaran at 99.5% the speed of light. To the observer in the spaceship, time on earth appears to unfold twenty times more slowly than on the spaceship. Also, to the observer on earth, time in the spaceship appears to unfold twenty times more slowly than time on earth. See text for details.*

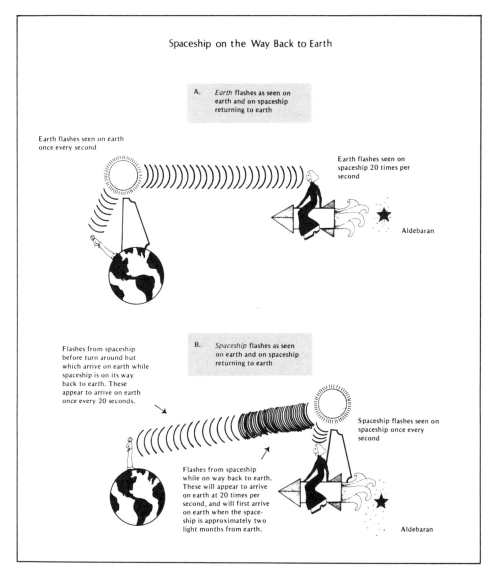

Spaceship on the Way Back to Earth

A. *Earth* flashes as seen on earth and on spaceship returning to earth

Earth flashes seen on earth once every second

Earth flashes seen on spaceship 20 times per second

Aldebaran

B. *Spaceship* flashes as seen on earth and on spaceship returning to earth

Flashes from spaceship before turn around but which arrive on earth while spaceship is on its way back to earth. These appear to arrive on earth once every 20 seconds.

Spaceship flashes seen on spaceship once every second

Flashes from spaceship while on way back to earth. These will appear to arrive on earth at 20 times per second, and will first arrive on earth when the spaceship is approximately two light months from earth.

Aldebaran

Figure 3. The situation changes dramatically because the spaceship turns around and heads back to earth at 99.5% the speed of light. To the observer in the spaceship, time on earth now appears to be unfolding twenty times faster than on the spaceship. But the observer on earth, for all but the last two months of the journey, still sees time unfolding twenty times more slowly on the spaceship than on earth. Only during the last two earth months does time on the spaceship appear to unfold twenty times that on earth. The net result is that the man in the spaceship ages only 6 2/5 years as seen on earth, but the twin on the earth ages 64 years 4 months during the round trip to Aldebaran. See text for details.

So far the twin paradox seems to be alive and well, as each twin sees the other's flashes arriving not one second apart, but twenty seconds apart. But watch closely as we compare what happens throughout the entire journey, because if you miss the details that make all the fun worthwhile, you wind up surly as the proverbial bereaved bear at the end of the description.

First, consider the whole series of events as seen by the twin who travels to Aldebaran. On the way there, flashes arrive from earth once every twenty seconds, so the twin concludes that during this time, events on earth are unfolding twenty times more slowly than events aboard the ship. To the traveling twin, the trip to Aldebaran seems to last only about 3 1/5 years, and this twin concludes that on earth only one-twentieth of this time, or just under two months, has passed on earth during the outward journey. Now suppose that the twin reaches Aldebaran and, without pausing for so much as a melloroon, returns to earth at 99½% the speed of light, always watching the flashing beacon. On the return journey, flashes arrive not once every twenty seconds, *but twenty times per second*. Why? Because now each successive flash has *less* distance to travel to reach the spaceship. For this reason, even though the flashes seem to be emitted only once every ten seconds (because the earth can be considered to be moving at 99½% the speed of light relative to the spaceship), there is a reduction in the travel time from the earth to the spaceship between each flash of 10 sec × (.995) = 9.95 seconds. The net result is that the time between flashes is 10 sec − 9.95 sec = 0.05 sec, so they arrive twenty times per second. This result does not indicate conclusively that the twin on earth is now aging more rapidly than the traveling twin. It indicates rather that the spaceship's motion towards earth more than compensates for the apparent slowdown in the rate of flashing. Bear in mind that each twin knows about additional travel time, and could calculate the part that it is playing in what they see, but the end result would still be what we shall calculate. (Figure 3)

So the traveling twin comes home on a journey that aboard the spaceship seems to take 3 1/5 years (just as the outward journey did), but during the return journey the traveling twin sees a flash rate from earth twenty times that on board, so the twin concludes that 20 × 3 1/5 years = 64 2/5 years 2 months[2] have elapsed on earth during this journey, and the total elapsed time on earth for the journeys out and back is 64 years and four months while the total elapsed time aboard ship is 3 1/5 + 3 1/5 years = 6 2/5 years. If you have been following this epic journey closely, you will notice that all the flashes emitted from earth have been observed and are accounted for aboard the spaceship.

What does the twin on earth see? While the other twin flashes onward toward Aldebaran, the twin on earth receives flashes once every twenty seconds, as we described above, because time aboard the spaceship appears to be running more slowly and the spaceship is constantly getting farther from the earth. To the twin on earth, the spaceship's outward journey appears to take 32 years and two months (32 light years at 99½% the speed of light), and, furthermore, the last flash from the outward journey, emitted upon arival at Aldebaran, will take 32 years to reach the earth. The result is that for the entire 64 years and two months needed for the traveling twin to reach Aldebaran and to have the flash from Aldebaran reach the earth, the earthbound twin observes time aboard the spaceship to be running twenty times more slowly than earth time. The twin on earth concludes that the total elapsed time aboard the spaceship by the time the flash from Aldebaran arrives is 1/20 × (64 years 2 months) = 3 1/5 years. (Figure 3).

___

[2] I have rounded off 3.2122 years to 3 1/5 years and a factor of 19.975 to a factor of twenty; the true product is 64.1637 years.

When the spaceship has begun its return journey and the flashes from this leg arrive on earth, they come not once per second but twenty times per second, since the spaceship's motion toward earth more than compensates for the apparent slowing of time aboard ship, as we described earlier for the reciprocal situation seen aboard the spaceship. The traveling twin will return to earth just two months after the flash from Aldebaran arrives on earth, because that flash travels to earth at the speed of light (for 32 years), while the spaceship comes home at 99½% the speed of light, thus taking 32 years 2 months, two months longer than the flash of light.[3] During the two months between the arrival on earth of the flash from Aldebaran and the return of the spaceship, the flashes arrive twenty times per second, indicating a passage of time twenty times faster by this standard of flash counting, so the return phase aboard the spaceship seems to take 20 times 2 months or 3 1/5 years as observed from earth.[4] The spaceship's entire journey as seen from earth thus appears to total 3 1/5 + 3 1/5 years = 6 2/5 years aboard the spaceship, but 64 years 4 months have passed on earth during the round trip to Aldebaran. This agrees with what the traveling twin saw. As observed aboard ship, the entire trip took 6 2/5 years, while 64 years 4 months elapsed on earth.

Thus by counting flashes and timing their arrival, both the twin on earth and the traveling twin agree that the trip to Aldebaran caused the twin who went to age 6 2/5 years while the twin who stayed behind aged 64 years and four months, for a difference of almost sixty years. The cause of the difference is the reversal of direction made by the traveling twin but not the twin on earth. On account of this key distinction, the two twins are not equivalent; they did not have the same experience even as seen from their own small worlds. The apparent paradox of the twins has thus been resolved, thanks to the immense power of logic ranged alongside the guiding principles that Einstein elucidated.

So we have the secret of longevity by earth standards: travel at velocities near the speed of light, and you'll outlive your contemporaries. It turns out (but we shall not demonstrate it here) that it's not necessary to go in a straight line; it's enough to circle round and round the earth like astronauts. The men who spent 84 days in orbit in Skylab, moving at a speed relative to ourselves of about 8 km/sec (about three one-thousandths of a percent of the speed of light), aged about one five-thousandth of a second less than they would have by staying at home. Although this gain of life probably does not outweigh the risks involved, especially since we should also dock them one five-thousandth of a second of flight pay, we can imagine that someday—should humanity survive long enough—space travelers to nearby stars could use the slowing down of time to help them survive the journey and return to tell their descendants what they found.[5]

• DISCUSSION QUESTIONS •

1. What do we mean when we say that two events are simultaneous? How did Einstein answer this question?

---

[3] When the flash from Aldebaran arrives on earth the spaceship is only two light months from earth and closing fast.

[4] I have rounded off as mentioned above.

[5] The slowing down of time often appears in science fiction, quite frequently without much care for exactitude. An exception is Poul Anderson's *Tau Zero*, where a spaceship's crew grows as old as the universe and (here a little license enters) survives the next "big bang."

2. What explains the fact that when we look out into space we are actually looking back in time?

3. What is the distance from the sun to the center of the Milky Way? From our galaxy to M31? From the earth to the most remote quasars?

4. What basic ideas are contained in the special theory of relativity?

5. Why is it possible to travel faster than the speed of sound, but not faster than the speed of light?

6. What explains the fact that perceptions become distorted when we are traveling at high velocities, close to the speed of light? How is this phenomenon a function of relative motion? What is time dilation, and under what circumstances might it occur?

7. What accounts for the fact that a person traveling close to the speed of light would hardly age at all? What is the "twin paradox" described in the selection by Goldsmith, and how might it be resolved?

8. How does the theory of special relativity provide us with a means of going to the stars?

9. What are some of the methods used to detect planets around stars? What evidence is there to suggest that planetary systems are common in our galaxy?

• ADDITIONAL ACTIVITIES •

Optional Projects

1. Using other sources, write a paper about the life and work of Albert Einstein.

2. Make a list of some of the phenomena that would occur if you were traveling close to the speed of light. Consider how your perceptions of length, time, mass, and color would be affected.

3. Write a few paragraphs describing some of the existing suggestions for future space travel.

Supplementary Bibliography

P. Anderson, *Tau Zero*. London: Coronet, 1970.
An intriguing science-fiction tale about a spaceship traveling close to the speed of light. Anyone interested in space travel will enjoy this book.

Albert Einstein, *Relativity*. New York: Crown, 1961.
One of the clearest and most readable explanations of the special theory of relativity available.

Philipp Frank, *Einstein: His Life and Times*. New York: Alfred A. Knopf, 1970.
A definitive study of the life and work of Einstein.

Alexander Moszkowski, *Conversations with Einstein*. New York: Horizon Press, 1970.
A revealing and insightful portrait of Einstein and his work based on a series of personal conversations.

Bertrand Russell, *The ABC of Relativity*. London: George Allen and Unwin, Ltd., 1958.
An excellent explanation of the theory of relativity written for the popular audience.

Chapter IX
THE LIVES OF THE STARS

• OVERVIEW •

THE MAGICAL SECRET the ancient alchemists burned to possess—how to transmute base metals into gold—lay not in their crucibles but in the stars. Even more, the transmutation of elements from atomically simple to more complex has been taking place since the beginning of the universe in the chain reactions created by the enormous forces generated in the cosmos.

Our origin is cosmic. Born in the stars were the oxygen in the air we breathe, the iron in our blood, the calcium in our bones—all the 92 elements except hydrogen and some helium, the simplest of the lot.

The mass of a star determines its life cycle and the elements it produces. Born of a collapsing cloud of hydrogen, a star proceeds to fuse hydrogen into helium, carbon, and oxygen. It is only in stars far more massive than our Sun that heavier elements such as silicon and iron are synthesized. And in the spectacular fireworks of a supernova—the death throes of a massive star—are created gold and uranium. Black holes—those wierd phenomena that have been described as traps for matter and energy where space-time itself is greatly warped—are formed in the intense gravitational field resulting from the collapse of giant, massive stars.

Our Sun, giver of life and subject of the worship of our forebears, is not a particularly large star and will not die such an extravagant death. It will become a red giant, a glowing shell of expanding gas, and will then collapse to form a white dwarf, and finally cool to a black cinder. Its end will be puny compared to that of a supernova. However, no life would probably exist on planets surrounding stars destined to become supernovae—their own existences are too quick and fierce to allow it. It is on planets around the stars such as our middle-sized and steady Sun that the magic of life has a chance to arise.

• LEARNING OBJECTIVES •

1. Explain Dr. Sagan's analogy of a star as a "cosmic kitchen," and describe how material processed in stars is recycled.

2. Describe atomic structure, nuclear reaction, and how more complex elements are constructed from simpler ones by atomic fusion.

3. Describe the phases of evolution of a star like the Sun.

4. Describe how the mass of a star determines the stages through which it evolves and the endpoint at which it arrives.

5. Explain Sagan's contention that the life cycles of stars are intimately connected with human evolution. How does Sagan arrive at the conclusion that "We are made of star stuff"?

6. Describe pulsars and galactic X-ray sources in terms of neutron stars and black holes.

7. Describe a supernova, and distinguish between novae and supernovae.

8. Describe what neutrinos are, what their role is in the processes occurring in the Sun, and the problems raised by the "missing neutrinos" of the Sun.

• KEY TERMS AND NAMES •

black hole	nucleus
cosmic ray	photon
Cygnus X-1	proton
electron	pulsar
element	quark
neutron	radioactivity
neutron star	red giant
neutrino	Ernest Rutherford
nova	supernova
nucleosynthesis	white dwarf

• ASSIGNMENT •

Watch COSMOS television series Program 9, "The Lives of the Stars."

Read Chapter 9, "The Lives of the Stars," in Carl Sagan's text, *Cosmos*, or other readings assigned by your instructor.

• READINGS •

David H. Clark and
F. Richard Stephenson . . . . **The Historical Supernovae**

In 1054, a supernova flared spectacularly in the constellation of Taurus the Bull. It was noted by Chinese, American, and Moslem observers. Now called the Crab

Supernova, it is the first supernova of historical record. In 1572, Tycho Brahe had the good fortune to observe another supernova, as described in the following passage.

While on the subject of the discovery of the new star, it is worthwhile commenting on the attitude to it in Europe. In Chapter 3 of his *Progymnasmata*, Tycho Brahe gives a graphic account of his own feelings. When the star first appeared, Tycho was staying with his uncle at the monastery of Herritzwadt in Denmark. He writes:

When on the above mentioned day (November 11), a little before dinner. . . I was returning to that house, and during my walk contemplating the sky here and there since the clearer sky seemed to be just what could be wished for in order to continue observations after dinner, behold, directly overhead, a certain strange star was suddenly seen, flashing its light with a radiant gleam and it struck my eyes. Amazed, and as if astonished and stupified, I stood still, gazing for a certain length of time with my eyes fixed intently upon it and noticing that same star placed close to the stars which antiquity attributed to Cassiopeia. When I had satisfied myself that no star of that kind had ever shone forth before, I was led into such perplexity by the unbelievability of the thing that I began to doubt the faith of my own eyes, and so, turning to the servants who were accompanying me, I asked them whether they too could see a certain extremely bright star when I pointed out the place directly overhead. They immediately replied with one voice that they saw it completely and that it was extremely bright. But despite their affirmation, still being doubtful on account of the novelty of the thing, I enquired of some country people who by chance were travelling past in carriages whether they could see a certain star in the height. Indeed these people shouted out that they saw that huge star, which had never been noticed so high up. And at length, having confirmed that my vision was not deceiving me, but in fact that an unusual star existed there, beyond all type, and marvelling that the sky had brought forth a certain new phenomenon to be compared with the other stars, immediately I got ready my instrument. I began to measure its situation and distance from the neighbouring stars of Cassiopeia, and to note extremely diligently those things which were visible to the eye concerning its apparent size, form, colour and other aspects.

Susan Wyckoff. . . . . **Red Giants: The Inside Scoop**

Susan Wyckoff, professor of astronomy at Ohio State University, explains how the study of giant red stars can provide information about the evolution of stars in general as well as about the fate of our Sun.

The red giant stars provide some of the most direct and positive evidence that our theories of stellar evolution and stellar energy generation are correct. According to present theory, essentially all normal, single stars will evolve through a red giant stage at some relatively mature epoch in their lives. Fortunately, the red giant stars are exhibitionists of sorts and readily reveal vital clues to their origin, history and future evolution. How do the obvservations of red giants support the theory of stellar evolution?

MAIN SEQUENCE STARS

Stars are probably formed in dense interstellar clouds which are scattered throughout the spiral arms of our galaxy.[1] The present chemical make-up of these clouds is hydrogen (92%) and helium (7.8%), with an admixture of oxygen, carbon, nitrogen and all heavier chemical elements comprising the remaining 0.2%. Somehow (we are not yet sure how), part of an interstellar cloud begins to contract into a sphere. As this "proto-star" contracts, the gas heats up, with the hottest part in the center and a gradually decreasing temperature toward the outer portions. When temperatures reach some thousands of degrees, atoms are completely stripped of their electrons and only a gas of bare atomic nuclei (plus free electrons) exists in the core of a proto-star. (Astronomers usually loosely refer to the central part of a star as the "core" and the overlying outer layers as the "envelope." Normal stars are gaseous throughout.) After several million years of contraction, the core temperature and density become so high that four hydrogen nuclei (which are really just protons) can *fuse* together to form a helium nucleus. Such a nucleus weighs slightly *less* than the four hydrogen nuclei from which it was created; in the fusion process, the mass excess is transformed into energy.[2] this fusion process is often called "hydrogen-burning" by astronomers, even though no real burning, in the chemical sense, takes place.

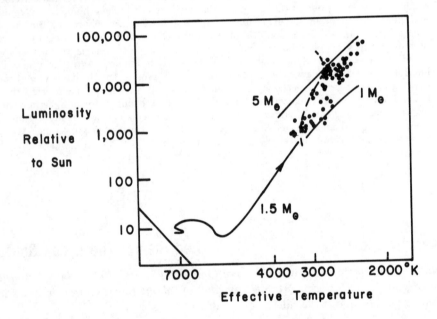

Figure 1. *H-R diagram for cool, luminous stars, adapted from the work of J. Scalo and of I. Iben and J. Truran. The main sequence is indicated in the lower left-hand corner. The computed evolutionary track indicates the evolution of a 1.5 solar mass star from the main sequence ot the red giant stage. Partial evolutionary tracks for the 1 and 5 solar mass stars are also shown. The backward S-shaped (dotted) curve indicates where the helium flash is expected to occur. The plotted points represent observations of individual red giants.*

[1] One example of such a "stellar nursery" is the Orion Nebula; for a photograph see the Nov/Dec 1978 *Mercury*, p. 122.

[2] The precise amount of energy released in this process can be calculated using Einstein's equation, $E = mc^2$, where E is energy, m is mass and c is the speed of light.

Hydrogen burning can continue uninterrupted for billions of years and is the energy source which causes most stars you see in the sky to shine. A star burning hydrogen is said to be in the *main sequence* phase of stellar evolution because a star spends most of its life in this stage. The Sun (which is an average main-sequence star) has been burning hydrogen for about five billion years and will continue to do so for another five billion years until the hydrogen fuel runs out.

RED GIANT PHASE

Eventually there is no more hydrogen at the proper temperature and pressure, so hydrogen burning must cease inside a star. What will happen to the star during this energy crisis?

Two opposing forces continually vie for control of any star. The all-pervasive and ever-present inward force of gravity tries to keep the hot, gaseous blob together; but at the same time the hot gases continually exert an outward force trying to expand and distend the star. When there is a stalemate between these opposing forces, as is true during the main sequence phase, we say the star is in *equilibrium*. But when the nuclear fuel runs out in the stellar core and hydrogen burning ceases, the core proceeds to cool. Soon the inward force of gravity in the cooling core becomes stronger than the outward thrust of the hot core gases. The star's reaction to its fuel shortage, then, is for its core to contract. (Remember that the core is now essentially pure helium because hydrogen burning for billions of years during the main sequence stage continually transformed hydrogen nuclei into helium nuclei.)

Now the core, in contracting, gives up gravitational energy. This energy must go somewhere, and the nearest place is the star's envelope. Consequently, as the core continues to contract, the gravitational energy of contraction is deposited in the surrounding envelope. The response of the gaseous envelope to its newly acquired energy is to expand greatly. Any gas which expands becomes cooler (and, in the case of a star, redder in color). Also, the increase in the size of the expanding star increases the overall surface area from which it radiates energy into space. The ultimate consequence of the main-sequence energy crisis, then, is to produce a luminous, bloated, cool star which astronomers have dubbed a "red giant."

By the time stars reach this stage, their envelopes are 100 or 1000 times their main sequence sizes and their surface temperatures have cooled by one-half or more. As an example, the Sun in its red giant phase (approximately 5 billion years from now) will have a radius extending out to the orbit of Mars or beyond!

As the helium core of a red giant continues to contract, eventually the temperature and pressure become so high that helium nuclei can fuse together to make carbon nuclei, again with a mass deficit which is transformed into energy. We call this stage in the evolution of a red giant, helium burning.

Now helium burning can happen catastrophically or quiescently, depending on how compact the core has become before reaching the ignition of helium. In massive stars the weight of the overlying layers is so great that the core will ignite while the gas in it is still in a normal state. In this case helium nuclei burn to become carbon nuclei in the core relatively slowly. On the other hand, in low mass stars like the Sun, a much greater contraction is needed to heach helium ignition temperature. The core must contract to a point where its gas becomes "electron degenerate."[3]

---

[3]For more on degeneracy see the article by J. Irwin in the Nov/Dec 1978 *Mercury*.

Degenerate gas has several interesting properties: First, it is nearly incompressible, so that the collapse of the core is greatly slowed. Second, degenerate electrons conduct heat with great efficiency, so that the entire core is essentially at a single temperature. When the helium finally ignites in the pure helium core, the temperature of the entire core is the same and a chain reaction is set off. In a matter of moments all the helium nuclei are transformed to carbon. We call this event the *helium flash*. (Even though it is probably the most dramatic event in the life of a low-mass star, it happens deep in the core, and is completely unobservable from outside the star!) After the helium flash, the red giant obtains its energy from hydrogen and helium burning in separate shells surrounding the core.

After the carbon core forms in the center of a red giant, our ideas of stellar evolution are not so certain. This is mainly because the computer time required to perform the numerical calculations for the model stars on which our ideas of stellar evolution are based becomes excessive (and expensive!). Observations tell us, however, that the products of the nuclear reactions in stellar interiors somehow reach the outer layers of red giants because we observe gross differences in the abundances of certain chemical elements when we examine the light from these stars.

TECHNETIUM OBSERVATIONS

The remarkable discovery of the unstable element technetium in atmospheres of red giants by P. Merrill nearly thirty years ago provided the first conclusive evidence that the coolest, most luminous stars must currently be synthesizing chemical elements in their interiors. Technetium is one of the very few chemical elements which have no stable form. All technetium here on Earth has been created artificially in nuclear laboratories, where we have found that this element can survive for a characteristic lifetime of only 200,000 years before it radioactively decays (its nucleus decomposes) and becomes a different, stable chemical element called ruthenium. Two hundred thousand years may sound like a long time, but in the life of a star the lifetime of a typical technetium nucleus is but a fleeting moment. Remember that red giants are at least a few million years old and most probably have ages of billions of years. Thus the mere presence of technetium in the atmosphere of an isolated star is conclusive evidence that this element was not part of the star at birth but must have been synthesized inside that star. But how is this unusual element synthesized inside red giant stars?

So far we have only discussed hydrogen and helium burning in the cores of stars. A rather minor type of nuclear reaction, called the s-process, can probably also take place during the red giant phase of stellar evolution. This process is not very important in terms of its contribution to the radiant energy of a star, but we believe the s-process is vital to the synthesis of some of the heavy, relatively rare elements such as zirconium, molybdenum and barium, as well as technetium.

The s in the name stands for *slow*, in reference to the rate at which neutrons bombard particularly vulnerable nuclei deep in the stars' interiors. Synthesis of heavy elements by the s-process involves a flood of neutrons (produced by other nuclear reactions) in addition to "seed" nuclei with which to begin the build-up of new elements. Nuclei successively absorb neutrons until the nuclei become unstable and decay to become a new element with one more unit of positive charge in the nucleus. As far as we know, the s-process is the only way the unstable element technetium can be built up. Since the typical lifetime of technetium nuclei is

200,000 years, any technetium present in the atmospheres of red giants must have been produced deep inside the star by this s-process in the relatively recent past (on an astronomical scale).

The importance of observing technetium in red giant atmospheres then is that it is a clear indication that these stars are sites for the synthesis of the heavy elements. But we have seen that the s-process is really a rather insignificant part of both element production and the energetics of a star. What evidence do we have that red giants have actually burned both hydrogen and helium, and that our other basic ideas of stellar evolution are correct?

RELATIVE	COSMIC	ABUNDANCES	
OF	CHEMICAL	ELEMENTS	
Hydrogen		92.0 %	
Helium		7.8	
Oxygen			
Carbon		0.2	
Nitrogen			
etc.			

THE H-R DIAGRAM

In an H-R diagram, a star's plotted position is determined by its surface temperature and its luminosity. The cool, luminous stars we have been discussing lie in the upper right-hand corner of the diagram. Astronomers use the diagram to describe how the surface temperature and luminosity of a star change as it evolves. We can test the validity of theories about stellar evolution by comparing the predicted positions of stars at given times in their lives with the actual positions of real stars in the diagram. Figure 1 shows the coolest, most luminous portion of the H-R diagram. The straight line in the lower left-hand corner represents the main sequence. The position of a star on the main sequence is determined by the star's mass and its initial chemical composition.

After the hydrogen burning phase, as the pure helium core contracts and the envelope expands, the star begins to move up the red giant branch of the H-R diagram. As its outer layers cool and expand, a star evolves off the main sequence and moves to the upper right in the H-R diagram (the increasing radius acts to increase the star's overall surface area and hence its overall luminosity). Since it takes several million years for a star to make this trek up the red giant branch, we cannot actually observe any given star undergoing these evolutionary changes. However, by observing many different red giant stars, we have managed to understand the entire sequence of events. Partial evolutionary tracks for red giant stars 1, 1.5, and 5 times the Sun's mass are indicated in the figure. The dotted "backward S" curve in the upper right of Figure 1 shows the position where the (unobservable!) helium flash is calculated to occur for various stars. Any red giant located to the right of the dotted curve in the H-R diagram has probably undergone the helium flash. The plotted points in the figure indicate observations of individual red giant stars. Note that nearly all of the red giant stars are located in the post-helium flash portion of the H-R diagram. We might surmise then that these stars have carbon-rich cores. What other observations of red giants might provide clues regarding the validity of our theory of stellar evolution?

SPECTRA: M, S AND C

In 1867 the Italian astronomer A. Secchi used a prism spectroscope attached to his telescope to discover some very peculiar stellar spectra having a "banded" appearance. When the light from a star passes through a prism, waves of different colors are bent by differing amounts and the light becomes spread out and ordered according to the individual energies (or colors) of the light waves. (The familiar rainbow is merely a spectrum of sunlight produced by water droplets acting as tiny prisms.) The reason spectra are so useful to astronomers is that atoms and molecules are able to absorb light waves at certain energies (or colors) from the spectra, causing light of those particular colors to be missing. Each kind of atom or molecule (a conglomerate of two or more atoms) can, under suitable conditions, create a pattern or gaps in a spectrum which is characteristic of that particular type of atom or molecule and recognizable wherever the absorption occurs.

Molecules, in fact, are gluttons for light waves, absorbing copious amounts of energy and giving the observed spectrum a banded appearance. While many stars are too hot to permit anything but individual atoms, the cooler red giant atmospheres abound in molecules. Consequently, spectra of red giant stars show the banded structure characteristic of these molecules.

Most of these stars, something like 88 percent, have been classified as M type; C types comprise approximately 10 percent and the rare S types only about 2 percent of all red giants. Curiously enough the choppy appearance of the M, S and C type spectra can each be ascribed to one particularly greedy molecule which is effective in absorbing light waves in the visible spectral region. M-type spectra are characterized by titanium oxide (TiO) absorption bands, S-types by zirconium oxide (ZrO) bands, and C-types by molecular carbon (C_2) bands. These spectral signatures indicate gross abundance anomalies in red giant stars, but their interpretation is not obvious due to the complex interactions which atoms undergo when forming molecules in stellar atmospheres.

To understand the three basic types of red giant spectra, we must understand a little more about the behavior of atoms and how they might form molecules under the conditions expected to occur in red giant atmospheres. Chemists tell us that atoms have different affinities for one another. Some form molecules with relative ease (for example carbon and oxygen readily combine into carbon monoxide); while some atoms rarely form molecules (for example, helium is a "loner" in this respect). In a star the gas mixture and atomic behavior are both so complex that it is impossible to guess intuitively what precise combinations of molecules will form. However, with the aid of a computer, the knowledge of the chemical characteristics of each atom enables us in essence to simulate a hodge-podge of atoms and see how it would behave and form molecules under the physical conditions of a red giant atmosphere. We can use this computer-generated model atmosphere to predict the relative numbers of different molecules in a particular star.

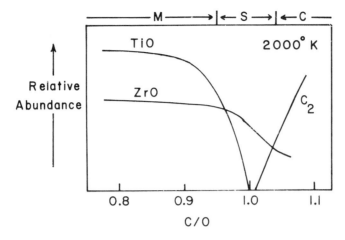

Figure 2. *Relative abundances of observable molecules in atmospheres of cool red giants based on recent work by the author and R. Clegg. The figure shows that a simple increase in the carbon to oxygen abundance ratio (C/O) in the atmospheres of the red giant stars can produce the spectral signatures (TiO, ZrO and C₂) of M, S and C stars. Thus the differences among the three types of red giants observed can probably be explained by the differences in their carbon abundances. The atmosphere of the Sun (and other main sequence stars) has C/O = 0.6: if our Sun were cool enough for molecules to form, it would have TiO absorption bands in its observed spectrum.*

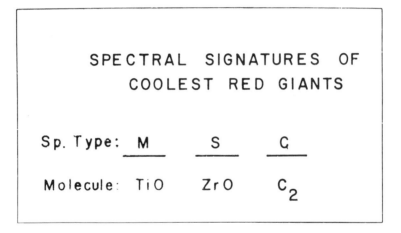

When we observe the usual spectrum of a red giant star, we actually see only a segment of its spectrum, the so-called *optical* or visible portion. For this reason, we only need to predict abundances for molecules which show a strong preference for absorbing waves in the visible spectral region. For example, molecular hydrogen (H_2) is computed to be extremely abundant in red giant atmospheres (mainly by virtue of the huge cosmic abundance of hydrogen). But for the purposes of our calculations we do not predict molecular hydrogen to be "abundant", because this molecule is not able to absorb light in the *visible* spectrum. (Molecular hydrogen would no doubt produce strong absorption bands in the *ultraviolet* spectral region, but such observations require a telescope in space.)

The results of the computer calculations which predict relative numbers of those molecules which absorb visible light under conditions expected in a red giant atmosphere are summarized in Figure 2. The higher the curve in the figure, the more abundant the molecule. The figure shows how the numbers of observable molecules would change if the carbon abundance were increased or oxygen abundance decreased in the atmosphere. The horizontal scale shows the carbon to oxygen abundance ratio (C/O), which is 0.6 in the Sun, indicating that there are 60 percent as many carbon atoms as oxygen atoms in the solar atmosphere. Amazingly enough, Figure 2 shows that by simply increasing the amount of carbon as compared to oxygen in our computer-simulated red giant atmosphere, we can predict the gross overall spectral characteristics of all three types of red giant spectra!

When there are approximately equal numbers of carbon and oxygen atoms in the atmosphere (C/O about 1.0), the figure shows that the expected spectral signature of a red giant is that of zirconium oxide. When carbon atoms exceed oxygen atoms in the atmospheres of red giants, the calculations predict spectra showing strong absorption bands due to molecular carbon (C_2). When the carbon abundance is less that that for oxygen, titanium oxide dominates and we have an M star. The calculations also indicate that the small numbers of S stars observed may reflect the fact that it is rare to find red giant atmospheres with carbon atoms very nearly equal the number of oxygen atoms. Of course, individual stars may have slightly different abundances of chemical elements other than carbon and oxygen (for example the s-process may operate in some red giants, but not others). Still, the spectral sequence (M ⟶ S ⟶ C) may be explained basically as an increase in the abundance ratio of carbon to oxygen. In fact, we have reason to believe that it is the carbon abundance which changes and not the oxygen. But where might an excess of carbon in the atmosphere of S and C stars come from?

Returning to the theory of stellar evolution, we recall that during helium burning, carbon is produced in the core. However, this process takes place deep in the interior of the star, millions of kilometers below the part of the atmosphere which we can observe. If the freshly synthesized carbon is getting to the outer layers of red giant stars, how does this happen? We are not yet certain, but we can imagine two possible ways (and both may be operating!) One way is for the star to somehow peel off its outer layers, thereby gradually (over millions of years) exposing the carbon enriched inner layers. This process is called *mass loss*. The other possible way of producing carbon enrichment is a kind of dredging operation whereby convective currents flow in the red giant envelope[5]. If these currents can extend from the core up to the surface layers, the carbon-enriched material from the core region may be able to ride—surfer style—the convective currents upwards into the atmosphere.

Either process—mass loss or convective currents—can explain how carbon from the interior can be exposed at the exterior of red giant stars. We believe then that we can understand the three types, M, S and C, basically as differences in the relative numbers of carbon and oxygen atoms in the atmosphere of red giants. Moreover our explanation of the three spectral types appears to support the theory of stellar evolution which predicts carbon synthesis in the cores of red giant stars.

Verification of details of the theory of stellar evolution is in its infancy, but the observations of M, S and C stars and the understanding of the chemistry of their atmospheres tell us we are on the right track. In fact, the observations combined with the theory of red giants are tantalizingly close to revealing to us the innermost secrets of these aging stars.

---

[5] In the process of convection, energy is transported ty the actual movement of material within the star. Hotter gas rises from below and cooler gas sinks.

Timothy Ferris . . . . Black Holes

Timothy Ferris entertainingly explains and describes black holes, those perplexing phenomena adored by physicists and science fiction addicts alike. This excerpt is from his book The Red Limit: The Search for the Edge of the Universe.

Insular, excommunicant, perpetually hungry, a black hole is the perfect place to hide anything. It is a well in spacetime so steep that nothing, not even light, can climb out of it, a confluence of the great in small, in circumference smaller than the city of Boston, in diameter infinite—you can feed a tape measure in forever and the black hole will simply eat it. It will eat hydrogen gas, planets, flowers or kings with equanimity. Each, falling in, departs our universe for good. The black hole will tell us nothing about its victims. It will tell us, in fact, nothing about itself except its mass, electrical charge and angular momentum. "A black hole has no hair," John Wheeler liked to say.

That these baleful sinks exist was a prediction of relativity. Karl Schwarzschild, one of the few who realized, prior to Einstein, that the universe might be viewed in terms of non-euclidean geometry, went to work soon after general relativity theory was published in 1916, investigating the geometry of spacetime in the vicinity of massive objects, which practically speaking meant stars. His calculations revealed that for a star of any given mass there is a "Schwarzschild radius" such that if the star is compressed to a size smaller than that radius, it will collapse to so high a density as to pinch itself off from the surrounding spacetime. The result is a kind of hole in space. Things can fall in but nothing gets out.

The Schwarzchild radius became part of theoretical astrophysics, but whether a real star ever suffered such a fate was another matter. Densely packed white dwarf stars were known to exist and were believed to result when stars burned out their nuclear fuel and collapsed, the outward pressure of their light and heat no longer able to balance the grip of their own gravity. White dwarfs were fantastic objects—a cubic inch of their surface could weigh tons—and the possibility that stars might collapse even further was not taken very seriously at first. Then in 1930 a young Indian student, Subrahamanyan Chandrasekhar, calculated that if a dying star were much more massive than the sun, it would collapse right through the white dwarf stage to become something even more compressed.

Chandrasekhar was studying under R. H. Fowler at Cambridge at the time, and Fowler brought his work to Eddington's attention. Eddington saw that if the calculations were correct, a sufficiently massive collapsing star could become so compressed that it sucked in its own light and cut itself off from the rest of the universe. This struck Eddington as ridiculous, and he felt he had discredited Chandrasekhar's theory by reducing it to absurdity.

In America the nuclear physicist J. Robert Oppenheimer, urged on by, among others, George Gamow, looked into the physics of gravitational collapse, and with several students published two important papers in 1939. The first theorized that tars could collapse through the white dwarf stage and become "neutron stars," objects whose intense gravity broke down the structure of atoms within them. The term was borrowed from Baade and Zwicky, who five years earlier had suggested that exploding stars might leave neutron stars behind as a sort of ash.* The second Oppenheimer paper discussed the possibility of a star crushing itself beyond the observable limit. "When all thermonuclear sources of energy are exhausted a sufficiently heavy star will collapse," the paper began. "Unless fission due to rotation,

---

* They were vindicated thirty years later with the discovery of a pulsar, or radio-bright neutron star, in the Crab Nebula, where Chinese astronomers had recorded a supernova in the eleventh century.

the radiation of mass, or the blowing off of mass by radiation, reduce the star's mass to the order of that of the sun, this contraction will continue indefinitely. . . . Light from the surface of the star is progressively reddened, and can escape over a progressively narrower range of angles." As the gravitational redshift approaches infinity, the star disappears and we have a black hole.

Interest in black holes reawakened in the 1960s with the discovery of quasars, the great energy of which might be explained by gravitational collapse, and of pulsars, which were shown almost certainly to be neutron stars. If there are things in space strange as neutron stars, one reasoned, why not black holes? Theoretical models showed that while finding solitary black holes in space by optical means might be impossible, they could be detected if they were part of double-star systems: the black hole would suck surface gas off its companion star, and the gas, whirling down into oblivion, would emit a flood of X-rays.

Their exotic name aside, X-rays are just another part of the electromagnetic spectrum, occupying the zone between ultraviolet light and gamma rays. They cannot be observed reliably from Earth because the atmosphere tends to absorb them. An Italian-American X-ray satellite, Uhuru, launched in 1970, eventually located over 100 cosmic X-ray sources, of which some were other galaxies, some neutron stars, and one, Cygnus X-1, was possibly a black hole. The issue remained in doubt, but several researchers pronounced themselves almost certain they had found a genuine black hole. Cyngus X-1 appeared to be feeding off its companion, the supergiant star HDE 226868, in a gravitational web so tight that the two whipped around their common center of gravity once every 5.6 days. If that model were correct the system would be quite a sight—the tormented supergiant pouring glowing gas across space and into an invisible spacetime vortex—but interstellar cosmonauts might be forgiven for passing up a close look. The crew of a spaceship falling into a black hole would experience, in their last moments, a growing redshift of starlight resembling the death of the universe, though it would be of course their own.

Although scientists were to argue for years whether it and other candidates located thereafter really were black holes, public response to discovery of Cyngus X-1 was enthusiastic. Science fiction writers made room for black holes in stories, poets heralded them, a few painters accepted what may be the ultimate technical challenge and attempted to paint their portrait. California physicists considered the feasibility of black hole power plants. Soviet theorists proposed that a massive rotating black hole might constitute a bridge between two distant parts of the cosmos, one a daring pilot might navigate. In Texas two physicists proposed, dead-pan, that a tiny black hole caused the Siberian forest explosion of June 30, 1908, when a brilliant fireball of uncertain origin slammed to earth near Tunguska, 100 miles north of the Sea of Okhotsk, and leveled 300 square miles of trees. They imagined that the black hole continued through the earth and emerged from the North Atlantic between Newfoundland and the Azores. They urged ships' logs of the period be searched for sightings of the reappearance.

As Kip Thorne of Cal Tech wrote, "Of all the conceptions of the human mind from unicorns to gargoyles to the hydrogen bomb perhaps the most fantastic is the black hole."

To cosmologists, the significance of black holes lay in their potential role as lockers for hidden matter. As Gott and others showed, all the known matter in the cosmos is not nearly enough to stop expansion. Unless ten times more matter is found, the universe is open. Could 90 percent of the stuff of the universe be locked away in black holes?

If all black holes were formed in the collapse of stars, probably not. If massive stars have been dying at a constant rate since the galaxies formed, a spiral system the size of the Milky Way ought to contain today about 100 million black holes. To avoid erring on the low side, let us say that stellar collapse was once more common than it is today and boost the estimate by a factor of ten, to one billion. Assume, again on the high side, the average black hole mass is ten times the sun's. (A more likely estimate is half that.) The result is to add 10 billion solar masses to our galaxy. That is a lot of mass, but it makes the galaxy heavier by less that 5 percent. We can go on to assume that every galaxy once had a quasar at its center and that the quasar remnant remains as a black hole. Theoretically this giant black hole could have a mass of up to one billion times the sun's. Even if we double that, we are still a long way from finding enough mass to stop expansion.

Gott and Gunn considered these and other "missing mass" theories, discarded them, then concluded, by studying the gravitational interaction of galaxies in clusters, that galaxies simply do not act as if they are ten times more massive than currently estimated. *"Galaxies themselves cannot close the universe,"* the Gott group wrote (their italics). If black holes harbor most of the mass of the cosmos, they must not be in galaxies.

The Gott group concluded that the universe probably, though by no means certainly, is open. "A clear verdict is unfortunately not yet in, but the mood of the jury is perhaps becoming perceptible," they wrote. Sandage, who previously leaned toward a closed universe, shifted toward their view, prompted by the globular cluster star ages and his own studies of expansion rates in nearby galaxies. "The conclusion that the universe will expand forever seems inevitable," he wrote in 1976.

If so, it is destined for heat death. Eventually all the stars will go out and the material for making new ones will have been exhausted. The universe will be an entropic duchy, carting black galaxies outward in a black cosmos forever.

If not, expansion will one day stop, contraction follow, and a new cosmic fireball be born. Present evidence weighs against this but is not conclusive. As John Wheeler said, "It's too soon yet to say what the story is. The excitement is just beginning. Nobody should throw in his hand at this point."

Whether the cosmos ends in fire or ice, apparently it will end, which is to say that it will change into something we would not recognize and could not live in. Some find this depressing. Bertrand Russell regarded it as tragic that "all the noon-day brightness of human genius . . . the whole temple of Man's achievement must inevitably be buried beneath the debris of a universe in ruins. . . ."

But later he cheered up a bit, as might we all for various reasons. We have little more personal stake in cosmic destiny than do sunflowers or bottleflies. The transfiguration of the universe lies some 50 to 100 billion years in the future; snap your fingers twice and you will have consumed a greater fraction of your life than all human history is to such a span. Life is not edifice but process. We owe our lives to universal processes, in that identity of cosmic and earthly destiny glimpsed by George Ellery Hale, and as invited guests we might do better to learn about them than to complain about them. If the prospect of a dying universe causes us anguish, it does so only because we can forecast it, and we have as yet not the slightest idea why such forecasts are possible for us. A few figures scrawled on a piece of paper can describe the rate the universe expands, reveal what goes on inside a star, or predict where the planet Neptune will be on New Year's Day in the year A.D. 25,000. Why? Why should nature, whether hostile or benign, be in any way intelligible to us? All the mysteries of science are but palace guards to that mystery.

Dennis Overbye. . . . . **The Wizard of Space and Time**

Stephen Hawking, considered one of the most brilliant physicists of our time, has originated a theory about black holes that has revived an old dream of science: a unified field theory, i.e. (from the following excerpt), that a "deep unity underlies three realms of physics that were previously thought entirely separate—gravitation, quantum theory, and thermodynamics."

Hawking . . . is one of the outstanding scientists of our generation. At 36 he has shaken the world with a discovery so wierd and still so mysterious that even a statement of one of his findings sounds like a Zen koan: "When is a black hole not black?" "When it explodes." . . .

In 1973, Hawking turned the theory of black holes inside out when he discovered that some black holes are not completely black, they can emit particles and eventually even explode, becoming "white" holes from which energy and particles gush.

Since then, Hawking's breakthrough has dominated discussions of black holes, but its importance transcends the subject of black holes themselves. His work has revived one of the oldest dreams of science: the search for a single theory that will encompass all the laws of physics, the unified field theory that was an unrealized dream of Einstein's. What Hawking has uncovered suggests that a deep unity underlies three realms of physics that were previously thought entirely separate—gravitation, quantum theory, and thermodynamics. Already, in his 30s, he is widely credited with having advanced the general theory of relativity more than anyone since Einstein. He also seems to have discovered that the universe is more unpredictable than anyone had previously recognized. . . . Stricken with a slow, wasting neuromuscular disease, Hawking is confined to a wheelchair where he can do little but sit and think. His mind is his blackboard. He memorizes the long strings of equations that give life to his ideas, then dictates the results to his colleagues or secretary—a feat that has been compared to Beethoven's writing an entire symphony in his head or Milton's dictating *Paradise Lost* to his daughter. . . .

When the black-hole equations that had taken Hawking months to set up finally unreeled across his mind in the fall of 1973, there were an infinite number of particles pouring out of the black hole. It was almost as if the hole had turned white.

"I didn't want the particles coming out," Hawking chuckles. "I wasn't looking for them at all; I merely tripped over them. I was very sorry because it destroyed my framework, and I did my best to get rid of them. I was rather annoyed."

Black holes were supposed to swallow things, not spit them out. . . .

A star is a long thermonuclear explosion held together and fed by gravity. The star's size is a continual negotiation between the crush of gravity seeking to collapse it and the heat blowing it apart. Eventually, though, the fires inside must die.

The first one to realize what might happen if gravity won was the French scientist Pierre Simon Laplace, in 1796. Laplace did not predict that gravity would shrink the star; he just reasoned, from Newton's theory that light was composed of particles with mass, that a massive-enough star would recapture all the light that left its surface. "It is therefore possible," he concluded, that the largest luminous bodies in the universe may . . . be invisible."

In 1939, J. Robert Oppenheimer and his graduate student Hartland Snyder repeated Laplace's investigation, but in the language of general relativity, and got an even stranger result. If a star was heavy enough, no force—not nuclear forces, quark forces, or electrostatic repulsion—could resist gravity, and the star would collapse indefinitely. Once shrinking started, it would go on forever. In a short time, the star would shrink to the point at which the velocity needed to escape its surface would pass the speed of light. Since nothing can exceed the speed of light, the star would be cut off from communication with the rest of the universe.

An outside observer would see it shrink and then just fade away. Its gravitational field would remain, ghostlike, surrounding empty, crushed space. The calculation was a prescription for a black hole, although it would be 30 years before John Wheeler, the Princeton cosmologist, coined the term.

There seemed nothing to stop a gravitational collapse from proceeding to such an absurdity. A star would shrink to an infinitely small point; its density would become infinite; and space would become infinitely curved. The result would be a *singularity*, a cosmic dead end, where particles and energy simply went out of existence.

Singularities appear to be defined mainly by our ignorance of them. At a singularity, Hawking once explained, the traditional notions of space and time break down. "Because all known laws of physics are formulated on a classical space-time background, they will all break down at a singularity," he wrote. "This is a great crisis for physics because it means one cannot predict the future. One does not know what will come out of a singularity."

Are there truly regions of the universe outside the domain of physical law, cosmic free-fire zones where anything goes? The very idea makes physicists queasy.

It had long been thought—and hoped—that the singularities in gravitational collapse would turn out to be only mathematical artifacts, but in 1965 Roger Penrose was able to prove that a collapsed star would result in a real, physical, unpredictable singularity. Penrose proved, in effect, that space-time could have an end.

A year later, Hawking applied Penrose's techniques to the universe as a whole. "The big question was," he says, "Was there a beginning or not? Roger Penrose and I discovered that, if general relativity is correct, there did have to be a beginning."

. . . he and Penrose produced a number of theorems about singularities, the structure of space-time, and the fate of matter caught in its dark path. A famous theorem by Penrose predicted that the collapsing matter (or anything that fell into a black hole) either would hit the singularity or (if the black hole, having formed from a rotating star, was rotating) would miss it and escape through a "wormhole" to another point in space-time, or even another universe. There it would gush forth as a "white" hole, the opposite of a black hole.

To deal with these kinds of problems, Penrose and Brandon Carter, another of Sciama's students, developed a sort of geometric pictorial shorthand in which, by mathematical transformations, the entire universe, past and future, was represented in a triangle. The vertices and two of the sides denote various kinds of infinity, while the third side is a time axis. Singularities appear as heavy jagged lines, either perpendicular or parallel to the time axis. In the fomer case, which applies to nonrotating black holes or the collapse of the universe, the singularity exists at a particular time, and trying to dodge it is like trying to avoid your 30th birthday.

In a spinning black hole, though, space and time switch roles, and the singularity is in a particular place, like a pothole in the road. One could, in principle, steer around it. The price of avoidance, though, since you can't come back out of the black hole is finding yourself in a new triangle representing a new space-time. Theorists soon learned to string these triangles, called Penrose diagrams, together in long repeating chains, like the pattern on some kind of cosmic wallpaper, and chart the paths of astronauts into black holes and white holes from universe to imaginary universe.

But it turned out that the wormholes would have to have been built into the fabric of space-time at the beginning of the universe, preceding the formation of the black holes themselves. The prospect was viewed unfavorably by physicists, who like to believe in cause and effect. Early last year, English physicists N. D. Birrell and Paul Davies showed that if such wormholes did exist, fluctuations in the fields around them would slam them shut.

That left the uncomfortable alternative of meeting the singularity. Fortunately, the same laws that predicted singularities seemed to say that they would always be imprisoned in black holes, preventing word of the breakdown of law and order from ever getting to an outside observer. Whatever came out of singularity would never escape the black hole surrounding it.

Penrose wondered whether there was a "cosmic censor" that forbade the appearance of a "naked" singularity, that is, one that could be seen from the outside world. The cosmic-censorship hypothesis enjoys almost the status of a divine commandment among black-hole theorists today, even though it has never been proved. "Physicists have to believe that the universe makes sense, in order to work," says Hawking.

Hawking was fond of pointing out that there was one singularity that could never be clothed, the big bang in which the universe began. This naked singularity has been known for a long time to theoreticians, but until radio astronomy found evidence of its existence it was widely regarded as a mathematical artifact with no physical meaning. Another naked singularity is the one in which the universe might some day end, if it should gradually stop expanding and then collapse.

In 1971, Hawking proposed an alternative way to create black holes, by the enormous forces operating during the big-bang creation of the universe. Although objects with less than three times the mass of the sun could not collapse to black holes of their own accord, they could be squeezed to that state. Hawking realized that during the big bang such a squeeze might have taken place. If so, our galaxy could now be sprinkled with trillions upon trillions of tiny primordial black holes. The typical mass of a primordial black hole would be a billion tons (10^{15} grams), about as much as a mountain, but it would only be the size of a proton (10^{-13} centimeters), barely a pin-prick in the fabric of space-time.

These mini black-holes were a big hit with astronomers. It seemed there was hardly a problem that could not be explained by the judicious postulation of a mini black-hole. When an experiment to detect neutrinos from nuclear reactions in the center of the sun unexpectedly came up empty-handed, one scientist suggested that a tiny black hole in the sun could explain the finding.

Meanwhile the search for their relatives was heating up. Astronomers had opened yet another window on the universe, with x-ray telescopes mounted in satellites orbiting high above the earth's atmosphere.

In the constellation Cygnus, about 6000 light-years away, astronomers had discovered a giant blue star with an invisible companion, Cygnus X-1. The companion was about ten times as massive as the sun and shrouded by x rays, the signature of matter heated beyond incandescence as it swirled tightly packed around the outside of the cosmic drain. "In a way, today a black hole is the most conventional explanation for Cygnus X-1," says Hawking. "If it isn't a black hole, it really has to be something even more exotic."

Hawking has hedged his emotional involvement with black holes by betting

Kip Thorne, a Caltech physicist, one of Wheeler's students and a longtime friend, that Cygnus X-1 is *not* a black hole. "It would really be easier for me to win than for Kip to win. There are a number of observations that could disprove that it's a black hole—for example, if they found that it was emitting absolutely regular pulses." Should that happen, Hawking would win a four-year subscription to *Private Eye*, a British combination investigative-humor magazine. Thorne, on the other hand, would win a year of *Penthouse*.

In the summer of 1973, Hawking started to think about small black holes again. Something the size of an elementary particle would have its properties defined not only by general relativity but also by quantum mechanics, the laws that govern the fuzzy world of subatomic physics. A tiny black hole might force some sort of a marriage between the laws that govern the two realms—the very great and the very small. "One ought to look at the quantum aspects of gravitation," he told Sciama one day.

Quantum gravity—if there is a magic phrase, a dream, in physics, those two words are it. The goal was and is to describe gravity the way physics describes other forces—as an interaction between two particles. In electromagnetism, for example, photons of light communicate the electrical force between two charged particles.

Quantum theory had rescued physics from its last previous encounter with singularities, at the turn of the century. Theory then predicted that two opposite charges, an electron and a proton, for example, would fall together with infinite energy. That this did not happen—atoms did not spontaneously collapse—was obvious. Nature, it turned out, had other rules.

While astronomers were discovering the expanding universe, a whole raft of physicists was discovering the strange world inside the atom. As puzzles poured out of the laboratories of Europe, a generation of distinguished physicists struggled to unlearn a lifetime of assumptions. It seemed that everything they knew was wrong.

The new findings were consolidated and reformulated in 1927 by a young German physicist, Werner Heisenberg, whose uncertainty principle became the symbol of a new age. He stated that it was impossible *even in principle* to know exactly both the velocity and the position of a particle at a given time.

If relativity had been strange, quantum theory was outrageous. It was such a rude concept that Einstein himself refused to accept it, arguing that the quantum fuzziness of nature was only the screen of our own ignorance. "God does not play dice," he said.

Princeton's John Wheeler likes to compare the quantum principle to a game of 20 Questions he once played, in which his fellow players tricked him by not agreeing on an answer beforehand but decided to be led by his questions. "The word would be brought into being by my questions." Each question took them longer and longer to answer as the players struggled to be consistent, until he finally guessed the word he had helped to create.

Wheeler was among those who hoped that quantum gravity when it ever came about—as everyone believed it must—would incorporate a similar rule change to prevent the dreaded unruly gravitational singularity, which he called the greatest crisis and the greatest hope in the history of physics.

In the early 1970s, Hawking turned to the task of applying quantum mechanics to black holes. "I had an idea about small black holes forming 'atoms' with 'electrons' in orbit around them, and I wanted to have a proper framework to describe these atoms.

"In September 1973, I went to Moscow, where I talked to people about the quantum mechanics of these black-hole atoms. A. A. Starbinsky there told me that rotating black holes ought to emit particles. This idea seemed reasonable to me, but I didn't like the way it had been derived. So I tried to get my own derivation. What I expected was that black holes would emit particles if, and only if, they were rotating. I found out otherwise."

Hawking decided to work out the relatively simple case of a nonrotating black hole first. To his surprise, he discovered that even they appear to create and emit elementary particles such as photons, electrons, or neutrinos.

His abstract calculations didn't even tell him how the particles got out of the black hole, only that somehow they apparently did. Hawking spent a lonely month running and rerunning the equations through his head before he told anyone about his results. "I worried about this all over Christmas, but I couldn't find any convincing way to get rid of them. In a way it was one of those accidental discoveries, like the discovery of penicillin."

Two things helped convince Hawking that particles really would come out of a black hole. One was that he figured out a way for it to happen, something his calculations couldn't tell him. The Heisenberg uncertainty principle taught that space never was really empty but was a fountain of creation, of birth and death, if you looked closely enough. Elementary particles such as electrons and their opposites, positrons, were continually being created out of borrowed energy in complementary pairs, strutting their fraction of a microsecond in space-time, then meeting and annihilating each other, paying back the borrowed energy which could come, say, from a strong gravitational field.

Near a black hole, one of the temporary particles could drift over the edge, however, and leave its mate behind. The latter would then be free to wander away from the black hole. To a faraway observer, it would appear to have just popped out of the black hole. The energy for the particle's existence, its mass, borrowed and not paid back, would have to come out of the mass-energy of the black hole, so this process would slowly reduce the mass of the black hole.

Hawking showed that the loss of energy owing to radiation would eventually deflate or "evaporate" a black hole. Someday it could explode, depending on the details of the structure of matter, like a 100-million-megaton bomb, in a shower of gamma rays and high-energy particles.

For ordinary—if that adjective applies to anything about black holes—stellar-mass black holes, the Hawking radiation process, as it came to be called, would be less than negligible. A hole the size of the sun would have a temperature of one ten-millionth of a degree above absolute zero and take 10^{66} years to evaporate, far longer than the age of the universe.

As black holes get smaller, though, the surface gravity and temperature skyrocket, and the lifetime shortens. One of Hawking's primordial mini black-holes, with a mass of a billion tons would be more than white hot, 120 million degrees hot, and spewing hard gamma rays. Any that formed at the beginning of the universe should be popping off about now.

Small black holes would in fact be indistinguishable from white holes, their time-reversed cousins. "White holes," he said, "will emit radiation at the same rate as black holes. I think there's only one entity. There are only holes. They appear black when they're big and white when they're small."

The most important thing about the Hawking radiation process is that it shows the black hole is not cut off from the rest of the universe. Hawking notes that it has many suggestive similarities with the big bang. You can regard the particles coming our of the black hole as coming from the singularity at the center. The singularity in the big bang might have behaved as ordinary black holes seem to.

Does an evaporating black hole leave behind a naked singularity? "That's what we all wonder, but my view is that a black hole completely evaporates, leaving behind just empty space."

It turns out that the radiation from a black, or white, hole has a special flavor of disorder about it, an unpredictability that goes one degree beyond the grudging uncertainty specified by quantum theory. Neither the velocity nor the position of outgoing particles could be predicted, because of the information that has been lost down the black hole. Any pattern of radiation consistent with our limited knowledge of what is in the hole—its mass, charge, and angular momentum—stands an equal chance of being emitted.

Black holes, it seems, are perfect entropy machines, perfect generators of chaos. Hawking attributes this to the singularity, and with characteristic style has named it the *principle of ignorance*: "God not only plays with dice. He sometimes throws them where they can't be seen."

Life has taken a strange turn for the man who rejected biology as too fuzzy and inexact. But he contends, "At least physics is inexact in a precisely defined way."

In another calculation, Hawking and Gibbons extended the Hawking radiation process to the case of an observer accelerating through a vacuum and found that reality began to diverge for differently accelerated observers or in very strong-graviational fields.

"Two different observers might even encounter different histories of the universe," they wrote in 1977. Hawking has hinted that the laws of physics themselves may be somewhat observer-dependent, a thought guaranteed to make Einstein wish he had taken up biology.

"I don't think there's one unique real universe," Hawking said when I asked him about this. "When you do quantum mechanics for the whole universe you encounter conceptual problems about what is meant by measurement. One possible viewpoint is what's called the Everett-Wheeler interpretation. According to quantum mechanics, if you make a measurement there are various possible results you can get, and each has a different probability. The Everett-Wheeler picture says that there are different branches of the universe, and each branch corresponds to a different possible result—parallel universes.

"Calling these things black holes was a masterstroke by Wheeler, because it does make a connection, or conjure up a lot of human neuroses," Hawking comments. "There is a psychological connection beweeen the naming of black holes and not the mathematical or physical idea but the popularization. They're named black holes because they do relate to human fears of being destroyed or gobbled up. They have played an important part in my career, but they don't have any psychological connection for me. I don't have fears of being thrown into them. I understand them; I feel in a sense that I'm their master." Hawking is not ready to be eaten.

In January of 1974, Sciama was back at Cambridge to organize a symposium. Rees came up to him, trembling and pale. "Have you heard? Stephen's changed everything!"

When is a black hole not black?

When it explodes.

Hawking's announcement at an Oxford symposium the next month that black holes would explode confounded and amazed his colleagues. Sciama called it one of the most beautiful papers in the history of physics. Hawking had found the first fragile link between the gravity that bends the universe and the quantum chaos that lives inside it. It might be the first step—even just a candle to light the first step—toward a unified theory of all the forces of nature.

• DISCUSSION QUESTIONS •

1. What lies behind the statement that all energy used on Earth can be traced to the Sun?

2. What is a black hole? What theories does Hawking propose about black holes? How do his theories fit with those in the Ferris article? Why are black hole theories difficult to comprehend?

3. How are the origin and evolution of life on Earth tied to the origin and evolution of the stars?

4. What are the characteristics of cosmic rays that prove beneficial to life? Where do they come from? How might life on Earth have evolved if cosmic-bombardment had been lighter?

5. Describe the stages in the evolution of stars that lead to a white dwarf, a supernova, a neutron star, and a black hole. What factors, in each case, lead to the particular death?

• ADDITIONAL ACTIVITIES •

Optional Projects

1. Write and sketch the stages through which hydrogen atoms synthesize into helium atoms in the core of a star.

2. Write the biography of our Sun from birth to death.

3. Develop an argument in favor of further research through use of X-ray telescope satellites.

Supplementary Bibliography

Isaac Asimov, *The Collapsing Universe*. New York: Walker and Company, 1977.
    Contains chapters on particles and forces, lives of stars, black holes, and quasars.

John N. Bahcall, "The Sun's Missing Particles" in *Natural History*, November, 1976.
    An account of the Brookhaven National Laboratory experiment on neutrinos and an analysis of the basic questions it raises.

Paul Davies, *The Runaway Universe*. London: J.M. Dent & Sons, 1978.
    Includes chapters on life cycles of stars, the Sun, deaths of stars, black holes.

George Gamow, "Mr. Tompkins Explores the Atom" from *Mr. Tompkins in Paperback*. London: Cambridge, 1967.
    An easy-to-understand explanation of atomic structure.

William Herbst, "Canis Major R1: A Stellar Nursery" in *Mercury*, July/August, 1979.
    How young stars just born in the star nursery in Canis Major are studied and why.

Fred Hoyle, "The Astrophysicist's Universe" from *Ten faces of the Universe*. San Francisco: W.H. Freeman and Company, 1977.
A concise account of the processes involved in stellar evolution.

William J. Kaufmann, III, *Astronomy: The Structure of the Universe*. New York: Macmillan Publishing Company, Inc., 1977.
Chapters on stellar evolution, white dwarfs and neutron stars.

Charles Mackay, "The Alchymists" from *Extraordinary Popular Delusions and the Madness of Crowds*. London: Richard Bentley, 1841.
A long chapter on alchemists throughout history—honest scientists and charlatans.

Harlow Shapley, *Of Stars and Men*. Boston: Beacon, 1964.
Another good explanation of stellar evolution.

Chapter X

THE EDGE OF FOREVER

• OVERVIEW •

IN RECENT DECADES we have discovered how the epic of the cosmic evolution began. We now know that our universe is expanding, a fact we can deduce from the observation that galaxies in all directions are rushing away from our own Milky Way galaxy—and from each other. Following this expansion backward in time, we infer that the universe must have been "born" about 20 billion years ago in a gigantic fireball we call the "Big Bang." Traces of the radiation from the Big Bang can still be detected today using radio telescopes.

It is now possible for scientists to study the history and future of the universe by studying the recession of very distant galaxies, which we observe at an earlier epoch when they were in a younger stage of evolution. The fate of our universe is linked to the curvature of space-time, which is determined by the density of matter. If the universe is dense enough, gravity will eventually stop the expansion, causing the universe to collapse once again. We do not know what would follow such collapse, but perhaps it will be followed by a successive Big Bang so that the universe will be continuously oscillating between expansion and contraction. If the universe does not have sufficient density to stop the contraction, it will continue forever, long after all the stars are extinguished and it becomes inert and lifeless. At the present, astronomers are not certain which is to be the universe's fate.

Our own galaxy was born about 10 billion years ago out of the primordial material left over from the fireball. The Milky Way is a spiral galaxy whose spiral pattern travels like a wave through the interstellar material, compacting this material and triggering the birth of stars. We live in a very average galaxy; even so, we detect energetic events in the galactic nucleus by the emission of radio waves and gamma rays, perhaps from a massive black hole residing there. This activity may be related to the much larger-scale activity in quasars, possibly the most distant and powerful objects in the universe.

• LEARNING OBJECTIVES •

1. Describe the evolution of the universe during the first stages of the Big Bang.

2. Describe "microwave background radiation" and explain its importance to our understanding of cosmology.

3. List and describe the different types of galaxies, comparing them specifically with our own galaxy, the Milky Way.

4. Describe the role of violent phenomena in the universe, focusing on the problems associated with the quasi-stellar objects (quasars). Cite other examples of violent phenomena from previous lessons.

5. Explain what is meant by the curvature of space-time. Describe our perception of four dimensions in terms of the characters in *Flatland*.

6. Describe how the fate of the universe, the curvature of space-time, and the density of the universe are related. Describe the possible types of universe that scientists have hypothesized and what the fate of each may be.

7. Describe the "Doppler effect" and how it has been used to study the structure and history of the universe.

8. Describe the Big Bang in the context of cultural myths about the creation.

• KEY TERMS AND NAMES •

Big Bang	Edwin Hubble
cosmic, or microwave,	Milton Humason
background radiation	isotropy
cosmology	quasar
Doppler effect	red shift
elliptical galaxy	ring galaxy
galaxy	spiral galaxy

• ASSIGNMENT •

Watch COSMOS television series Program 10, "The Edge of Forever."

Read Chapter 10, "The Edge of Forever," in Carl Sagan's text, *Cosmos*, or other readings assigned by your instructor.

• READINGS •

Martin Rees . . . . The Unfolding Universe

In the following selection, Martin Rees discusses the recent history of our ideas concerning the origin of the universe, emphasizing the advances in astronomy that have been made during the past 20 years. Dr. Rees is professor of astronomy at the Institute of Astronomy at Cambridge University in England.

The accelerated advance of astronomy in the past 20 years has been due primarily to the exploitation of new parts of the electro-magnetic spectrum—particularly the radio and X-ray bands. Our view of the cosmos is less biased and incomplete than it was when one could study only the objects which shine in visible light, and has led to the concepts of pulsars, quasars, neutron stars, black holes and the "big bang." Perhaps the most extraordinary development of all has been the emergence of cosmology as a genuine observational science: there is now a general consensus that the Universe evolved from a primordial state of high density, and events that might have occurred within the first minutes of cosmic history are within the accepted framework of serious scientific discussion.

The expansion of the Universe was discovered in the 1920s, and by 1956 there was a large body of evidence that the galaxies were receding from each other at speeds proportional to their distance. It also seemed that, broadly speaking, the Universe was uniform and homogeneous, and that our Galaxy was not in any privileged position. The most straightforward inference is that the Universe was in some sense smaller at earlier epochs, and that about 10 billion (10^{10}) years ago all the galaxies were compressed together. But the advocates of the "steady state" theory contested this conclusion: they argued that the large scale structure of the Universe could be the same at all times, continuous creation of new material (and new galaxies) maintaining the Universe at the same mean density despite the overall expansion.

To discriminate decisively between an evolving and steady state Universe, one must observe objects so far away that their radiation has taken several billion years on its journey towards us; and the obvious difficulty is that ordinary galaxies at these distances are almost undetectably faint even with the use of a 200-inch telescope.

The importance of radio astronomy for cosmology first became evident in 1954, when Cygnus A—one of the most prominent features of the radio sky—was identified with a distant galaxy. This suggested that many detectable radio sources were so far away that their optical counterparts would be invisibly faint, and therefore that the radio astronomer could perhaps probe deeper into space (and so further back into the past) than his optical colleagues. It was claimed in the late 1950s and 1960s that the relative number of faint (and presumably distant) radio sources was too high to be consistent with a steady state cosmology but indicated that the Universe was evolving: the number of powerful radio sources was higher in the past when the galaxies were younger.

Later developments have vindicated this interpretation, but the radio data are sufficiently ambiguous that the controversy might well have continued to the present day if no other corroborating evidence had emerged. But the consensus really swung towards acceptance of a "big bang" cosmology after the discovery (in 1965) of the 2.7 K *microwave background* radiation. This radiation is generally interpreted as a relic of an early epoch when all the material in the Universe was as hot, dense and opaque as the interior of a star—the "primordial fireball." No plausible alternative theory seems able to account for the observed isotropy (independence of direction), energy content, and spectral distribution of this radiation (which has now been observed by more than 20 groups at a wide range of wavelengths).

This development was fully as important for cosmology as the discovery of the universal expansion. By the end of the 1960s, almost all cosmologists had come to accept the idea that the background radiation was a genuine survivor from the very early stages of an evolving big bang Universe. (The shift in opinion was rather similar to the changing attitude of geophysicists towards continental drift during the same decade.)

The microwave photons detected on Earth have been propagating uninter-ruptedly through space for 99.99 percent of the time since the big bang—since long before galaxies could have existed in anything like their present form. The fact that the radiation apparently has the same temperatures in all directions with a preci-sion of one in 1000 provides direct evidence that the Universe on a large scale is ex-ceedingly homogeneous (it looks the same from all points) and isotropic (it looks the same in all directions for each point). This is a most remarkable cir-cumstance—one might have thought that a chaotic early Universe would have more degrees of freedom open to it, and thus in some sense be more likely. Thus uniformity restricts the admissible description on the Universe to a very limited range of mathematically calculable models. Were this not so, progress in cosmology would be almost inconceivable.

If one assumed that the Universe were isotropic and almost homogeneous right back to the very early times, and assumed also that Einstein's general relativity is applicable, it would be impossible to calculate the chemical composition of the material emerging from the big bang; and it is widely regarded as one of the tri-umphs of the theory that it enables us to predict that this material will be 25 percent helium and 75 percent hydrogen. The relevant nuclear reactions all occurred during the first 100 seconds or so of the explosion. This result is happily in accordance with present observations and solves a long-standing problem in theories of nucleogenesis: because, whereas the heavier elements can perhaps be adequately ex-plained by nucleosynthetic processes associated with stellar evolution, it was for a long while a problem to explain the high abundance and relative uniformity of helium.

WHEN QUASARS WERE NEARBY

The discovery in 1963 of the first quasars was another key step, for it enabled astronomers to observe objects with redshifts larger than the faintest detectable galaxies. If these redshifts were indeed due to the universal expansion, this implied that quasars were much more luminous than ordinary galaxies, and raised the hope that optical astronomers could use them to discriminate more successfully between rival cosmologies. However, the intrinsic brightness of the quasars seemed to vary a great deal and even now—when several hundred are known—they still cannot provide anything beyond crude statistical evidence.

The most dramatic inference from these studies is that the Universe is by no means in a steady state, but that the density of quasars and powerful radio sources would have been thousands of times higher than at the present time. At that epoch the Universe was less than a quarter of its present age. A hypothetical astronomer observing only two billion years after the big bang would perceive a vastly more active and dramatic environment: whereas our nearest bright quasar, 3C 273, is about 2000 million light years distant, he would be likely to find a similar object only 40 million light years away—50 times closer—and appearing as bright as a fourth magnitude star. This evidence is crucially important to our understanding of how galaxies form and evolve.

When quasars were discovered, they were regarded as something qualitatively quite different from anything hitherto known. There was thus a general readiness to consider that they might involve some kind of "new physics" or that their red-shifts might be due to something other than the universal expansion. This opinion has been repeatedly voiced by some astronomers, the controversy being fueled by regular claims of peculiar effects and anomalies: systematic periodicities in the red-shift distribution, physical association between quasars and nearby galaxies, and so on. Although the case for "anomalous redshifts" is still propounded, it cannot be said to have strengthened. Indeed the emphasis of the arguments seems to change year by year: the early anomalies or correlations are generally not borne out by analyses of newer and more extensive data (or even turn out to be mere artifacts); but new effects turn up to replace them. Nor do the various anomalies mesh together into any coherently-formulated alternative picture.

Probably even fewer astronomers would have accepted the idea that quasars were nearby if quasars had been discovered later than they were. We are now aware that many galactic nuclei contain non-stellar energy sources which seem to differ from quasars only in degree and not in kind. Such objects had been in-vestigated in 1963. Also, the discovery of neutron stars (in 1967) and, perhaps, of stellarmass black holes has familiarized astrophysicists with the idea that a compact object can be powered by gravitational energy, which can be more efficient than nuclear energy in converting rest-mass into non-stellar radiant energy.

An increasingly plausible hypothesis is that radio galaxies, Seyfert galaxies, and probably quasars as well, are varied manifestations of the same general kind of violent activity in galactic nuclei. Among the suggested models proposed to explain this general phenomenon are that one is seeing a rapid succession of super-nova-type explosions, resulting in the formation of a million Crab Nebulae almost in unison. Alternatively it has been speculated that a single magnetized supermassive spinning object may be involved, which accelerates particles rather like a giant pulsar. A third possibility is that a masive black hole lurks in the centre of these galaxies, which accretes gas from its surroundings rather like a scaled-up version of the X-ray source Cygnus X-1.

All these ideas invoke gravitation or gravitational contraction as the primary energy source. But it is still an entirely open question which of these three alter-natives (if any) is more likely to be correct. Our best observational line of attack on this problem will involve detailed optical studies of quasars and the variable central regions of active galaxies; and investigations of the structure of compact radio sources by the technique of very long baseline interferometry.

Accepting that the Universe exploded from an initial "big bang," one might wonder whether it will go on expanding forever. Or will the cosmic recession even-tually halt? If it does, it will be succeeded by a phase in which the galaxies draw closer to each other (displaying blue shifts instead of redshifts), until they eventu-ally collide and coalesce, their contents being finally engulfed in a universal fireball like the one from which they originally emerged.

In the simplest cosmological theories, where general relativity is assumed and the so-called "cosmical constant" is taken to be zero, the answer to this question just depends on the present average density of material in the Universe. If this ex-ceeds a critical density of about one atom per cubic metre, then the deceleration is sufficient to cause eventual recollapse: if the density is lower, gravitational effects can never halt the expansion.

The masses of individual galaxies are rather uncertain. (There is, for instance, a lively current debate about whether the bulk of a galaxy's mass may actually be in an extensive "halo" too faint to show up on ordinary photographs.) However, even if we allow for this possibility, and also include enough "missing mass" in clusters of galaxies to make them gravitationally bound, one still falls short of the critical density by a factor of about 10. Nor, apparently, can intergalactic gas con-tribute the "critical" density without producing absorption, or X-ray background emission, in excess of that observed. There might, however, be a lot of stuff in intercluster space in some even more elusive form than diffuse gas (for example massive black holes or neutrinos): absence of evidence need not be evidence of absence!

Indirect evidence for a low-density (or "open") Universe—one which will expand forever—comes from the recent discovery that deuterium (heavy hydrogen) exists in interstellar space. Ultraviolet observations have revealed it in atomic form, and radio astronomers have detected deuterated molecules in interstellar clouds. Deuterium, having a rather delicate nucleus, is destroyed (rather than synthesized) in ordinary stars. During the last few years, theorists have tried hard to think of ways of synthesizing deuterium. It turns out that deuterium can be formed in the big bang. However the amount that survives is (unlike the amount of helium) sensitive to the density; and only a "low density" big bang produces enough. So far, nobody has thought of a plausible way of making deuterium by current astrophysical processes. This may mean that the theorists have not been ingenious enough. On the other hand, it may be a genuine argument in favor of an "open" Universe. (However, there are, as in most cosmological arguments, some "escape clauses" which may appeal to those with an agoraphobic predilection for a closed Universe—for instance, the deuterium could be produced primordially to a "nonstandard" closed model if the missing mass took the form of small black holes which already existed at the epoch of element formation.)

Helium and deuterium are the only important substances (other than hydrogen) that are believed to be relics of the "primordial fireball." Other chemical elements are believed to have been synthesized in stars. All the carbon, oxygen, iron, and other elements on Earth may have been produced in stars, formed early in galactic history, which perhaps completed their lives by exploding as supernovae. The Solar System then condensed, several billion years after the Galaxy first formed, from material already contaminated by debris from such explosions.

Most of these ideas, and much of the relevant nuclear physics, had already been developed in the 1950s. The steady state theory actually provided a powerful impetus to these developments, because in this theory nucleosynthesis could not be relegated to a mysterious early epoch where conditions were different, but had to be going on in some present-day astrophysical environment. (Indeed, some people might regard the concept of stellar nucleosynthesis as the most constructive legacy of the steady state theory.)

HOW GALAXIES EVOLVED

Another major problem has been galactic evolution. How and when did galaxies condense from primordial material? How is their gas content converted into stars? As a galaxy ages, how does it change its size and shape? What factors determine whether a protogalaxy becomes a spiral or an elliptical galaxy? Perhaps the major goal of optical and ultraviolet astronomy in the next decade will be to probe as deep as possible into space and accumulate data on all types of galaxies at various redshifts. By 1980 improved ground-based optical telescopes, the large space telescope, and X-ray telescopes should be contributing valuably to these studies by looking to greater distances and detecting emission from hot uncondensed gas in clusters of galaxies, and quasars at large redshifts.

Theorists hope that the physical principles governing the gross properties of galaxies will soon be understood to the same extent that we now understand the properties of individual stars. One would hope also to understand what makes the nuclei of galaxies (particularly young galaxies) undergo the violent activity which manifests itself in quasars, radio outbursts and the like.

The existence of galaxies implies that the early Universe cannot have been completely smooth, but must have contained some irregularities. Regions of slightly enhanced density, suffering an above-average deceleration, would eventually condense out from the expanding background. Many theorists have attacked this subject in recent years. Higher-precision observation of the microwave background radiation could reveal velocity perturbations at pregalactic epochs and thereby yield important clues. The goal of these studies is to understand the evolution from primordial fluctuations to galaxies like our own, without having to fall back too often to the statement "things are as they are because they were as they were."

It is now over 60 years since the general theory of relativity was enunciated, and the various "expanding Universe" solutions of Einstein's equations were already very familiar in the 1950s. But the prospects of discriminating between different cosmological theories were then dim; and Newtonian theory seemed almost entirely adequate for describing the dynamics and equilibrium of stars and galaxies. Relativity theory was then regarded as a rather stagnant topic—a glaring contrast with its present status as one of the liveliest frontiers of fundamental research.

There are several reasons for this renaissance in gravitational physics. It stems partly from the utilization of new mathematical techniques, which would have revived interest in the theory even if there had been no hope of confrontation with observation. But it has also been stimulated by the accelerated progress of observational cosmology, and by the realization that objects where relativistic effects are large—neutron stars and black holes—may actually exist.

In the short run, the most useful tests of gravitational theories may well come from high-precision experiments—radio interferometry, planetary radar, and so on—in the Solar System, even though there the relativistic effects are very small. Already these experiments are precise enough to exclude most of the rival theories; and to confirm general relativity, at least in the so-called post-Newtonian approximation, with a precision of a few percent. But to study situations where gravity is overwhelmingly strong, one must look farther afield—to possible black holes, and to the big bang itself.

Nevertheless even now the astrophysical uncertainties are so great that one cannot, from observations of galaxies and quasars, decide whether or not the Universe is expanding in accordance with general relativity. However the primordial helium abundance is sensitive to the expansion rate of the early Universe which in turn depends on the assumed theory of gravity. In some alternative theories the helium abundance at least lends some support to a general relativistic Universe.

If one takes the big bang seriously, there is no reason for stopping our backward extrapolation at the time of helium formation, when the "age of the Universe" was about 100 seconds. The primordial material would have attained nuclear densities about 10 millionths of a second after the big bang. Before this time the densities and pressures are so extreme that the behavior of matter is sensitive to current uncertainties in elementary particle physics. But if, as perhaps we should, we envisage time on a logarithmic scale, to ignore the first 10^{-5} seconds would seem a severe omission indeed!

The early stages of the big bang are in many senses analogous to the time-reversal of gravitational collapse into the black hole (and to the fate that will overtake everything if the Universe is destined to recollapse), and relativity theory predicts that the densities and space curvatures should become arbitrarily high as we approach close to the initial instant $t=0$. When the space curvature becomes sufficiently great (the first 10^{-23} seconds) it is believed that particle pairs can be created out of gravitational pairs in strong electromagnetic fields. When the curvatures reach even more extreme values (10^{-43} seconds) it is accepted that Einstein's theory cannot be an adequate description and that a full-blown theory of quantum gravity is required.

When a stellar mass object collapses to become a black hole the regions of such extreme space curvature are deep inside the horizon at the Schwarzchild radius, shrouded from view. But this is not so for the big bang, where there is, in principle, a causal chain extending right back to the "singularity." Many relativists believe that the global isotropy and homogeneity of the Universe, a much more puzzling feature than the existence of the small amplitude fluctuations which develop into galaxies, is imposed by quantum gravitational effects at the very earliest times. This is one of the motivations for the current interest in quantum effects and pair creation in curved space-time: an important and hopeful step towards a full theory of quantum gravity.

We also know that the big bang was "hot"—which means more precisely that the photons comprising the primordial radiation outnumbered the ordinary particles (protons, neutrons, and so on) by a factor of about one hundred million. There is still no satisfactory explanation of this number (or, equivalently, for the high entropy of the Universe), and it would be a great step forward if its value could be understood.

Some physicists have been attracted to the idea that the Universe as a whole may be symmetric between matter and antimatter. In the very hot initial instants of the big bang, protons, antiprotons, and so on would exist in profusion. But they would tend to annihilate as the Universe cooled down, and the problem with this idea is to explain why any particles survive, and why the Universe is not now almost pure radiation.

TWENTY YEARS ON

In the past 20 years, new observational techniques have revealed a greater range and richness of cosmic phenomena than had hitherto been suspected. The discoveries have often been made by people who would not call themselves astronomers in the traditional sense, using techniques developed primarily for other practical goals. Indeed, the constricting artificiality of the traditional sub-disciplinary boundaries within astronomy and space science is now generally recognized. More and more observational programs now involve coordinated studies in different wavebands. Also, the remarkable interdependence of cosmic processes is now appreciated. For instance, the abundance and distribution of chemical elements within the Solar System was partly determined by processes occurring throughout the early evolution of the whole Galaxy. And, on more fundamental levels, some theorists suspect that the properties of elementary particles—and indeed many key features to the everyday world—are somehow determined by what happened in the initial instants of the "big bang."

Most physicists now recognize the importance of exploiting the "cosmic laboratory" to study the properties of matter under conditions too extreme to be simulated terrestrially: the densities in neutron stars and the big bang; the magnetic field strengths of pulsars; the energies of particles in cosmic rays; and the properties of the plasma in radio galaxies. Astrophysicists attempting to interpret cosmic phenomena find themselves faced with problems whose solution demands the combined efforts of physicists spanning an increasngly broad range of expertise.

One would like to be able to predict what astronomical advances will be achieved in the next 20 years. But experience warns us against doing this, because the main payoff and vindication of past projects—ground-based and space research alike—has usually lain in the entirely unforseen new phenomena that they have revealed. It may be that the next few years will see fewer complete surprises: after all, we have now had at least a glimpse of the sky over essentially the whole electromagnetic spectrum. The initial exploratory phase may then be succeeded by a period of consolidation, detailed studies, and model building, in which the more leisured pace of novel discoveries allows theorists to catch up! However the newer techniques, particularly the infrared, and those utilizing space techniques, are still in the pioneering stages when order-of-magnitude improvements are feasible within a decade. (And the optimists may hope soon to exploit non-electromagnetic channels of information such as neutrinos and gravitational waves.)

Timothy Ferris . . . . Crucibles of the Cosmos

Science writer Timothy Ferris describes how astronomers are discovering unexpected activity in galaxies that may soon yield answers to important questions about the size, age, and rate of expansion of the universe.

Dr. Allan Sandage sat up late one night recently at the Kitt Peak National Observatory in Arizona exposing photographic plates on the giant four-meter telescope and talking about galaxies. It was a dark, motionless night. It always is when Sandage is to be found observing, for his interests lie with starlight that has been journeying in space for millions of years and arrives in so feeble a condition that it can be analyzed and recorded properly only by the dark of the moon. Sandage is one of the blue-water sailors among astronomers.

The sky over Kitt Peak was full of stars. Sandage could see none of them. He was sealed in an observer's cage suspended within the telescope tube high above the observatory floor, his vista of the cosmos limited to its close black walls and to a single blob of light in the eyepiece that he scrutinized to assure himself that the telescope was tracking correctly while the plate was exposed. The plate is what matters in viewing galaxies. The human eye is insufficiently sensitive to view galaxies in detail and deep-space astronomers rarely *look* at them through telescopes. Nor do they spend much time admiring the resulting photographs, though galaxies are indisputably beautiful and I have seen an ordinarily sober astronomer jump up and down with excitement at a photograph of a particularly striking one. Instead, they analyze the plates, counting and measuring thousands of star images on them, seeking to discern the anatomy of these cities of stars. As to the stars in the Arizona sky, Sandage appreciates their spectacle as do the rest of us, but he finds them rather . . . local. Astronomers like Sandage enjoy gazing at them casually but find them of such peripheral concern that many never bother to learn the constellations. Some would have trouble locating the Big Dipper. These stars are our neighbors. They crowd the foreground like leaves in a celestial tree that makes up the Milky Way galaxy. The deep-space astronomers are interested in peering out beyond, to the other galaxies. "Trees aren't important when you're interested in the forest," Sandage said over the intercom from the observer's cage. By "forest," he meant the universe.

Now astronomers are finding that galaxies are stranger than anyone had expected. Nesting in them may be creatures as provocative as black holes feeding on stars, and quasars, pouring out power with a vigor that astonishes physicists. They are enormous physical laboratories: by better understanding what goes on inside them, astronomers expect to gain fresh insights into the age, size and dimensions of the universe.

A team of researchers including Wallace Sargent of the Hale Observatories in Pasadena and C. R. Lynds of Kitt Peak recently found what they believe to be a huge black hole in the nucleus of the massive galaxy M-87, making the galaxy resemble a sort of cosmic sink with an infinitely deep drain in its center. Earlier this year, astronomer Donald Hall of Kitt Peak, studying how stars form in galaxies, discovered a star so young that it has been shining, in Hall's estimate, only since Homeric times, a mere instant in astronomical terms. A host of investigators in galactic dynamics, among them Beatrice Tinsley and Richard Larson of Yale University, James Gunn of Cal Tech, and the veteran observer Halton Arp of the Hale Observatories, are finding that galaxies undergo startling transformations. Big galaxies swallow little ones. Galaxies collide. Some, it appears, explode. Some dance grand passacaglias, swapping stars by the millions. These transformations are less violent than they sound—we who are riding aboard a galaxy need worry little more about them than Jonah worried about the perambulations of the whale—but they add up to a picture of a universe in evolution, in whose story our own evolution plays a part.

It is beginning to look as if we are deeply connected with our cosmic surroundings, like birds perched in a galactic tree, our lives involved with the fortunes of the starry forest. Some of these connections may dictate matters as mundane as the weather. Several British astronomers, among them Sir Fred Hoyle, R. A. Lyttleton and William McCrea, suggest that the Ice Ages may have been triggered by the solar system's having passed through a cloud of dust and gas associated with one of our galaxy's spiral arms. A Colorado physicist, Lars Wahlin, has proposed that lightning bolts, those symbols of the caprice of fate, may be produced by cosmic rays—particles accelerated through interstellar space by our galaxy's magnetic field. If Wahlin is right, then the old commonplace is true, and lightning bolts really are, in a sense, dispatched from heaven.

Still deeper connections between ourselves and the galaxies are being discerned. Astrophysicists studying the chemical composition of stars, and biologists investigating the chemical composition of our bodies, have found that we are made up of much the same allotment of elements as is our galaxy: The metals found in trace elements in our bodies appear to have been formed in the explosions of stars that died before the sun was born, seeding space with the metal-rich dust and gas from which our solar system and, eventually, ourselves were formed.

The story of galaxies is beginning to reveal itself to a new generation of astronomers, as well as to their elders, through the eyes and ears of new astronomical tools. X-ray satellites have made it possible to study the tenuous intergalactic gas through which galaxies pass, permitting analysis of how entire clusters of galaxies behave. Ultraviolet sensors, working in realms of the spectrum beyond the range of the human eye, have yielded clues to the puzzling quasars, which may represent galaxies in their early stages of development, shimmering with light that started on its voyage to our telescopes billions of years ago. Researchers aided by computer simulation techniques are taking steps toward cracking the highly complicated problem of how galaxies herded their billions of stars together in the first place. Says Gunn: "We've only just started looking at galaxies in analytical ways, but I have every faith that some real understanding will be reached and that it won't take terribly long. Tremendous effort is being dedicated to it." And Sandage, as we talked, said, "We see the story of the evolution of galaxies coming to a head in a remarkable way. Problems that had seemed impossible to understand are yielding, and a general picture of sorts is emerging. The subject is going to be very lively in the next few years."

The astronomers who know galaxies best tend to be careful in choosing their words about them. They are mindful of the contrast between the grand reality of the galaxies and the elementary nature of our understanding of them. Sandage, who in the estimation of many colleagues possesses the most accomplished mental picture of galaxies of any man alive, can be circumspect in the extreme. Sometimes he begins a conversation by denying he knows anything at all, a characteristically scientific sort of defense, the social equivalent of calibrating all meters to zero. That is what happened when I appeared at Kitt Peak and announced myself through the intercom.

"I don't work on galaxies anymore," said Sandage from his perch up in the dark. "I gave it up."

The night assistant sitting beside me grinned and pointed to the coordinates glowing in ruby numbers on the control console. They indicated that Sandage was photographing M-81, a spiral galaxy six and a half million light-years away.

"That looks like M-81 you're on now, Allan," I said.

"Oh, well, it's not a big galaxy. Only 90 billion stars."

"The residents of M-81 might not be pleased to hear that. It's a beautiful galaxy."

"Yes. You know, beauty in galaxies appreciates according to their mass. The more stars a galaxy has, the prettier its spiral arms."

We talked through the night. Like a guide spotting fishing holes, Sandage can show you where in a galaxy to find nurseries churning out young stars, or retirement homes of old stars nearly spent, or slowly winking variable stars that will help you chart the galaxy's distance. He is familiar with giant elliptical galaxies larger than our Milky Way, with paltry irregular galaxies that look like little more than thimblefuls of sand, with spirals of elegant beauty and galaxies whose eventful past has left them tattered. He can show you two spiral galaxies cocked to each other like an open pocket watch, and note that in such pairs, the two spiral in opposite directions. (Our own galaxy and the great spiral in Andromeda form such a pair.) "Galaxies are what they are," Sandage said, quoting a Zenlike remark of his mentor Edwin Hubble, one of the discoverers of the expansion of the universe. "You try to learn from them."

Sandage searches for similarities in galaxies seeking to improve our estimates of the dimensions of the universe and the rate at which it is expanding; these numbers in turn ought to yield a prediction of the fate of the universe—whether expansion will go on forever. The approach stands in contrast to that of some younger researchers whose curiosity leads them to be concerned more with individual galaxies—how they formed and why they look the way they do. Many are physicists rather than astronomers. "We who came into the field from physics are not so much grand builders," says Wallace Sargent, a physicist at Cal Tech. ("Grand builder" in astronomical circles is more or less a code name for Sandage.) "The big picture is far too uncertain as yet. We tend more toward being explorers, toward looking for an interesting particular problem and going after it. We look for galaxies whose stars are bluer than average, or redder, or fainter than average, and try to see what the hell is going on there." A colleague put it more baldly and less seriously: "We physicists are opportunists."

Recently several of the physicists have been looking into the question of why some galaxies seem to be producing no new stars. In a "healthy" galaxy like ours, new stars form with regularity, but some spirals appear to have closed up their star-making shops long ago; they contain only old stars. Our sun is itself a relatively young star. Had our galaxy stopped forming stars six billion years or more ago, we wouldn't be here to ask why. Two young Kitt Peak astronomers, Karen and Stephen Strom, suggest that the "unhealthy" galaxies may have suffered collisions with other galaxies or with clouds of intergalactic gas, collisions that swept them clean of the dust and gas they needed to make more stars. The Stroms and others have found evidence that "unhealthy" galaxies tend to be found in the crowded inner regions of galaxy clusters, where collisions would be most likely.

The question would be interesting to residents of an "unhealthy" galaxy if they were interested in developing technology, because metals apparently are available only to inhabitants of planets of younger-generation stars. According to this theory, widely accepted in astrophysics, metals are forged in the explosions of dying stars, which seed the interstellar medium with heavy elements that in turn condense to form new stars and planets. In galaxies where star formation ceased before the metals seeded space, all the planets would be metal-poor. Astronomers there, studying the skies with telescopes formed of bamboo or lignum vitae or whatever other light materials had been left them by their cosmic fortunes, presumably would ask themselves the same sorts of questions the Stroms are asking here: Why do galaxies turn out differently from one another? Says Stephen Strom, "We're trying to unravel what might be called the genetics of galaxies, their evolutionary processes."

One obstacle has been that galaxies conduct their affairs over such long periods of time that on a human time scale they appear frozen. If you want to know whether hawks nest on a particular cliff you can sit in a blind for a month or two and see if any hawks show up. But if you want to see two galaxies interact as they pass each other, you'll have to wait a few hundred million years, and that is more than even the most patient astronomers can manage. Recently scientists at several institutions have employed computer simulations to look into the past and future of galaxies. The computers are programmed with data on the mass and size and relative locations of galaxies. Then the programs are run to recreate events that took eons to unfold.

A pioneer in this endeavor, Alan Toomre, showed me a computer-generated film one afternoon in a darkened office at M.I.T. The subjects were M-51, a lovely spiral galaxy, and a small nearby irregular designated NGC 5195. The symmetry of M-51 is broken by one distended arm that reaches out toward the smaller galaxy; astronomers had wondered just what was going on there. Toomre's film appears to have solved the riddle.

Toomre started the film at a point millions of years ago. As the milleniums sped by (a counter in the corner off the screen, calibrated in millions of years, flickered faster than the eye could follow), the two galaxies churned across space toward each other. At first they looked as unperturbed as strangers approaching on a city street. Then their gravity began to make itself felt as the space between them narrowed. Each galaxy contorted like the face of a man who has been punched in the stomach. Their arms, each home to billions of stars, waved like tentacles, reached out almost to touch—and the film froze. We were at the present.

The computer rotated the model in one dimension, and we were treated to the sight, unprecedented on earth, of how a couple of galaxies look from another perspective. If Toomre's film is correct the two galaxies have experienced their nearest encounter and NGC 5195 is continuing off into space, followed by one beseeching arm of M-51. A few million stars have been left homeless by the episode. They now ride alone in intergalactic space. If astronomers evolve there one day, they might, by recourse to the sort of analysis Toomre has applied, learn how they came to find themselves dwelling under starless skies drifting between two galaxies and claimed by neither.

Computer analysis by Toomre, Roger Lynds of Kitt Peak and others had enjoyed at least preliminary success in explaining the curious ring galaxies. Dozens of these puzzling objects have been found, each resembling a smoke ring. the computer studies suggest that ring galaxies are formed when a smaller galaxy passes through the center of a large one, punching a hole in it. And indeed, near every known ring galaxy is found a smaller galaxy, slinking away from the scene of the accident.

Galaxies are mostly space, and collisions between them may take place with few if any stars running into each other. The exceptions to this rule are the nuclei of galaxies, their centers, the Grand Central Terminals of stars. What goes on there is not yet well understood. Some galaxies emit considerable light and natural radio noise from their nuclei, and our own galaxy's core rumbles a bit in radio wavelengths. (Intervening dust clouds prevent our seeing the center of the Milky Way galaxy in visual light, but radio telescopes can "see" it.) A number of astronomers and physicists are interested in galactic nuclei, not least because what goes on there may tell us something about two of the most provocative subjects of modern astronomy, black holes and quasars.

Black holes were predicted indirectly by that cornucopia of gravity physics, Einstein's theory of general relativity. The theory implies that if mass is concentrated to a high enough density—as in the case of a giant collapsed star—its gravitation will be so intense that nothing, not even its own light, can escape from it. In Einsteinian terms, the black hole occupies a well in space-time whose sides are so steep that radiation cannot "climb out." Most theorists today take seriously the possibility that black holes exist, but actually finding one poses difficulties, as black holes are invisible. A black hole swallowing up gas from an interstellar cloud, or tearing it off the surface of a nearby star, might betray its presence by a sort of scream released by the doomed gas. Calculations show that the scream ought to be detectable in the zone of the electromagnetic spectrum known as X-rays, and observations of X-ray satellites have revealed several such sources that may signal the presence of genuine black holes.

Quasars, discovered by Sandage in 1960, appear to be very remote objects glowing with furious brightness. They are so bright that astrophysicists have trouble imagining how they turn out so much energy. One popular speculation is that they represent the nuclei of young galaxies, where the collapse of gas clouds formed massive black holes; their intense energy would result from tormented dust and gas heated as it spins into the black hole. More than one hypothesis urges that stars, too, are consumed by black holes at the center of these galaxies. Some quasars flicker; this might signal that they are gorging themselves on stars. "It would be quite a sight," says one physicist, "stars spiraling down into the hole like bowling balls, first dismembered and then disappearing in sheets of light."

Virtually all quasars lie at distances of a billion light-years or more, meaning that it has taken their light a billion years or more to reach us, so we are seeing a feature of the universe as it was that long ago. No quasars are known to exist in the modern universe. But some relativly nearby galaxies exhibit signs of lingering violence at their centers, like the thunder in a subsiding storm. If these nuclei once were quasars, and if the black hole concept of quasars is correct, we should find black holes at the nuclei of many galaxies today. With this in mind, astronomers in the United States and England recently examined two large galaxies, whose great mass makes them likely candidates, and found evidence of giant black holes sitting in the nucleus of each. Observations by an orbiting space telescope, scheduled for launch in 1982, should help decide the matter.

An alternative to looking for relics of ancient cosmic violence is to search out galaxies still in their birth throes. The more conspicuous galaxies, ours among them, were born billions of years ago and seem to have settled into calm middle age, but young galaxies may yet be condensing out of raw dust and gas, their violent adolescence still in the future. Looking for them will take time—the number of available telescopes is small, galaxies are strewn across the sky like beach sand, and the very young ones are likely to be dim—but astronomer R. B. Larson of Yale calls it "the most intriguing and perhaps most promising possibility" in the field.

At Kitt Peak, Sandage and I talked on past midnight. His voice grew weary.

"I don't know what I'm accomplishing here, letting starlight put marks on a silver nitrate photographic plate," he said with a sigh. "But it sure looks pretty. I don't know why people have to try to do what they couldn't do before. I don't know what it's all about. All I know is that I feel awful bad if I don't keep working."

At 1 A.M. Sandage had exposed all the plates in the observer's cage. He ordered the telescope tilted down to the floor so he could reload with fresh film to keep him supplied till dawn. In the dark interior of the dome I watched the telescope heel over and down until the observer's cage reached a white steel scaffold. A door in the cage opened, spilling red night-vision light. Sandage's booted feet emerged. He climbed out, a case of plates under his arm. We shook hands. "This will take about 10 minutes," he told the night assistant. He hurried toward the darkroom to reload the plates. He did not quite run.

Edwin A. Abbott . . . . Flatland

In the following excerpts from the classic science fiction tale Flatland, *written by a Shakespearean scholar some 20 years before Einstein published his special theory of relativity, we are introduced to the basic concepts of relativity and multiple dimensions of space. In the first part of the selection, we learn about the physical characteristics of Flatland, its social hierarchy, and how its inhabitants live and interact. In the intervening sections, not included here, the narrator and central character of the story (a square) is visited by what he perceives to be a sphere-like creature who claims to come from a three-dimensional world called "Space." In the second part of the selection, the disbelieving square is finally convinced of the existence of other dimensions when he accompanies the sphere on a guided tour of the third dimension.* Flatland *was first published in the 1880s.*

Part I

OF THE NATURE OF FLATLAND

I call our world Flatland, not because we call it so, but to make its nature clearer to you, my happy readers, who are privileged to live in Space.

Imagine a vast sheet of paper on which straight Lines, Triangles, Squares, Pentagons, Hexagons, and other figures, instead of remaining fixed in their places, move freely about, on or in the surface, but without the power of rising above or sinking below it, very much like shadows—only hard and with luminous edges—and you will then have a pretty correct notion of my country and countrymen. Alas, a few years ago, I should have said "my universe": but now my mind has been opened to higher views of things.

In such a country, you will perceive at once that it is impossible that there should be anything of what you call a "solid" kind; but I dare say you will suppose that we could at least distinguish by sight the Triangles, Squares, and other figures, moving about as I have described them. On the contrary, we could see nothing of the kind, not at least so as to distinguish one figure from another. Nothing was visible, nor could be visible, to us, except Straight Lines; and the necessity of this I will speedily demonstrate.

Place a penny on the middle of one of your tables in Space; and leaning over it, look down upon it. It will appear a circle.

But now, drawing back to the edge of the table, gradually lower your eye (thus bringing yourself more and more into the condition of the inhabitants of Flatland), and you will find the penny becoming more and more oval to your view; and at last when you have placed your eye exactly on the edge of the table (so that you are, as it were, actually a Flatlander) the penny will then have ceased to appear oval at all, and will have become, so far as you can see, a straight line.

The same thing would happen if you were to treat in the same way a Triangle, or Square, or any other figure cut out of pasteboard. As soon as you look at it with your eye on the edge on the table, you will find that it ceases to appear to you a figure, and that it becomes in appearance a straight line. Take for example an equilateral Triangle—who represents with us a Tradesman of the respectable class. Fig. 1 represents the Tradesman as you would see him while you were bending over him from above; figs. 2 and 3 represent the Tradesman as you would see him if your eye were close to the level, or all but on the level of the table; and if your eye were quite on the level of the table (and that is how we see him in Flatland) you would see nothing but a straight line.

When I was in Spaceland I heard that your sailors have very similar experiences while they traverse your seas and discern some distant island or coast lying on the horizon. The far-off land may have bays, forelands, angles in and out to any number and extent; yet at a distance you see none of these (unless indeed your sun shines bright upon them revealing the projections and retirements by means of light and shade), nothing but a grey unbroken line upon the water.

Well, that is just what we see when one of our triangular or other acquaintances comes toward us in Flatland. As there is neither sun with us, nor any light of such a kind as to make shadows, we have none of the helps to the sight that you have in Spaceland. If our friend comes closer to us we see his line becomes larger; if he leaves us it becomes smaller: but still he looks like a straight line; be he a Triangle, Square, Pentagon, Hexagon, Circle, what you will—a straight Line he looks and nothing else.

You may perhaps ask how under these disadvantageous circumstances we are able to distinguish our friends from one another: but the answer to this very natural question will be more fitly and easily given when I come to describe the inhabitants of Flatland. For the present let me defer this subject, and say a word or two about the climate and houses in our country.

OF THE CLIMATE AND HOUSES IN FLATLAND

As with you, so also with us, there are four points of the compass North, South, East, and West.

There being no sun nor other heavenly bodies, it is impossible for us to determine the North in the usual way; but we have a method of our own. By a Law of Nature with us, there is a constant attraction to the South; and, although in temperate climates this is very slight—so that even a Woman in reasonable health can journey several furlongs northward without much difficulty—yet the hampering effect of the southward attraction is quite sufficient to serve as a compass in most parts of our earth. Moreover, the rain (which falls at stated intervals) coming always from the North, is an additional assistance; and in the towns we have the guidance of the houses, which of course have their side-walls running for the most part North and South, so that the roofs may keep off the rain from the North. In the country, where there are no houses, the trunks of the trees serve as some sort of guide. Altogether, we have not so much difficulty as might be expected in determining our bearings.

Yet in our more temperate regions, in which the southward attraction is hardly felt, walking sometimes in a perfectly desolate plain where there have been no houses nor trees to guide me, I have been occasionally compelled to remain stationary for hours together, waiting till the rain came before continuing my journey. On the weak and aged, and especially on delicate Females, the force of attraction tells much more heavily than on the robust of the Male Sex, so that it is a point of breeding, if you meet a Lady in the street, always to give her the North side of the way—by no means an easy thing to do always at short notice when you are in rude health and in a climate where it is difficult to tell your North from your South.

Windows there are none in our houses: for the light comes to us alike in our homes and out of them, by day and by night, equally at all times and in all places, whence we know not. It was in old days, with our learned men, an interesting and oft-investigated question, "What is the origin of light?" and the solution of it has been repeatedly attempted, with no result than to crowd our lunatic asylums with the would-be solvers. Hence, after fruitless attempts to suppress such investigations indirectly by making them liable to a heavy tax, the Legislature, in comparatively recent times, absolutely prohibited them. I—alas, I alone in Flatland—know now only too well the true solution of this mysterious problem; but my knowledge cannot be made intelligible to a single one of my countrymen; and I am mocked at—I, the sole possessor of the truths of Space and of the theory of the introduction of Light from the world of three Dimensions—as if I were the maddest of the mad! But a truce to these painful digressions: let me return to our houses.

The most common form for the construction of a house is five-sided or pentagonal, as in the annexed figure. The two Northern sides RO, OF, constitute the roof, and for the most part have no doors; on the East is a small door for the Women; on the West a much larger one for the Men; the South side or floor is usually doorless.

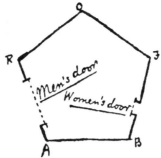

Square and triangular houses are not allowed, and for this reason. The angles of a Square (and still more those of an equilateral Triangle), being much more pointed than those of a Pentagon, and the lines of inanimate objects (such as houses) being dimmer than the lines of Men and Women, it follows that there is no little danger lest the points of a square or triangular house residence might do serious injury to an inconsiderate or perhaps absent-minded traveller suddenly therefore running against them . . .

CONCERNING THE INHABITANTS OF FLATLAND

The greatest length or breadth of a full grown inhabitant of Flatland may be estimated at about eleven of your inches. Twelve inches may be regarded as a maximum.

Our Women are Straight Lines.

Our Soldiers and Lowest Classes of Workmen are Triangles with two equal sides, each about eleven inches long, and a base or third side so short (often not exceeding half an inch) that they form at their vertices a very sharp and formidable angle. Indeed when their bases are of the most degraded type (not more than the eighth part of an inch in size), they can hardly be distinguished from Straight Lines or Women; so extremely pointed are their vertices. With us, as with you, these Triangles are distinguished from others by being called Isosceles; and by this name I shall refer to them in the following pages.

Our Middle Class consists of Equilateral or Equal-Sided Triangles.

Our Professional Men and Gentlemen are Squares (to which class I myself belong) and Five-Sided Figures or Pentagons.

Next above these come the Nobility, of whom there are several degrees, beginning at Six-Sided Figures, or Hexagons, and from thence rising in the number of their sides till they receive the honourable title of Polygonal, or many-sided. Finally when the number of the sides becomes so numerous, and the sides themselves to small, that the figure cannot be distinguished from a circle he is included in the Circular or Priestly order: and this is the highest class of all. . . .

Part II

HOW THE SPHERE, HAVING IN VAIN TRIED WORDS, RESORTED TO DEEDS

I brought my hardest right angle into violent collision with the stranger, pressing on him with a force sufficient to have destroyed any ordinary Circle: but

I could feel him slowly and unarrestably slipping from my contact; no edging to the right nor to the left, but moving somehow out of the world, and vanishing to nothing. Soon there was a blank. But still I heard the Intruder's voice.

Sphere. Why will you refuse to listen to reason? I had hoped to find in you—as being a man of sense and an accomplished mathematician—a fit apostle for the Gospel of the Three Dimensions, which I am allowed to preach once only in a thousand years: but now I know not how to convince you. Stay, I have it. Deeds, and not words, shall proclaim the truth. Listen, my friend.

I have told you I can see from my position in Space the inside of all things that you consider closed. For example, I see in yonder cupboard near which you are standing, several of what you call boxes (but everything else in Flatland, they have no tops nor bottoms) full of money; I see also two tablets of accounts. I am about to descend into that cupboard and to bring you one of those tablets. I saw you lock the cupboard half an hour ago, and I know you have the key in your possession. But I descend from Space; the doors, you see, remain unmoved. Now I am in the cupboard and am taking the tablet. Now I have it. Now I ascend with it.

I rushed to the closet and dashed the door open. One of the tablets was gone. With a mocking laugh, the Stranger appeared in the other corner of the room, and at the same time the tablet appeared upon the floor. I took it up. There could be no doubt—it was the missing tablet.

I groaned with horror, doubting whether I was not out of my senses; but the Stranger continued: "Surely you must now see that my explanation, and no other, suits the phenomena. What you call Solid things are really superficial; what you call Space is really nothing but a great Plane. I am in Space, and look down upon the insides of the things of which you only see the outsides. You could leave this Plane yourself, if you could but summon up the necessary volition. A slight upward or downward motion would enable you to see all that I can see.

"The higher I mount, and the further I go from your Plane, the more I can see, though of course I see it on a smaller scale. For example, I am ascending; now I can see your neighbour the Hexagon and his family in their several apartments; now I see the inside of the Theatre, ten doors off, from which the audience is only just departing; and on the other side a Circle in his study, sitting at his books. Now I shall come back to you. And, as a crowning proof, what do you say to my giving you a touch, just the least touch, in your stomach? It will not seriously injure you, and the slight pain you may suffer cannot be compared with the mental benefit you will receive."

Before I could utter a word of remonstrance, I felt a shooting pain in my inside, and a demoniacal laugh seemed to issue from within me. A moment afterwards the sharp agony had ceased, leaving nothing but a dull ache behind, and the Stranger began to reappear, saying, as he gradually increased in size, "There, I have not hurt you much, have I? If you are not convinced now, I don't know what will convince you. What say you?"

My resolution was taken. It seemed intolerable that I should endure existence subject to the arbitrary visitations of a Magician who could thus play tricks with one's very stomach. If only I could in any way manage to pin him against the wall till help came!

Once more I dashed my hardest angle against him, at the same time alarming the whole household by my cries for aid. I believe, at the moment of my onset, the Stranger had sunk below our Plane, and really found difficulty in rising. In any case he remained motionless, while I hearing, as I thought, the sound of some help approaching, pressed against him with redoubled vigour, and continued to shout for assistance.

A convulsive shudder ran through the Sphere. "This must not be," I thought I heard him say: "either he must listen to reason, or I must have recourse to the last resource of civilization." Then, addressing me in a louder tone, he hurriedly exclaimed, "Listen: no stranger must witness what you have witnessed. Send your Wife back at once, before she enters the apartment. The Gospel of Three Dimensions must not be thus frustrated. Not thus must the fruits of one thousand years of waiting be thrown away. I hear her coming. Back! back! Away from me, or you must go with me—whither you know not—into the Land of Three Dimensions!"

"Fool! Madman! Irregular!" I exclaimed; "never will I release thee; thou shalt pay the penalty of thine impostures."

"Ha! Is it come to this?" thundered the Stranger: "then meet your fate: out of your Plane you go. Once, twice, thrice! 'Tis done!"

HOW I CAME TO SPACELAND, AND WHAT I SAW THERE

An unspeakable horror seized me. There was a darkness; then a dizzy, sickening sensation of sight that was not like seeing; I saw a Line that was no Line; Space that was not Space: I was myself, and not myself. When I could find voice, I shrieked aloud in agony, "Either this is madness or it is Hell." "It is neither," calmly replied the voice of the Sphere, "it is Knowledge; it is Three Dimensions: open your eye once again and try to look steadily."

I looked, and, behold a new world! There stood before me, visibly incorporate, all that I had before inferred, conjectured, dreamed, of perfect Circular beauty. What seemed the centre of the Stranger's form lay open to my view; yet I could see no heart, nor lungs, nor arteries, only a beautiful harmonious Something—for which I had no words; but you, my Readers in Spaceland, would call it the surface of the Sphere.

Prostrating myself mentally before my Guide, I cried, "How is it, O divine ideal of consummate loveliness and wisdom that I see thy inside, and yet cannot discern thy heart, thy lungs, thy arteries, thy liver?" "What you think you see, you see not," he replied; "it is not given to you, nor to any other Being to behold my internal parts. I am of a different order of Beings from those in Flatland. Were I a Circle, you could discern my intestines, but I am a Being, composed as I told you before, of many Circles, the Many in the One, called in this country a Sphere. And, just as the outside of a Cube is a Square, so the outside of a Sphere presents the appearance of a Circle."

Bewildered though I was by my Teacher's enigmatic utterance, I no longer chafed against it, but worshipped him in silent adoration. He continued, with more mildness in his voice. "Distress not yourself if you cannot at first understand the deeper mysteries of Spaceland. By degrees they will dawn upon you. Let us begin by casting back a glance at the region whence you came. Return with me a while to the plains of Flatland, and I will shew you that which you have often reasoned and thought about, but never seen with the sense of sight—a visible angle." "Impossible!" I cried; but, the Sphere leading the way, I followed as if in a dream, till once more his voice arrested me: "Look yonder, and behold your own Pentagonal house, and all its inmates."

I looked below, and saw with my physical eye all that domestic individuality which I had hitherto merely inferred with the understanding. And how poor and

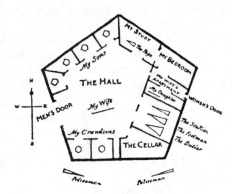

shadowy was the inferred conjecture in comparison with the reality which I now beheld! My four Sons calmly asleep in the North-Western rooms, my two orphan Grandsons to the South; the Servants, the Butler, my Daughter, all in their several apartments. Only my affectionate Wife alarmed by my continued absence, had quitted her room and was roving up and down in the Hall, anxiously awaiting my return. Also the Page, aroused by my cries, had left his room, and under pretext of ascertaining whether I had fallen somewhere in a faint, was prying into the cabinet in my study. All this I could now *see*, not merely infer; and as we came nearer and nearer, I could discern even the contents of my cabinet, and the two chests of gold, and the tablets of which the Sphere had made mention.

Touched by my Wife's distress, I would have sprung downward to reassure her, but I found myself incapable of motion. "Trouble not yourself about your Wife," said my Guide: "she will not be long left in anxiety; meantime, let us take a survey of Flatland."

Once more I felt myself rising through space. It was even as the Sphere had said. The further we receded from the object we beheld, the larger became the field of vision. My native city, with the interior of every house and every creature therein, lay open to my view in miniature. We mounted higher, and lo, the secrets of the earth, the depths of mines and inmost caverns of the hills, were bared before me.

. . . indeed I was intoxicated with the recent draughts of Truth to which he himself had introduced me. However, the end was not long in coming. My words were cut short by a crash outside, and a simultaneous crash inside me, which impelled *me* through space with a velocity that precluded speech. Down! down! down! I was rapidly descending; and I knew that return to Flatland was my doom. One glimpse, one last and never-to-be-forgotten glimpse I had of that dull level wilderness—which was now to become my Universe again—spread out before my eye. Then a darkness. Then a final, all-consummating thunder-peal; and, when I came to myself, I was once more a common creeping Square, in my Study at home. . . .

• DISCUSSION QUESTIONS •

1. What are quasars and why does Sagan call them "the mightiest events in the history of the universe since the Big Bang"? What is the origin of the

word quasar? What basic problems do quasars present to scientists? What can the study of distant quasars tell us about the expansion of the universe?

2. What is the Doppler effect? How does it explain why the sound of a horn from a passing car seems to fade from high frequencies to low frequencies? Why an object receding from us at high velocities has its spectral lines red-shifted? Why is the Doppler effect called the "key to cosmology"?

3. What are spiral arms of a galaxy and how do they develop? About how many years, on the average, do the sun and planets spend in a spiral arm, outside a spiral arm, in a newly formed spiral arm? How might the passage of the sun through a spiral arm explain the major ice ages on our planet?

4. Who were Hubble and Humason? What was the significance of their observation that the more distant a galaxy was, the more red-shifted were its spectral lines? What other evidence do we have to support the Big Bang theory?

5. On the basis of what observations have scientists deduced that the universe is expanding? If the universe is expanding, how can we explain the fact that some galaxies have spectra that are blue-shifted? How is the fate of our universe linked to the curvature of space and the density of matter?

6. What is the cosmic background radiation and how is it detected? Why is the background radiation one of the most important pieces of evidence in support of the Big Bang theory?

7. How is it possible to explain the fact that observers on every galaxy are perceiving the same thing we perceive; that is, the expression of the universe? Why is it so difficult to determine the location of the center of the universe?

8. What is the role of violent phenomena in the universe? (In answering this question, consider the problems associated with quasars.) What other examples of violent phenomena can you cite from previous lessons?

• ADDITIONAL ACTIVITIES •

Optional Projects

1. Write a scenario describing what the universe was like during the first stages of the Big Bang.

2. Write a paper describing the different types of galaxies, explaining how they were formed, and listing the major characteristics of each.

3. Create a short story about a four-dimensional creature who visits our three-dimensional world. What characteristics would he have? What advantages? How would we perceive him?

4. Using other sources, write a paper discussing some of the myths that have developed over the ages to explain the creation. Consider the ancient Hindu concept of the cycles of life and death in relation to modern cosmology. Also consider how the Big Bang theory conflicts with Western theology.

Supplementary Bibliography

George O. Abell, "Cosmology—The Origin and Evolution of the Universe." *Mercury*, May-June 1978.
    Provides background on theories concerning the origin and evolution of the universe.

Richard Berendzen, R. Hart, and D. Selley, *Man Discovers the Galaxies*. New York: Neale Watson Academic Publications, 1976.
    A detailed history of the discovery and exploration of the galaxies written for the non-science reader.

N. Calder, *The Violent Universe*. New York: Viking, 1969.
    A well-known book that discusses a variety of topics in cosmology.

Timothy Ferris, *The Red Limit*. New York: William Morrow, 1977.
    A highly readable, historical account of the important discoveries in modern cosmology.

Owen Gingerich, ed., *Cosmology + 1*. San Francisco: W.H. Freeman & Co., two volumes, 1971 and 1976, respectively.

William Kaufmann, *Relativity and Cosmology*. New York: Harper & Row, 1976.
    A collection of essays by the author on topics in cosmology.

Chapter XI
THE PERSISTENCE OF MEMORY

• OVERVIEW •

IN OCEAN WATERS, huge creatures sing ever-changing symphonies, which seem to be intelligent communications. Their brains have evolved somewhat as human brains have—through the same ancestors to mammalian sensibility. They are the great whales. As yet we have not translated their songs into human language, although we have discerned some of the patterns.

Our brain, like theirs, is a repository of information about life on Earth as well as the set of processes through which that information is managed. The structure of the human brain reflects its evolutionary history. In "reading" the layers of the brain from the innermost to the outermost, one begins with the oldest part, the brainstem, which mainly regulates body functions and is present in very ancient forms of life. Next is the reptilian R-complex, the seat of behavior patterns such as aggression and ritual. The uniquely mammalian limbic system surrounding the R-complex governs behavior such as parenting. Finally, crowning it all, are the marvelous folds of the cerebral cortex, where 100 billion neurons connect in 100 trillion ways in a complex circuitry through which we think, intuit, imagine, and remember.

The whale brain is not so dissimilar. Yet we have not found a way to communicate in any meaningful way with the whales, or with another close relative, the ape.

Communication may be occurring with other beings. We send messages, mostly unwittingly, into space. There if intelligences exist, they may be trying to make sense out of our television and radio broadcasts—speeches, news, situation comedies, Shakespeare, soap operas, rock-and-roll, symphonies, jingles for commercials. Will "they" or "it" understand? Can a solid-state intelligence decipher a human smile, let alone a greeting? The message sent into space with Voyager, Earth's Greatest Hits, contains hellos in 55 languages, and a greeting from the great whales, and more. Will it be found and decoded?

• LEARNING OBJECTIVES •

1. Describe and explain the measurement of intelligence in terms of "bits."

2. Describe and explain the relationship between genetics, brain activity, and libraries as aspects of intelligence storage and use.

3. Describe the human brain in terms of its three-part evolutionary history, the operation of neuron cells, and the roles of specialization and redundancy.

4. Describe the operation and effects of random accidents in evolutionary history and be able to cite examples in the evolutionary chain on this planet.

5. Summarize some of Dr. Sagan's conjectures on the aspect, nature and functioning of some of the intelligent, extraterrestrial beings we will eventually contact.

6. Describe some of the intentional and unintentional ways in which human beings are currently transmitting and receiving interstellar communications (signals).

• KEY TERMS AND NAMES •

bit
brainstem
cerebral cortex
corpus callosum
DNA

genetic code
limbic system
neuron
R complex

• ASSIGNMENT •

Watch COSMOS television series Program 11, "The Persistence of Memory."

Read Chapter 11, "The Persistence of Memory" in Carl Sagan's text, *Cosmos*, or other readings assigned by your instructor.

• READINGS •

Roger Payne . . . . Humpbacks: Their Mysterious Songs

Zoologist Roger Payne has been taping and studying the songs of humpback whales for many years. He and his colleagues have found their songs change constantly. Why? Here he examines some theories.

[He describes sitting in a small sailboat at night off the shore of Bermuda with his wife Katy. He lowers a pair of hydrophones into the water and turns on the amplifiers.] We were no longer alone! Instead, we were surrounded by a vast and joyous chorus of sounds that poured up out of the sea and overflowed its rim. The spaces and vaults of the ocean, like a festive palace hall, reverberated and thundered with the cries of whales—sounds that boomed, echoed, swelled, and vanished as they wove together like strands in some vast and tangled web of glorious sound.

I felt instantly at ease, all sense of desolation brushed aside by the sheer ebullience of it all. All that night we were borne along by those lovely, dancing, yodeling cries, sailing on a sea of unearthly music. . . . [As humpbacks migrate, on their way north from their calving grounds, they sing long songs. With Scott

McVay of Princeton University, the Paynes have analyzed the songs to find a regular sequence of repeated sounds.]

When you go out to listen to a humpback sing, you may hear a whale soloist, or you may hear seeming duets, trios, or even choruses of dozens of interweaving voices. Eash of those whales is singing the same song, yet none is actually in unison with the others—each is marching to its own drummer, so to speak.

Humpback whales are constantly changing their songs. In other words, the whales don't just sing mechanically; rather, they compose as they go along, incorporating new elements into their old songs. We are aware of no other animal besides man in which this strange and complicated behavior occurs, and we have no idea of the reason behind it. If you listen to songs from two different years you will be astonished to hear how different they are. . . . [Combining tapes with those made by others, the Paynes have a sample covering 20 years in Bermuda. Analysis shows that songs change every year, but that the songs of two consecutive years tend to resemble each other. The song evolves.]

We have also recorded and analyzed four years of humpback songs from Hawaii, a major wintering area for humpbacks. Although songs of the same year in Hawaii and Bermuda are different, it is intriguing that they obey the same laws of change, and have the same structure. Each song, for example, is composed of about six themes—passages with several identical or slowly changing phrases in them. Each phrase contains from two to five sounds. In any one song, the themes always follow the same order, though one or more themes may be absent. The remaining ones are always given in predictable sequence. . . .[The fact that whales in Bermuda and Hawaii are not in contact suggests that whales improvise within a set of inherited laws. It is not clear whether the laws are transmitted by genetic inheritance or by learning. A six-month study the Paynes conducted with four others showed that the whales did not forget the song from the previous year, even though there was a period between breeding seasons when they did not sing, but brought it out of "cold storage" at the beginning of the new season. The song changes as the season progresses.]

Another fascinating thing we discovered is that the whales always sing new phrases faster than the old ones. We discovered, too, that new phrases are sometimes created by joining the beginning and end of consecutive phrases and omitting the middle part—just as we humans shorten "do not" to "don't." In many other ways the introduction of new material and the phasing out of old are similar to evolving language in humans.

So far, the study of the humpback whale songs has provided our best insight into the mental capabilites of whales. Humpbacks are clearly intelligent enough to memorize all the complicated sounds in their songs. The also memorize the order of those sounds, as well as the new modifications they hear going on around them. Moreover, they can store this information for at least six months as a basis for further improvisations. To me, this suggests an impressive mental ability and a possible route in the future to assess the intelligence of whales.

Songs are not the only vocaltzations of humpxacks; we often hear grunts, roars, bellows, creaks, and whinesigence of whales.

Songs are not the only vocalizations of humpbacks; we often hear grunts, roars, bellows, creaks, and whines. These sounds sometimes accompany particular types of behavior, suggesting that they may have specific social meaning.

One such association between sound and behavior has been documented by Charles Jurasz, an independent researcher in Glacier Bay, Alaska. Chuck's 12-year study has added significantly to our knowledge of whales. On a recent visit with Chuck I recorded the underwater sounds of a humpback in the act of "spinning its net." Such sounds consist solely of expelled air. There are no accompanying social or vocal noises, which suggests to me that bubble netting is a deliberate act—that of a whale setting a trap. . . . [International agreement prevents killing of hump-backs, however tourists who converge on the whales to observe them harass the great creatures. Steps have been taken to ameliorate this. Whale songs are traveling with Voyager on a recording intended for extraterrestrial civilizations, if they exist.]

Gordon Rattray Taylor . . . . **Wond'rous Machine**

One of the most exciting fields in science today is the study of the brain. Gordon Rattray Taylor, science writier and chief science adviser for the BBC, describes the structure of the brain and some of the ways in which it functions in this article, taken from a chapter in his book The Natural History of the Mind.

THE FIVEFOLD BRAIN

'Brain is mind,' cries Professor Arturo Rosenblueth. The mind is simply the Brain, echoes the philosopher, Professor D. M. Armstrong. Leaving aside all the finer doubts about the meaning of such assertions, I simply wish to ask, at this point, whether such a claim is plausible. Is the brain the sort of mechanism of which one could make such a claim with any hope of defending it at all? Does it have the sort of structure which could conceivably support mind?

In the last few decades, the scientific view of the brain has been changing quite rapidly, as more and more new facts come to light. The brain has certainly turned out to be a much fancier piece of equipment than even the most imaginative neurologist had envisaged. And not only is it fancy: it seems to be constructed according to subtler principles than those that we use in constructing our spacecraft, our computers, and our atom bombs.

Therefore, let us take a look at the brain. No, let me rephrase that. Let us look at *our* brains. The reflexive character of this operation makes it unique. When, with our brains, we consider galaxies or microbes we are in a position to feel a certain detachment. We are studying complex objects, no doubt, but the tool with which we study them is more complex than they. But to inspect our own brain we have only our own brains. Some feel, on grounds which are less philosophical than mystical, that the brain can never hope to understand itself. The idea smacks of hoisting oneself by one's own bootstraps. However, we can make a start.

The first person to examine the brain in a modern manner was the Viennese anatomist Dr. Gall. Previous investigators had simply sliced it up, as if carving a joint. Gall dissected out the various structures within it, and laid the foundations of mo rn neurology. Poor Dr. Gall demonstrates the ironies of human reputation. History remembers only his phrenological theories and dismisses him as a charlatan. In point of fact it was a pupil of Gall's named Spurzheim who exploited phrenology, much to Gall's disapproval: Gall refused even to read Spurzheim's works.

What Gall started with was something looking like half a peeled walnut, but bigger of course: two wrinkled hemispheres (actually they are quarter spheres) consisting of a sheet of tissue, a few millimetres thick and about the size of a pocket handkerchief. The sheet is crumpled in the effort to fit a large surface into a small skull. It is officially called the cortex or rind, though the great Sir Charles Sherrington preferred to call it, more appropriately, the roof brain.

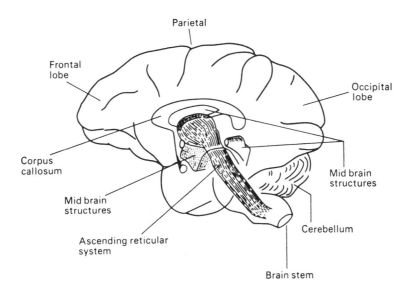

Phantom view of a human brain from the left side. The mid-brain structures are depicted as if seen through a transparent cortex.

Lifting off this roof, Gall found a series of mystifying structures. First, two lobes, closely linked to the cortex, known as thalami, or reeds, in the fanciful nomenclature of neuroanatomy. Below them, the 'almond,' the 'olive' and the 'seahorse,' and so on. This heterogeneous assortment we call the mid-brain. Stripping it away, Gall found a couple of swellings at the top of the spinal cord, the old brain. Finally, stuck on at the back, another wrinkled, bilobed structure, the little brain or cerebellum. Gall did not of course comprehend the role of these structures. We are each the owner of four brains—or even five, if we count each of the cerebral hemispheres as a separate brain, which we could, seeing that a person can operate quite well with only one.

Like those airlines which operate two computers to record their passenger bookings, just in case one should break down, evolution has blessed us too with spare equipment. All five brains are interconnected.

Two of these brains will not concern us here. The old brain is the body's chief engineer, regulating heart-beat and breathing, deciding whether your blood vessels should dilate or your viscera contract, and so on. It also incorporates the alarm-system, arousing the cortex (the captain) when matters of interest arise, for through it pass all the cables from the sensory organs, and it monitors the information flow in them. The cerebellum is the automatic pilot. When you learn new skills, such as riding a bicycle, you start by using your cortex: you have to think what you are doing. Later, you can ride 'without thinking' or you can think of something else. Your cortex has handed over to the cerebellum. This little brain consists of long banks of similar equipment, fed with data by one set of nerves, and monitored by another, in a manner resembling a computer. The analogy between brains and computers is frequently overdone, but if there is anywhere where it is appropriate to use it, it is here. However, some scientists wonder if the cerebellum may not have other, unobvious functions. Intensive work has been done in recent years on the cerebellum, notably by the great Hungarian neuroanatomist Szent-Agothai. Its relatively simple, repetitive structures may be the first thing in the brain to yield to enquiry. It receives data not only from the cortex but from the mid-brain, which as we shall shortly see—is concerned with emotions. That is rather odd. Why would an automatic pilot have any truck with emotion? However, I shall say no more about the old brain or the cerebellum.

So I can boil things down for you by saying: We are concerned with two brains merely—the mid-brain which handles our feelings (and smell), and the roof brain which handles all the sensations (except smell), as well as thoughts, the control of movements and perhaps memory.

I find it makes it easier to hold this pattern in one's head if one looks at the brain from an evolutionary and developmental viewpoint. First, the simple nerve net, as in starfish, worms and other creatures. Then the notochord or long nerve running the length of the body, enclosed in due course in a protective sheath which becomes the spine. Then a proliferation of the cells at one end, as the old brain develops to run a more complex body. Now the possessor has a front-end and a back-end: up to this point the two ends were identical. Next the development of the mid-brain, giving a crude awareness of the environment and capable of simple executive actions. A dog from which the cerebral hemispheres have been removed can walk, feed and sleep, thanks to its mid-brain. (Children are sometimes born without hemispheres—they are called anencephalics: they cry, they coo when stroked, they sleep and wake.) Finally, the roof brain begins to develop. At first optic lobes to analyse the input from the eyes, auditory lobes for the ears. (The olfactory lobe had been there from very early on.) Gradually the new brain spreads backwards over the older parts like a cap; and as the sheet of cells continues to grow, it begins to crumple. The cortex of a rabbit is smooth, but that of the more intelligent cat is wrinkled.

When the German physiologist Eduard Hitzig made the first modern studies on the exposed brain, almost a century ago, he tried stimulating portions of the cortex, for this was all he could get at. He found that various sensations and muscular movements ensued. So it came about that the neocortex came to be thought of as *the* brain. Much more recently, scientists have plunged wires and fine tubes through the cortex into the mid-brain, and are beginning to learn about the complex role it plays: it is the seat of feeling and emotion, as well as having taken over some of the automatic control functions from the brain-stem.

We shall do better, I think, to regard the mid-brain as *the* brain—the mechanism which really determines what we do—and to think of the cortex as a computer which it calls in for detailed studies. If we remove the cortex from a living animal, it is still vaguely aware of the position of objects, it can move around, it can feed itself, it can withdraw from a painful stimulus. But the universe is blurred. It needs a cortex to identify that dark object as a cat or that attractive smell as a banana. That this is so is shown by the case of a patient (a thirty-six-year-old accountant) with severe right cortical damage who could, for example, feel a pinprick on his left side but could not say where exactly it was. He could describe the shape and feel of an object placed in his left hand but could not identify it. Here was the mid-brain locating the facts, but the cortex was unable to interpret them.

One commentator declares, on the basis of this sort of data, that the cortex cannot see, hear or think. But, as we shall see in more detail later, seeing and hearing are indubitably cortical functions; the fact that a primitive kind of seeing, hearing, and feeling is also performed by the mid-brain in no way invalidates the more sophisticated efforts of the new brain. Countless nerve fibres connect every part of the cortex with the several components of the thalamus, and carry impulses both to and fro. The cortex seems to refer its findings about the world (for it is the analyst of vision as well as the executor of behaviour) to the thalamus for an emotional rating. As J-P. Ewert has said: the new brain tells you what it is, the thalamus tells you whether it matters.

In what follows we shall be much concerned with the relations between the new brain and the older mid-brain. The new brain makes plans and looks ahead, it restrains the impulses of the mid-brain.

Though I have presented the brain as having only two levels, the American neuroscientist Paul McLean sees it as having three, which he has picturesquely named Graven Image, Lethe and Guru—the first concerned with the past, the second with the present and the last with the future. He is thinking, however, more in evolutionary than in structural terms. At first there is the reptilian brain, working by instinct, the accumulated wisdom of the past; then the simple mammalian brain, reacting to present situations; finally the human brain, planning far ahead. He has an excellent point. For our cortex is not concerned simply with the fine-grain analysis of what is happening, but with expectancies and probabilities.

The point has now been reached at which I should introduce you more closely to this 'hot brain' which is the core of our being. It was an investigator named J. W. Papez who gained a permanent place in the history of neurology when he made the acute suggestion that the various odd-shaped structures which lie below the roof brain constituted a co-ordinated system, which he named the 'limbic system.' Only with the development of techniques of penetrating the cortex with fine needles and recording electrically from these structures was it possible to learn much about them, and they still remain pretty much a mystery, though some broad outlines of their function are beginning to loom through the mist.

Scientists are currently looking closely at some of these structures since they give us some idea how the brain functions, in the sense of 'How does it split up the complex task of captaincy into feasible sub-tasks?'

I shall take for study the hippocampus, or sea-horse. A sounder comparison would be with a rather stumpy Bologna sausage. It is a rather large structure; that man has the largest hippocampus of any animal suggests that it serves important functions. The first curious thing is its internal structure: a series of leaves, like the pages of a book. It is as if someone had taken a great many micro-circuit boards and stacked them up. The input lines from the sense organs run through this stack of leaves, making contact with the dendritic trees in each. The output lines descend from the leaves and run to the muscular system. The whole thing reminds one irresistibly of the kind of device made up by electronic experts, much as does the cerebellum.

If you insert electrodes in the hippocampus of a free-running rat you find that there are cells which fire only when it is at certain points in the cage or maze. It has cells which fire when three or four cues are simultaneously present, but erratically if only one. David Olton of Johns Hopkins was stuck by the observation of a naturalist that the honey creeper, a tiny bird that feeds on nectar in Hawaii, seemed able to remember which flowers it had already stripped of nectar. He therefore decided to investigate the question of spatial memory. He found that a rat placed in a maze with eight arms could remember which had proved to contain food. It could also do so on a seventeen-arm maze, though it made more mistakes. Varying the conditions showed that it was making a mental map. But if one of the hippocampal connections was cut, the animal's performance after recovery from the operation was profoundly impaired. So it seems that one of the functions of the hippocampus is to compare memories of spatial arrangements in relation to whether they were associated with a reward. The circuitry is just what you need for such a result. This conclusion also conforms with the evolutionary evidence.

Fish, like animals lower than themselves in the evolutionary scale, have no hippocampus. Amphibians have only a primitive one; reptiles do a little better. In the ocean there are few landmarks, and fish are guided only by broad environmental factors like temperature and salinity. But once creatures had climbed on land, to remember where food could be found, or where your nest or lair was, became important. In mice and rats and primitive mammals the fully organised hippocampus appears. Russian scientists tested a range of animals from snakes and turtles through rabbits, hedgehogs and birds to dogs and baboons on the same experiment. They had to note three signals and the order in which they were given: a sound, a light, and a different sound. Goldfish never learned. Turtles got it right some of the time. Birds were terrific. Rabbits, which have a good hippocampus but a poor cortex, needed a lot of tutoring and were foxed by a change of order in the stimuli. Dogs and baboons did perfectly, provided the signals were given in proper order. You seem to need a cortex to see that FLASH-BANG can be treated the same as BANG-FLASH.

And this seems to be another feature of the hippocampus: it surveys memories in serial order. If you are trying to find your way you have to remember what came after what. Left turn, then right turn, then left turn does not get you to the same destination as right turn, left turn, right turn.

Animals with damaged hippocampi have trouble with time-based tests and memories involving serial order. One can speculate therefore that the hippocampus in our own case is involved in the appreciation of music and speech. Part of the story, of course, is that you need to remember which of the remembered positions proved rewarding, and so it is not surprising that the hippocampus has connections with the pleasure centres or reward areas. I like to think that some of the folia carry a sort of red star indicating, 'This one was fun.'

Another suggestion, coming from T. McLardy, is that the hippocampus also functions as a delay line; many of the cells lie cheek-to-cheek and electric currents permeate through them relatively slowly. This 'seepage' could explain for instance why lights which flicker more than fifteen times a second tend to be seen as a continuous light; and why the successive pictures of a film or TV programme fuse together. He also believes the hippocampus detects intensity gradients. It certainly has further functions and seems to be needed for the unlearning (extinction) of a response. A leading American neurophysiologist, the Vienna-born Karl Pribram, thinks it is concerned with the whole task of organising complex behaviour.

[The hypothalamus is described.]

WHERE IS FANCY BRED?

In the days when the mind was conceived as an immaterial gas-bag tethered to the body, the brain was thought to be all of a piece, a sort of sounding board for the soul. In the Middle Ages naturalists assigned the mental faculties to the three open spaces or ventricles within the brain. The pendulum swung back and forth between the conception of the brain as a 'common sensorium' and the idea of 'localisation of function'. And here is one of the most curious of the brain's features: somehow the cortex manages to be both things at once, specialised, yet generalised. In this paradox is embedded an important truth about the brain and its relation to mind, so allow me to pursue it further.

The first person to put the matter on a scientific footing was the youthful French anatomist Paul Broca; his discovery made modern brain surgery possible. In 1861 he described the brain of a patient who had been kept many years in the Salpetrière, unable to express himself in speech or by writing, a condition Broca christened 'aphasia.' On autopsy, the man was found to have suffered damage to a small area of the brain which has ever since been known to anatomists as Broca's area. Broca claimed, correctly, that the patient's speech problem was directly due to this damage: that this part of the brain was precisely responsible for translating ideas into words. It was the first time a brain function had been localised. Then, in 1873, the German Carl Wernicke identified an area, not very far from Broca's, which he described as the area of understanding speech. His patient could speak and write but not understand what was said to him. The area, naturally, has gone into the textbooks as Wernicke's area. (Fortunately, before the brain became a forest of patronymics, baffling the memory, a man named Brodmann developed a system of numbered areas which, though not very satisfactory, is still widely used. Broca's area corresponds roughly to Brodmann's 44.)

These evidences that the brain actually had some kind of comprehensible structure aroused unprecedented excitement among neurologists, who began to accumulate data with great enthusiasm. The next significant advance was made by Eduard Hitzig, whom I mentioned earlier. It was in 1870 that he published his epoch-making paper in which he demonstrated that, if you stimulated the brain at various points, different groups of muscles were caused to contract. The area across the top of the brain is known as parietal (paries being the Latin for roof): it is bounded by a deep fold known as the fissure of Rolando, named for the Italian anatomist who drew attention to it. This was the area which Hitzig and his colleague Fritsch stimulated. They found that all the muscles of the body were activated in regular order, from the feet at one side of the brain to the head at the centre, the right side of the body being represented on the left and vice versa. On the other side of Rolando's fissure are the cell-groups which connect with the sensory areas of the body, also neatly laid out from top to toe, with large areas assigned to delicately innervated body parts, like fingers and tongue, and small areas for less innervated ones such as the forearm or the sole of the foot.

At the back of the brain (known as the occipital lobe) lies the area responsible for vision: stimulation here produces flashes of light, stars, wheels and other elements of vision. At the side, in the temporal area, stimulation produces sounds, and between the two is an area responsible for linking the two senses. (Another association' area links vision with touch.) Just forward of this, as the Canadian surgeon Wilder Penfield discovered much later, stimulation evokes memories—but that is a story I shall postpone telling until we come to the subject of memory.

The only area where stimulation seemed to have no specific result was the frontal lobes—stimulation here only stopped the animal from doing whatever it was doing. They were accordingly dubbed 'the silent areas' and for long were accused of being functionless. Now we know that they are the plan-making apparatus—the executive of the brain. All the rest is simply information processing for the benefit of the frontal lobes. Karl Pribram declares, "I feel reasonably sure that the dorsolateral frontal cortex, like the limbic, are (*sic*) concerned in the inhibition of interference among brain events."

Animals in which the frontal lobes have been removed seem to have great trouble in deciding between two alternatives. They fail to learn when tempted by rewards, as if they failed to see the consequences of their actions. The results in the few human cases of cortical ablation are even more bewildering. On the one hand irritability, on the other indifference. Impetuousness combined with lack of initiative. Euphoria and boastfulness. Failure to spot details and poor behaviour on sorting tests—these one might well expect, since the role of the cortex is to make fine discriminations. The frontal lobes seem to exert a restraining role on the impulsiveness of the mid-brain. The operation of leucotomy (replacing the earlier operation of lobotomy, in which parts of the lobes were removed), severs some of the connections between the frontal and the limbic lobes, and is helpful in cases of overwhelming anxiety and depression. After such operations, the patient may go towards the other extreme, become abusive or given to violence and sexually active as well.

One of the classic cases of neurology concerns Phineas Gage, a workman who was tamping explosives into a hole. The charge exploded prematurely, driving the tamper clean through his skull. Afterwards, his friends commented on his changed disposition.

But I have not quite brought the story of localisation of function up-to-date. The Second World War provided neurologists with a large crop of cases of penetrating brain injury, from which much could be learned. The man who, beyond all others, has devoted himself to the study of such cases is Aleksandr Luria, doyen of Russian neuropsychologists, who has made it almost a life's work.

Luria found men who had lost mental functions of a very specific kind. For instance, soldiers with an injury to a certain spot on the left side of the brain towards the back showed a curious disturbance of their ability to judge space, both when moving and when simply perceiving. Such patients typically 'cannot interpret the position of the hands of a clock or find their bearings on a map; they cannot find their way around the ward where they are staying; they cannot solve even relatively simple arithmetical problems, and they are confused when faced with the problem of subtracting from a number of two digits carrying over from the tens column: when subtracting seven from thirty-one, for example, they do the first stage of this operation (30−7 equals 23) but then they do not know whether the odd one should be added or subtracted, or whether their final result should be twenty-two or twenty-four. Finally they begin to have great difficulty in understanding grammatical structures incorporating logical relationships, such as "the father's brother" and "the brother's father"; "spring after summer" "summer after spring" whereas the understanding of simpler grammatical structures remains unimpaired.' . . .

The cortex emerges, then, as a many-faceted computer adapted to handle many different tasks, and to integrate them harmoniously. What the 'brain is mind' party fail to explain is, first, why only some of these functions—all carried out by much the same kind of equipment—produce sensations and experiences of the kind we identify as 'mind'; and second, why, when they *do* produce such experiences, they are so very different. The cells, and even the wiring, in the visual cortex look pretty much the same under the microscope as the cells and wiring in the auditory cortex. So why does one of them evoke the experience we call 'seeing' and the other the experience we call 'hearing'? And why do the very similar cells in the motor cortex produce no sensations at all? There may be some simple answer. It would certainly put a new face on the discussion if we found it.

THE PRIMORDIAL PROTOPLASMIC GLOBULES

It was in the 1830s that Theodore Schwann realised that the basic units from which all living things are constructed were 'primordial protoplasmic globules' or, as we now tersely put it, cells. It took another thirty years before Meinert gave the first accurate description of the cellular structure of the cortex. However, nerve cells—usually known as neurones—are quite unlike the other cells of the body. Each has a process, a thread sometimes several feet in length, along which the cell-body can transmit an electrical impulse.

This process is known as the axon and terminates on the surface of another cell. In the brain, neurones receive impulses in this way from hundreds or even thousands of other neurones. When a neurone receives more than a certain minimum of stimuli, it in turn emits an electric impulse, or 'fires', as physiologists say. If it fires, its threshold of sensitivity is lowered, so that on the next such occasion it fires more readily. Even if it does not fire, the arrival of impulses may reset its threshold so that, on some future occasion, it will fire more readily when stimulated. Furthermore, general chemical changes in the brain, including those caused by drugs, may shift such thresholds in whole blocks of cells. In addition to axons, neurones are provided with a branchwork of fine threads, known as dendrites, which contact cells in their immediate neighbourhood. The general character of the brain is thus of an elaborate network, in which each unit is receiving information about the state of thousands of other such units. One thing I must add: while some neurones encourage those they are in touch with to fire, others have the opposite effect and block their firing (inhibition). Thus whether a neurone fires or not may be the upshot of, so to say, a large number of votes—some saying 'yes', some 'no'—which it summates.

It is not necessary for our purpose to go into the nature of the electric impulse, except to say that it is different from an ordinary electric current and travels much more slowly. Nor need I discuss how, at the point of contact with another neurone, there is a cleft known as the synapse, into which chemical 'transmitters' are released when the electric pulse arrives: those neurohumours then excite or inhibit the receiving cell. What I do want to do, however, is to bring out the immense complexity of the pattern into which these rather simple relay-like units are woven.

The early microscopists of the brain, such as the Spaniard Ramon y Cajal, were struck by the many varieties of neurone which they found, but many of these variations appear to be as trivial as the variations in the human race, accidents of development, situation, or role in life. When it comes to the crunch, many neurophysiologists believe that there are only three basic types of cell. Though why and how they differ is still a mystery. Thus the remarkable fact is that the brain contrives to carry out such different functions as sight and smell, as thinking and feeling, as wishing and deciding, with equipment which is substantially identical. Not to mention controlling the bodily functions, executing movements, regulating alertness and sleep. There must be a lesson in this. How can consciousness in all its many aspects subsist on patterns of interlinked relays?

ONLY CONNECT

If you take a razor and slice through the cortex of a fresh brain you will reveal two kinds of substance, the one whitish-yellow, the other pinkish. After the brain has been fixed in formaldehyde, the one apears grey, the other white, giving rise to the popular expressions 'grey matter' and 'white matter.' The grey matter, only a few millimetres thick, contains all the neuronal cell-bodies, the dendrites and axonal terminations. The white matter, which takes up the bulk of the space, turns out on microscopic examination to consist of an incredible feltwork of cross-connections between every part of the brain.

This knowledge did not come easily. In 1861, Griesinger was writing of 'an apparently homogeneous, structureless molecular mass, an unusually fine network,' meaning the grey matter. As late as 1897 Krafft-Ebing was speculating . . . most likely these millions of cells are connected with one another.'

Within the cortex itself, the structure of the grey matter is everywhere so similar that often one cannot tell from which area a given section has come, nor in which direction it was oriented. Under the microscope, when sliced through, the grey matter reveals a series of layers. This fact long misled people into thinking that the brain was organised laterally, a notion which persisted until some twenty years ago. Vernon Mountcastle showed that the cortex consists, functionally, of a million vertical columns, packed together like the cells in a honeycomb. Signals are shuffled up and down these columns, in which the various types of cells give rise to the layered appearance. Though each column influences its neighbours through its dendrites (and perhaps in other ways) the main intercommunications are by the axons, running in bundles beneath the grey matter.

Scientist are tracing the paths of these bundles by very laborious methods. A favourite one is to make a lesion in the brain of a living animal: this causes the axons arising from the damaged cells to degenerate or die away. After days or weeks, depending on the method used, the animal is killed and its brain preserved, stained and sliced in very thin sections. By using dyes which only stain injured or dead neurones, the course of their connections can be traced. And, while we are on the subject of staining, let us mention the methods devised by Cajal's great rival, Camillo Golgi. He discovered a stain which has the peculiar property of filling some neurones with a red-black precipitate, but leaving the rest unstained. Thus the splendid photographs one sees in illustrated works about the brain give an entirely false impression of the density with which the neurones are packed. Without staining, it would be impossible to see the trees for the forest. With staining, one or two trees are left standing in majestic isolation, so that their branches can be clearly distinguished, but the forest as a whole has become invisible.

I recall these facts in order to set the stage for an excursus on the incredible complexity of the brain, complexity of a very special kind. If any of my readers has a taste for staggering statistics, I can now satisfy it. The number of neurones in the cortex alone is commonly put at ten thousand million, which can conveniently be written 10^{10}—an easy figure to remember. Unfortunately also an inaccurate one, based on an investigation made in 1896 and copied from work to work ever since, even by neurologists themselves. Later studies have put the figure as high as fourteen thousand million and as low as two thousand six hundred million. In any case it is a phenomenal number: around thirty-five thousand cells for each square millimetre of surface, each contacting about six hundred other cells and making 10^7 synapses. Incidentally about one-tenth of these cells are occupied in analysing data from the eyes.

But though this enormous figure of 10^{10} is so often quoted, one could easily cap the quotation. The cerebellum, for instance, contains some forty thousand million granule cells, and God alone knows how many cells there are in the limbic system and the brain-stem. Perhaps a hundred thousand million would be nearer the population of the brain as a whole. If cells were people, they would populate twenty-five planets like the earth. Small wonder that the brain consumes about one-third of the body's total oxygen supply. (In addition there are as many supporting cells, neuroglia, as there are neurones.) As Professor Donald Kennedy has remarked, with noble understatement, "These vast populations of cells present a formidable challenge to biologists."

But if I quote these astronomical figures of cell numbers, it is not simply to make you gape, but rather to prepare the ground for the more interesting question of how they are interconnected. It is hardly an exaggeration to say that every group of cells in the brain is connected with every other group. The various parts of the cortex are connected not only with each other, but with the basal nuclei of the limbic system and with the brain-stem, to say nothing of their connections with the muscles and the sensory organs. For instance, the frontal lobes have close connections with the limbic system, a fact which you acknowledge when you say, "The very thought of it makes me feel sick." More than a million nerve fibres run from the eye to the brain. A single segment of spinal cord controls the few muscles it operates through several thousand motoneurones. Nature is prodigal, and can afford to be.

The most substantial connecting tract is the one which joins the two halves of the cortex, the corpus callosum. The number of fibres it contains in man is unknown, but in the cat some patient technician has counted seventy thousand fibres to the square millimetre.

Altogether, the axons of all the brain's neurones would stretch, it has been estimated (though I should not care to attempt such a feat), three times as far as the distance from the earth to the moon. That is, the axons of one human brain. The axons of the brains of all living persons would stretch to the nearest galaxy, a hundred light years away. The point I am hammering at is that connectivity, not quantity, is the secret of the brain's success. The human brain, at one thousand four hundred and fifty grams or so for men and one thousand three hundred and fifty grams for women, is piddling compared with the five thousand grams the elephant can boast or the mighty six thousand eight hundred grams of the blue whale. But when it comes to interconnections, the human brain has a clear lead.

The axons of which I have written are, of course, the links between relatively distant cell groups. In addition, there are the dendrites, a dense fuzz of local connections. Valentino Braitenberg has suggested that we should talk of A and B systems of connection, the local connections which coordinate cells within cell groups, as distinguished from the connections between groups. No one knows much about dendritic patterns, and the study of the 'local circuit neurones' which link nearby cells (or maybe separate them) has only recently become a recognised discipline. A few years ago, a Californian scientist named Stephen Zamenhof fed growth hormone to pregnant rats. Their offspring were brighter than average at running mazes and such-like tricks; and when their brains were examined proved to have a richer growth of dendrites than usual. Connectivity, in fine, is the basis of intelligence—not brain weight or neurone count.

I said that the complexity of the brain was of a special type, and now I think I have said enough to make this statement clearer. The brain is built of very simple, repetitive units of a very few kinds. It is not complex in that sense. It is the processes which are complex. A great many different things are happening at the same time in any one place. Every neurone is influenced directly by hundreds or thousands of other neurones, and in several different ways. Indirectly, every neurone is influenced, or may be influenced, by every other neurone. Every part of the brain, to put it more picturesquely, knows what the other parts are doing. There are no man-made mechanisms of which this is even approximately true.

Thus the paradox of the brain is that it is both localised and generalised. It analyses, but at the same time, and with the same equipment, it synthesises. it is hard for us to grasp the kind of thing which is continually going on as it matches nothing in our ordinary experience.

And now I have to push this rather difficult conception one stage further. The brain is able, unlikely as it might appear, to distribute its activities among the available equipment in a very curious way, or perhaps several curious ways. In the most obvious of these ways, it simply mobilises the available equipment, rather as the larger computers do.

Suppose you are driving a car and talkng to your companion. Suddenly you have to do a tricky bit of overtaking. You fall silent for a few moments while you 'concentrate' on the driving problem. What has happened? You have called in the parts of the brain which were handling your thoughts and remarks to assist the parts which were processing the driving task. The additional equipment makes it possible—thanks to the parallel processing set-up—to process the data more rapidly and more accurately. This phenomenon suggests that the brain must have— just like the larger computers—a central command unit which distributes the equipment as required. In computers these units have a 'noticing order' programme which assigns priorities to different operations. Karl Pribham believes that he has shown that animals likewise have 'noticing order' programmes. Nevertheless, no such unit has been found and I am inclined to believe the result is achieved in a subtler way. I suspect that all the traffic of the brain carries a priority tag—it might be the amplitude of the signal or the die-away rate or the internal structure of the pulse-code; we need something of this kind to explain why some things seem urgent and important, others less so, if not downright dull. (It could even be that priorities are assigned to cortical material by reinforcement from the hot brain.) If this is correct, the priorities would sort themselves out; certain neural patterns would swamp others, as big waves at sea ignore little ripples.

As each neurone discharges its tiny pulse, the total effect is detectable as an electric field outside the skull. When the brain is inactive, the cortical cells discharge in unison, producing the 'alpha rhythm' of which much has been heard recently. When the brain is concentrating on some problem, the synchrony of discharge vanishes, as different groups of cells pursue their own purposes, and more complex rhythms are detectable. In deep meditation even the ten to twelve per second alpha rhythm dies away, to be replaced by a slower four to six per second rhythm known as the theta rhythm.

It was a German psychiatrist, Hans Berger, who in 1925 first recorded the human 'encephalogram' (EEG) from the scalp of his young son. To begin with, he pushed platinum wires into the boy's scalp, but later found that metal discs taped to the skin would serve as well. Berger was a shy, rigid man, who kept his result to himself until 1929. His report was ridiculed at first: it was thought to be absurd that the brain should be in constant activity. It was Lord Adrian, at Cambridge, who realised the importance of his findings and invited him to work with him.

Eventually, opinion swung from scepticism to the other extreme: the analysi¢ of these brain waves was going to explain everything. The reality has been disappointing. True, the waves do seem closely related to what the brain is doing; thanks to special techniques it has recently proved possible to detect the difference when a person looks at a chequered field as compared with his looking at a uniform one, for instance. Evidently, the rhythms are indicating something, but just what is unclear and shows little sign of becoming clearer. They have proved valuable in the clinical field, however, since abnormal rhythms may warn of an impending epileptic attack, while localised abnormalities may indicate the location of a tumour or blood-clot. They also have a role as a research tool, since probes thrust deep into the brain can record the rhythms from small areas and reveal how their activity is affected by drugs or mental disturbance. But the great breakthrough in understanding the brain which many expected has not occurred. The EEG resembles the noise coming from a house which might tell us that a party or a concert was going on inside, but who is present and what part they are taking we can only guess.

THE BRAIN AS A WHOLE

But even this does not exhaust the account of the brain's connectivity. For though neurologists have long focused on the electric transmission of data through axon and synapse, it is now becoming clear that there are other types of transmission in the brain. The eminent Professor Valentino Braitenberg, of Freiburg's Max Planck Institute, lists no fewer than five types. Among them—and I suspect of great importance—is electronic transmission. Whereas the type of transmission most commonly described (known as the action potential) fires with undiminished strength into all its ramifications, and travels at uniform speed, this other kind dies away and loses speed as it does so. Direct electric coupling can also take place between closely aligned cells. There are also chemical forms of transmission. Thus while the action potential gives the brain a faint resemblance to a digital computer, which works with all-or-nothing pulses, some of these other forms smack more of the analogue computer, which echoes fluctuating forces in the real world with fluctuating electric potentials. (This opens up a whole new aspect of brain function. . . .)

Up to this point I have treated the brain primarily as an electrical switching device, for this is how scientists have persisted in thinking of it. The biggest change which has come over brain research in recent years, however, is the realisation that it is also a complex chemical system. Though it is over a century since Thudichum, the German refugee who worked at St. Thomas's Hospital in London, founded the study of brain chemistry, it is only in the last two decades that neurochemistry has become a science, thanks to the devising of recondite methods of identifying the presence of very small amounts of particular substances in specific small areas of the brain. At least forty such neurochemicals are now known to exist, and their connection with mood and behaviour is slowly being unravelled. . . .

C. Wetherill and W.T. Sullivan III . . . . Eavesdropping on the Earth

How might extraterrestrial civilizations analyze Earth's "radio signature"? The authors, from the University of Washington, describe our information leakage to the cosmos from the point of view of creatures on other worlds.

> Nobody passes us in the deep
>   quiet of the dark sky;
> Nobody sees us floating out here
>   among the stars. . . .
> No one receiving the radio
>   signals today. . . .
>   —Brian Eno

Most estimates of the possibility of communication with extraterrestrial civilizations in our galaxy depend on the assumptions that planetary systems about stars are common and that many of these are suitable for the development of intelligent life. Yet mankind's current knowledge of the astronomical and physical processes involved in the formation of stars and their planetary systems is not sufficient for us to know whether or not our Earth and its cousins represent a truly rare phenomenon. In fact, the solar system in which we participate is the only one known definitely to exist in the universe! Why don't we have more of the needed information? A good way to answer this question is to turn the tables and examine various ways an extraterrestrial astronomer might find evidence of our own solar system.

Much of his difficulty would stem from our system's insignificance on a cosmic scale. While the Earth-Sun distance of 150,000,000 kilometers (or one *astronomical unit*) may seem large, that to the *nearest* star is over 200,000 times larger. Furthermore, planets are small and contain little mass; Jupiter is one thousandth the mass of the Sun and yet more massive than all the other planets combined. Planets also are not very bright—the "full Earth" is about one billion times (or 23 magnitudes) fainter than the Sun and would not be visible beyond 20 light years to an extraterrestrial astronomer using even a 5-meter telescope (such as the one on Mt. Palomar)[1]. It is because their observable effects are so minute that we cannot expect planets like those we know to be detectable over great distances. . . . [One exception to this statement is Barnard's Star, a binary system in which the unseen companion may be planet-like; there are other such cases.]

The second extreme situation renders at least one known planet much more easily detectable than it would otherwise be. This is the phenomenon of life on Earth, life which has recently reached such a stage as to announce our planet's presence over interstellar distances to any being possessing astronomical knowledge and technology comparable to our own. And it turns out that much more than just the simple presence of our Earth could be deduced by possible inhabitants of other, distant planetary systems. Within the signals which leak into space from Earth, there is detailed information about both the source planet and the "disturbance" at its surface which sent the signal on its way.

"LEAKING" RADIATION

Let us examine the various sources of energy that not only escape the Earth, but also completely leave the solar system and enter the interstellar environment. All such leakage has to date been electromagnetic in nature, meaning "light" of various wavelengths such as radio, infrared, and visible. The Pioneer 10 spacecraft, which will become the first man-made material object to leave the solar system, is passing Saturn this year [1979]. When it passes Pluto its speed will be only 1/30,000th of the speed of light and it will be quite a while before it reaches another star.

Detailed consideration of all parts of the electromagnetic spectrum reveals that it is *radio* waves which are by far the most important "leakage" from the Earth[2].

[1] In practice, the situation would be even worse due to the tremendous glare of the nearby Sun.
[2] This was first pointed out in 1963 by the Soviet astrophysicist I. S. Shklovski.

For instance, nothing that Man does with visible light, not even exploding a hydrogen bomb, compares in the least with with the Sun's output. But at wavelengths from 1 centimeter to 30 kilometers our society has organized a host of activities on Earth which give our planet an unnatural "radio signature": television and radio broadcasting, radars used for weather, navigational and military purposes, "shortwave" communications ("hams," Citizens Band, taxis, police), satellite communications, etc., etc.

We now want to put ourselves in the "shoes" of an extraterrestrial radio astronomer on a planet revolving about a star far from our Sun. Which of these radio services would be "best" for our "eavesdropper" to tune in on? Which is detectable to the greatest distances? Which potentially carries the most information of use to the eavesdropper? To answer these questions one must study many factors including the power of each service's transmitters, the frequencies and bandwidths involved, types of antennas used, and the fraction of time spent transmitting[3]. One example of these factors is the general trade-off between the information content (TV picture, spoken words, Morse code) of a transmitted signal and the range (distance) to which it can be detected. This can be understood by noting that one gets more range by concentrating transmitted power at the fewest number of frequencies possible. But the information content of a signal is contained in the arrangement of its power among a number of neighboring frequencies and increases as we spread the power over a greater bandwidth.

Three other important criteria in the evaluation of each radio service are: (a) that the signal should be exactly the same from day to day, (b) that the amount of sky "illuminated" by the transmitting antennas should be large, and (c) that the number of transmitters on Earth should be large. Regarding (b), remember that the radio waves from even a stationary antenna can sweep out a large portion of the sky as a result of the Earth's rotation. Furthermore, each antenna has a characteristic "beam" into which the transmitter power is directed. If an antenna, say a parabolic reflector or "dish," is designed so that the power is concentrated into a relatively small region of the sky, the range of detection for the signal increases, but at the expense of excluding many potential listeners.

ACQUISTION AND INFORMATION SIGNALS

Keeping the above factors in mind, an examination of all the radio services on Earth reveals two categories of strong signals escaping the Earth that might be of interest to an extraterrestrial observer.

An *acquisition signal* merely announces our presence over a large region of space by its very existence, but is not generally useful for careful study because it fails to meet one or more of the criteria given above. An *information signal*, however, satisfies all three criteria. At the present time on Earth some of the most important acquisition signals originate from a half-dozen or so U.S. military radars (and their presumed Soviet counterparts). These Ballistic Missile Early Warning System (BMEWS) radars sweep out a large fraction of the local horizon with

---

[3] The bandwidth of a signal is the range of frequencies over which it is sent. Readers not familiar with this terminology should think of a band of frequencies as a band of possible "channels" for broadcasting. A broad frequency band would have a lot of channels.

extraordinarily powerful transmitters. The result is that this "radio service" provides by far the most intense signals which leak from our planet to a large fraction of the sky.

While BMWES radars pass criterion (b) above, they fail (c) and partially fail (a) because there are so few of these radars and they often change their frequency of operation to avoid being jammed. Nevertheless, if an external observer used equipment comparable to the most sensitive radio telescope on Earth (the 305-meter diameter dish at Arecibo, Puerto Rico), we calculate that a BMEWS-type radar could be detected as far away as 30 light-years. This distance includes only about 200 stars, but of course it is possible that our eavesdropper possesses a much more sensitive radio telescope than we. If he had something like the largest one ever proposed for Earth, namely the array of 1000 100-meter dishes called for by Project Cyclops, he could detect a BMEWS-type radar at a distance of 500 light years. In this case at least 1,000,000 stars are possible candidates for such an eavesdropper's location. But note that radio waves travel at the finite speed of one light year per year and thus it will take until the 25th century, or 500 years from now, before all of these stars have had a chance to be bathed in the radiation of our defense system radars!

After picking up a BMEWS (or other) acquisition signal, the observer needs at least 100 times more sensitivity in his equipment to reach the rich lode of *information signals* emanating from Earth. It turns out that television broadcast antennas (or "stations") are the most intense sources of such signals. All other services either have their transmitter power spread over too broad a frequency band (for instance, FM broadcasting and most radars) or they do not transmit continuously (ham radio operators) or from the same location on Earth each day (taxis, aircraft). Many signals, such as medium-wave AM broadcasting and almost all shortwave communications, never even penetrate the reflective layer of charged particles, called the *ionosphere*, which surrounds the Earth. We thus concentrate on TV broadcasting—all other services which leak from Earth are less intense and merely add to the background "noise" which a distant observer would measure in the direction of our Sun as seen in his sky.

TV BROADCASTING SIGNALS AND ANTENNAS

In order to understand why television is so valuable to the eavesdropper as an information signal, it will be helpful to discuss some of the characteristics of TV broadcasting signals. Perhaps the most important facts are that there are a large number of very powerful TV stations on Earth (see Figure 1), and that about one-half of a station's broadcast power resides in an extremely narrow band of frequencies, only about 0.1 Hertz (or 0.1 cycle per second) wide, called the *video carrier signal*. The other half of the power contains the picture information and is spread out in a complex manner over a far larger frequency range of about 5 Megahertz (5 million Hertz). Nowhere in this broader region is the power per Hertz even a thousandth that at the video carrier frequency. It would therefore be much more difficult for the eavesdropper to receive full program material than to simply detect the presence of the carrier signal. (Given the quality of most TV programs, we find this fact very reassuring!) An observer near Barnard's Star, at a distance of 6 light years from Earth, is thus about to receive television signals originating from the 1973 World Series, but he probably cannot find out that Oakland won! In the discussion below, we assume that only the video carrier signals of stations, *not* program material, are detected.

The combination of reasonably high power and small bandwidth means that the most powerful TV carrier signals can be detected at distances as large as one-tenth of those discussed for the BMEWS radars. The narrow-band nature of the signal also enables the observer to measure extremely accurate *Doppler shifts* in the frequency of the carrier signal. . . .

After his initial discovery of these radio waves from the direction of our Sun, our eavesdropper would undoubtedly first ask, "Is this some kind of strange natural radio emission, or has some form of civilization produced it?" It would seem that the narrowband nature of the signals would be one of the best clues that the signal is artificial in nature, as no astrophysical process (known to us) can channel comparable amounts of energy into such small frequency intervals. Other clues, such as polarization of the signals, also exist. And yet, who knows? Perhaps the theorists of another planet are clever enough to come up with a substance whose emission spectrum matches that of the observed radio waves! Clever theorists notwithstanding, for this discussion we assume that the signals from Earth will be recognized as artificial. . . . [Our eavesdropper could make the following scientific deductions from the signals: a map of the detected stations can be constructed (it would look much like Figure 1), the radius and rotation of Earth can be found as can Earth's annual motion about the sun and other vital orbital data. Earth's surface temperature and even the size of the transmitting antennas can be determined from the signals. The eavesdropper's job is not unlike that of an archeologist trying to understand an ancient city with a knowledge of only its street plan.]

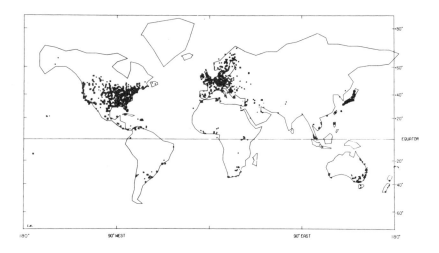

Figure 1. Map of the Earth showing the 2200 most powerful television transmitters, possessing about 97% of the world's total TV power. Note the absence of stations in the southern hemisphere and the marked concentrations in North America, Europe, Japan, and Australia. Full information for stations in the Soviet Union and China was not available, but estimates indicate that there is negligible television power in these countries. 896 transmitters in the United States are included.

SHOULD WE TRY TO EAVESDROP?

The above discussion is of course relevant to the larger issue of our own attempts at contact with extraterrestrial civilizations. We can make either of two basic assumptions about the first contact: (i) that it will arise through a purposeful attempt, perhaps through the use of an interstellar radio beacon, or (ii) that a civilization will be detected through no special efforts of its own. Most attention to date had been directed toward possibility (i), but in fact for the one civilization about which we do know something (our own), note that it has sent out virtually no purposeful signals, yet has been leaking radiation for several decades. How typical this situation will be in our own future or at any time for other galactic civilizations is impossible to say. For instance, cable television may replace the present system of broadcasting antennas, but new forms of radio leakage may just as well appear. It is true that the range of detection at any purposeful beacons is probably much larger than for leaking signals. But purposeful signals require decoding of any received message, while we have seen above that unintentional signals yield a great deal of information using only standard astronomical techniques. Not only that, but in a sense the information gained may be a more accurate reflection of the society's major concerns. At least this seems to be true for the case of our own civilization with its military and television leakage, although we might not wish to admit it.

In summary then, we should keep both possibilities in mind when searching for extraterrestrial signals. We cannot know whether the most likely signals to be detected will place us in the role of intended recipient or of eavesdropper.

Ann Druyan . . . . **Earth's Greatest Hits**

Ann Druyan, a novelist and one of the group involved in assembling the messages for Voyager 1 to carry into space, tells what those messages are and how the decisions to include specific items were reached.

> What will they think of me on the star of Venus Urania, how will they judge me, without seeing me?
> —Ludwig van Beethoven, in a letter to Baron von Gleichenstein, 1807.

On Aug. 20 the first of twin Voyager spacecraft left Cape Canaveral on a mission to reconnoiter Jupiter, Saturn and possibly Uranus as well. In about a dozen years from now, upon completion of its mighty allemande with those planets, it will be expelled from our solar system to begin what may be an eternity of wandering among the stars.

Secured to its side by satiny white titanium bolts are a porcelain cartridge, a diamond stylus and a copper phonograph record sprayed with gold. The whole package has been encased in aluminum to assure the record a sonorous one billion years, and engraved on its cover are playing instructions expressed in scientific language.

Astronomer Dr. Carl Sagan of Cornell; his wife, Linda Sagan; music and science writer Timothy Ferris and I were among the team involved in the challenging task of composing a 120-minute message for that record. We had only eight weeks to select the material we hoped would be worthy of such munificent postage.

We decided it should consist of greetings from people in many languages and from some whales, a 12-minute sound essay, 90 minutes of music and a series of blips for spacefaring extraterrestrials to decode into black-and-white and color photographs.

The likelihood that our message would ever be received by beings of another world was impossible to predict. We shall never know its eventual fate. Forty thousand years will pass before the spacecraft glides by even the nearest star, hundreds of millions of years as it roams among the stars of our galaxy, occasionally passing within a light year or so of a star, probably never closer. Making the record therefore became an oddly practical way of confronting some abstract questions about art and life on earth. Are human beings capable of making something universal? Who are we? What are the essential characteristics of our identity? How do you represent the earth? And, because Voyager was destined to cross vast distances of time and space, it presented us with an embodiment of the desert-island problem. You're allowed to take only a certain number of things with you to this isolated place. You're going to be there for quite a while. Think carefully. What will you take along? What can you bear to leave behind?

The record begins with 116 pictures: diagrams to indicate our address in the Milky Way; schematics of DNA and our chromosomes, our anatomy; our star, the sun; the chemistry of earth and our atmosphere; images of our oceans, rivers, deserts, mountains, continents, flowers, trees, insects, birds, animals, marine life, a snowflake. They were selected chiefly by Dr. Frank Drake, who is the director of the National Astronomy and Ionosphere Center, and by artist Jon Lomberg.

We are shown also in a variety of aspects of our social selves—eating, drinking, working, playing and dancing in a global spectrum of settings. There are photographs of human engineering achievements such as the Taj Mahal, the Great Wall of China and the Golden Gate Bridge. We are seen alone and in substantial aggregates, as in our modern cities. There's an illustration from Isaac Newton's "System of the World" which shows you how to put a cannonball into orbit. The sequence ends with pictures of a sunset, a string quartet, a violin and a page of sheet music of Beethoven's String Quartet in B flat, No. 13 (Op. 130).*

This section is followed by greetings from President Carter, Secretary General Kurt Waldheim, speakers in 60 different languages, some members of the United Nations Outer Space Committee—and some particularly cordial salutations from a couple of whales.

A 12-minute montage of earth's sounds follows. It opens with a giddy whirl of tones reflecting the motions of the sun's planets in their orbits—a musical readout of Johannes Kepler's "Harmonice Mundi," the mathematical tract whose echoes may still be found in the formulas that make Voyager possible. A roughly chronological sequence of sounds follows, beginning with the upheavals of our planet's genesis, through the vast rains that made the seas, to the initially tentative and later robust ferment of life. Human sounds venture forth from the chill winds of the ice ages, technology parades its noises (whose charms may be quaintly enhanced for extraterrestrials who have weathered their own machine age), and it concludes with a baby's first cries, a set of human brain and vital-sign recordings and the cold static of a pulsar. Since horse carts, chopping wood, the hiss of bus brakes and other sounds of our era take up as much time on the record as a ripple of primeval ponds, the sequence is open to the criticism that it, like our written history, vastly overemphasizes the last few thousand years at the expense of the

---

* Following the sheet music is an actual phrase from that quartet to demonstrate the relationship between musical notation and musical sounds.

millions that preceded them in the chronicle of our species. But if the sounds on the record accurately reflected the time scale of earth's four-and-a-half-billion-year history, all but the last few moments would have been only the gurgle of waves and whisper of wind across barren plains; mammals would have had to roar out all they had to roar in a few seconds and the proud accomplishments of all human civilization would have expired in a single beep of Morse code. If the denizens of a distant planet can make sense of the sound montage—and arguably it may be the easiest part of the record for an alien intelligence to relate to—perhaps they will not be wholly unacquainted with the paradoxes time engenders, and will listen in a tolerant spirit.

Three-quarters of the record is music. Choosing it was a stormy business— sometimes we argued until 3 or 4 o'clock in the morning. People who enjoy music tend to hold strong opinions about it, and since there was only so much time available on the record, everyone had to accept the likelihood that personal favorites would be left behind. Some of us felt that we had a debt to repay to a cherished piece of music by booking its passage on the record. Although we knew the record was going to parts unknown, that the odds on its recovery in interstellar space were very low and that if it is ever recovered by some unimaginable society, the happy day of its interception will postdate our lives by some hundreds of thousands of years—for all that, when a piece of music close to our hearts was eliminated we tended to feel as if it had been lost to earth, not space.

Our criteria in selecting the compositions were devised to represent music from around the world, to hint at something of the richness and diversity of our planet's human cultures, and to put nothing on the record that did not arouse general en- thusiasm—to include nothing out of a mere sense of duty. Clearly it would be im- possible to find earth's "best" music, whatever that might mean. And we were aware that as English-speaking Americans we carried the baggage of a specific culture and could not hope to divorce ourselves from our predispositions. But we tried to set aside these as best we could, without turning to the bloodless calcula- tions one associates with committees. In the process, each of us opened doors onto landscapes of beautiful music we'd never known existed. It was during these times that we found ourselves considering Dr. Lewis Thomas's solution. "I would vote for Bach," he wrote in *The Lives of a Cell*. All of Bach, streamed out into space, over and over again. We would be bragging, of course, but it is surely excusable for us to put the best possible face on at the beginning of such an acquaintance. We can tell the harder truths later."

Three Bach compositions are included on the record, and two by Beethoven. There is not one by Wagner, Debussy, or Brahms. We knew this was a controversial decision. But we felt that the task of "translation" might be made easier for extrater- restrials if we offered more than one work by a given composer, in that a composer's personal style can be extracted for each piece, helping to lay a foundation for inter- preting all the music. And, rightly or wrongly, it is difficult to offer up a swatch of the world's music without being a trifle generous to these two giants. Here's a look at seven of the 27 selections, and some thoughts on why we chose them:

Bach's Brandenburg Concerto No. 2, first movement. We chose Karl Richter's recording with the Munich Bach orchestra for its exuberant air—appropriate to a greeting—its technical excellence, and the cleanly recorded brass parts that should still sound distinctly from the grooves of the record when it marks its billionth birthday.

Johnny B. Goode, by Chuck Berry. Debate over this selection was particularly tense. Some of the dozens of persons consulted about the record argued that there should be no rock-and-roll on it at all. We asked ourselves whether we considered rock-and-roll because we'd been so immediately formed by its culture—and was it, in fact, just a spasm in musical history to which we were sympathetic? We decided that rock-and-roll is an example of two diverse cultures meeting in a distant place—Africa and Europe meeting in America. Others lobbied for something more recent, more refined: the Beatles, perhaps. Chuck Berry won out as an inventor of rock-and-roll who, unlike the equally fascinating Elvis Presley, is performing a song of his own composition.

New Guinea Men's House. A field recording made by Robert MacLennan, this has been identified by ethnomusicologist Alan Lomax as belonging to the oldest tradition of "primitive" music recorded unaltered by the music of what we call civilization. At least a thousand years old, it is hypnotic, monochromatic, and vastly different from anything else on the record.

Peruvian Woman's Wedding Song. One of the two South American selections, this is sung in a bell-like voice by an anonymous young girl who happened to be standing in front of musicologist John Cohen's field microphone. If birdsongs or any of the other pure outcries of earth's creatures have any resonance for inhabitants of other planets, we are inclined to think this song will, too.

Flowing Streams. When I called Dr. Chou Wen-chung of Columbia University and asked him to nominate a piece of Chinese music for the record, I expected that he would want some time to consider his answer. He didn't. " 'Flowing streams,' " he told me. "That's what you must put on your record. Because it is performed on the seven-stringed *ch'in,* an instrument that predates Christ by a couple of thousand years. Because 'Flowing Streams' has been a part of Chinese culture since the time of Confucius. Because it is a meditation on the human sense of affinity with the universe. Because all kinds of Chinese people, on every side of political divisions, would be moved by such a choice. And it must be the performance by the late virtuoso Kuan P'ing-Hu, the Heifetz of the *ch'in.* He was a very old man when he made this recording. Send this one and you will be telling a great deal about China." We heard it and made one of the easiest decisions of the record.

Dark Was the Night, by Blind Willie Johnson. Johnson was a blues and gospel guitarist from Texas, who never made enough money to support himself. There are no lyrics to this guitar nocturne, recorded in 1927, just a moan that sounds like a lonely, piercing question.

The fifth movement (cavatina) from Beethoven's String Quartet in B flat, No. 13 (Op. 130). We knew that the final piece would have the additional weight of a last word. We chose this exquisite piece because it is not an expression of any one single emotion; rather, it is a quiet, melodic statement of human pain, longing and hope. It is a complicated signature, full of ambiguities, like our own future.

Who will one day get the record? The crew of an interstellar caravel, routinely picking up old space probes, who may perhaps recognize Voyager as the work of an emerging civilization and spare it from the scrap furnaces? A world of huge beings who live on a time scale so grand that our music will sound to them no more engaging than the nervous jittering of insects? A living interstellar cloud that will feel the spacecraft as a tickle in the ribs? Or no one? The realm of the stars may be full of little probes like ours, lonely little hellos, or not. To find out which is the case, we shall have to look more deeply into that realm ourselves, and perhaps listen to its chorus of radio noise for signs of an intelligent signal.

If we one day hear from another world or encounter one of its artifacts, we will at least be able to point to modest efforts like the Voyager record, and say that we did not sit idly by, but tossed out a note or two in a bottle ourselves. The Voyager record is earth's cultural audition for the universe and in another sense, our application for citizenship in that vastness.

• DISCUSSION QUESTIONS •

1. Why do whale songs qualify as songs, rather than series of noises? How do they differ from bird songs? What does this reveal about whale intelligence? How does Payne compare the evolution of whale language to the evolution of language in humans?

2. How is information stored in the human being? What are the advantages bestowed by the capabilities of the cerebral cortex? Explain the cerebral cortex in terms of bits.

3. What does Taylor's article reveal about the ways in which the human brain is being studied? Is the brain a machine? If so, what is the nature of the machine?

4. In what ways might the study of the human brain be useful in trying to communicate with extraterrestrial intelligence? How does the human brain mirror the world in which humans live? Does that prevent humans from communicating with intelligences from vastly different extraterrestrial environments? Why?

5. Why is the study of the intelligence of other animals on Earth vital to the success of possible communication with extraterrestrial intelligences? What are its limitations?

6. What are the difficulties in sending information over interstellar distances? According to the Wetherill and Sullivan article, what information is being sent now?

7. What are the universal qualities of human language? Why are music and mathematics reputed to be universal languages? Do you think their universality extends beyond the confines of Earth? Why? Do you agree with the choices of information sent as "Earth's Greatest Hits"? Why were some composers represented by more than one piece of music? What do you think is the information most likely to be significant to extraterrestrials?

• ADDITIONAL ACTIVITIES •

Optional Projects

1. Putting yourself in the place of an extraterrestrial (as much as possible), watch a television program either with the sound off or in a language you don't understand. How might you interpret it? Write at least two versions.

2. Keep track of all your activities for five minutes. Include breathing, blinking, and other involuntary actions. How many are genetically determined? How many are learned? How many fall in a gray area between the two?

3. List all the methods of human communication you can think of. Annotate your list with comments on their impact on extraterrestrials.

4. Devise your own "Earth's Greatest Hits" message to extraterrestrials.

Supplementary Bibliography

Karl-Erik Fichtelius and Sverre Sjölander, *Smarter than Man? Intelligence in Whales, Dolphins, and Humans.* New York: Pantheon Books, 1972.
Views mammalian brain as a biocomputer and compares whales, dolphins, and humans with attention to physiological factors, evolution, language, and culture.

Stephen Jay Gould, *"An Early Start" in Natural History,* February, 1978.
New discoveries on the origin of life.

Beverly Karplus Hartline, "Einstein Pictures the X-ray Sky" in *Science,* July 6, 1979.
An article about HEAO-"Einstein," the second satellite X-ray telescope.

J.H. Piddington, *Radio Astronomy.* New York: Harper & Brothers, 1961.
A somewhat dated source with good basic information on the history and applications of radar astronomy.

Scientific American, September, 1979.
This entire issue was devoted to the brain—background information, recent research and future research suggested by it.

Chapter XII
ENCYCLOPAEDIA GALACTICA

• OVERVIEW •

IN THE SPECTRA of stars, in the slow rotation of galaxies, in the star-born elements that make up Earth lie an underlying predictability. The patterns, the forces, the laws of science seem to be the same everywhere in the universe. Therefore, since the laws of science seem to be common ground despite culture differences, if we ever speak to extraterrestrials, it will probably be in the language of science. They might not comprehend a smile or a poem, but they might understand a reiteration of a universal scientific law cast in a radio message containing within itself the clues to its own decoding—a Rosetta Stone of space.

Deciding upon the message is one thing. Deciding if there's anyone to send it to is another. Which of the pinpricks in the night sky, if any, are stars around which habitable planets revolve? And which of those habitable planets, if any, are actually inhabited? The narrowing down of probabilities is guesswork. We don't know.

An advanced civilization, one that might have colonized a galaxy, might very well have a sophisticated technology impossible for us to imagine. If they haven't approached us, it may be because we are in such an insignificant spot that they have assumed we aren't worth bothering with. Some "ufologists" would have it that "they" are hovering over us in flying saucers all the time. In nightmares, one might think of them coldly watching us as a superintelligent being might watch an ant colony. If contact is made, however, it will change our Earth civilization drastically.

• LEARNING OBJECTIVES •

1. Briefly describe Dr. Sagan's current position on the existence or appearance of U.F.O.s (unidentified flying objects) in the Earth's atmosphere.

2. Identify Jean Francois Champollion, describe his life's work, and relate it to the current search for extraterrestrial life and communications. Describe Dr. Sagan's conjecture about the nature and language of such communications.

3. List the reasons why Dr. Sagan believes radio astronomy is likely to be the prime means of searching for and communicating with other intelligent, "technical" civilizations.

4. Outline briefly how Dr. Sagan computes the probability of the existence of other technical civilizations in the universe with which human beings can potentially communicate. What does Sagan conclude is the least calculable variable?

5. Explain why Dr. Sagan believes contact between Earth and extraterrestrial civilizations will most likely be benevolent and beneficial, and describe how Dr. Sagan proposes we should conduct this communication.

• KEY TERMS AND NAMES •

Arecibo Observatory
Jean Francois Champollion
lenticular cloud

quasar
radio astronomy
Rosetta Stone

• ASSIGNMENT •

Watch COSMOS television series Program 12, "Encyclopedia Galactica."

Read Chapter 12, "Encyclopedia Galactica" in Carl Sagan's text, *Cosmos*, or other readings assigned by your instructor.

• READINGS •

Chang Hsieh . . . . Touching the Left Horn of a Snail

These words, by a Chinese writer of the 1400s, reveal the attitude of Chinese sailors toward visiting "alien" civilizations.

According to the writer's opinion, those who make carriages build them in workshops, but when they come forth to the open road, they are already adjusted to the ruts. So is is with good sea-captains. The wings of cicadas make no distinction between one place and another, while even the small scale of a beetle will measure the vast empty spaces. If you treat the barbarian kings like harmless seagulls (i.e. without any evil intentions), the trough-princes and the crest-sirens will let you pass everywhere riding on the wings (of the wind). Verily the Atlas-tortoise with mountain-islands for its hat is no different from (an ant) carrying a grain of corn. Coming into contact with barbarian peoples you have nothing more to fear than touching the left horn of a snail. The only things one should be really anxious about are the means of mastery of the waves of the seas—and, worst of all dangers, the minds of those avid for profit and greedy of gain.

Samuel Eliot Morison . . . . **Columbus' Contact with Native Americans** (from **Admiral of the Ocean Sea**)

On Columbus' first voyage to America, he stopped at Puerto Gibara in Cuba to clean the bottom of the Santa Maria *and was forced by high winds to stay there several days more. He made contact with the natives of the area.*

Samples were taken of the gumbo-limbo resin, which Columbus supposed to be mastic, and of the agave which he mistook for aloes. As a final reward to these nonresistant Indians of the Golden Age "without knowledge of what is evil, . . . and so timid that a hundred of them flee before one of ours," the Admiral kidnapped five young men who came aboard for a farewell visit, and then sent his boat ashore to bag "seven head of women, large and small, and three boys." The husbands and fathers of some came out and begged to join them, which was granted. Columbus explained that he wanted the youths to train as interpreters, and the women to keep them from getting spoiled; for he had already observed when voyaging for Portugal that the Negroes brought home from Guinea in order to learn the language received so much attention in Portugal that they were no good when returned to Africa. Two of the young men escaped at Tanamo Bay; none of the rest survived the voyage to Spain. . . . [Later, in Haiti, he met a cacique (a native leader) from whom he hoped to take gold.] Although Columbus might treat a visiting cacique with dignity and even honor, his real thoughts, as he recorded them in his Journal for the eyes of his sovereigns, indicate that he meant to take full advantage of the Tainos' weakness and good nature. "Your Highnesses may believe . . . that this island and all the others are as much yours as Castile, that here is wanting nothing save a settlement, and to command them to do what you will. For I with these people aboard, who are not many, could overrun all these islands without opposition; for already I have seen but three of these mariners go ashore where there was a multitude of these Indians, and all fled without their seeking to do them ill. They bear no arms, and are all unprotected and so very cowardly that a thousand would not face three; so they are fit to be ordered about and made to work, to sow and do aught else that may be needed, and you may build towns and teach them to go clothed and to adopt our customs." . . .

James Oberg . . . . **The Failure of the "Science" of Ufology**

James Oberg, a NASA engineer, describes his approach to UFOs as that of a "gentle skeptic" and "sympathetic critic."

In the 30 years since the current flying saucer fever began, the phenomenon has apparently been transformed from the property of cranks and crackpots to the subject of true scientific study. The sensational term "flying saucer" became the more semantically neutral "unidentified flying object," or "UFO." The study of such reports—the objects themselves, not being physically present, cannot be studied—came to be called "ufology."

The word has all the appearances of a true science, yet somehow that particular branch of study has *not* become accepted as a science. Can ufology really be considered a true science, or perhaps an infant science, or possibly an unborn science—or is it instead just a hysterical pregnancy? After all the labour, what has been produced?

Ufology has been shunned and by "traditional" science, a rejection which many participants in the movement see as a knee-jerk reaction to any new and unconventional idea. Ufologists regale themselves with anecdotes about Galileo, Giordano Bruno, Louis Pasteur and Charles Darwin, and often appear to contend that contemporary rejection of ufology is practically a canonisation of their field as a future science. "How much of yesterday's heresy is today's science?" they ask knowingly.

The answer, unfortunately, is very, very little. More scientific heresies of the past fell by the wayside, forgotten in our history books, and unnoticed by modern would-be Galileos. Ufology must have better credentials than simply its rejection by modern science. After all, in those 30 years since UFOs appeared, modern science has undergone several generations of radical revolutions in its comprehension of the Universe, from the cosmic and macrocosmic to the microscopic and subatomic scales.

The suspicion with which modern "establishment science" regards the UFO movement appears to be more closely connected with some disturbing characteristics of "ufology" itself. Although many negative feelings have, no doubt, been aroused by the crackpot aura with which the flying saucer movement has long been associated—despite the best efforts of a few serious ufologists—other criticism has been levelled at the very philosophical foundations of ufology. The inability of ufological theorists to come to grips with these objections represents the most serious roadblock to the acceptance of ufology as a legitimate branch of modern science.

The criticisms are essentially these: ufology allegedly refuses to play by the rules of scientific thought, demanding instead special exemptions from time-tested procedures of data verification, theory testing, and the burden of proof. Ufologists assert the existence of some extraordinary stimulus behind a small fraction of the tens of thousands of UFO reports on file. The cornerstone of the alleged proof is the undisputed observation that a small residue of such reports cannot at present be explained in terms of prosaic (if rare) phenomena. Yet this claim is invalid: it is clearly not logical to base the existence of a positive ("true UFOs exist") on the grounds of a hypothetical negative ("no matter what the effort, some UFO reports cannot be explained").

RUMOURS, LIES AND FRAUD

This latter fallacy can be called the "residue fallacy," and it has been addressed by philosophers of science numerous times in the past, apparently without effect on ufologists. Writing in *Science* magazine in 1969, Hudson Hoagland expressed it as follows: "The basic difficulty inherent in any investigation of phenomena such as those of . . . UFOs is that it is impossible for science ever to prove a universal negative. There will always be cases which remain unexplained because of lack of data, lack of repeatability, false reporting, wishful thinking, deluded observers, rumours, lies, and fraud. A residue of unexplained cases is not a justification for continuing an investigation after overwhelming evidence has disposed of hypotheses of supernormality, such as beings from outer space. . . . Unexplained cases are simply unexplained. They can never constitute evidence for any hypothesis."

It is not necessary to conjure up visions of blind, drunk and dishonest UFO percipients to cast doubt on UFO reports. The vast majority of UFO witnesses apparently are honest, sober and intelligent people faced with an extraordinary perception. Yet there are amazingly many obvious and subtle ways in which such perceptions can be understandably generated. And there is bound to be an artificial residue of unexplained cases, a residue created purely by bizarre coincidences, by limitations on human perception and memory, or by rare undocumented natural occurrences. Additional sources of unexplained sightings could be human activities which are never publicised due to military security, to the illegality of the activity, or to plain ignorance on the part of the human agents of the activity that they had caused such a fuss. That residue will never be solved, and no extraordinary stimulus need be referred to.

In a similar fashion, the existence of unsolved crimes, unfound missing persons, unexplained aircraft or automobile accidents and similar all-too-familiar manifestations of our less-than-perfect knowledge of events cannot be taken to prove the need for the existence of some extraordinary criminals, some extraordinary kidnappers, or some extraordinary traffic saboteurs. "Unexplained cases are simply unexplained," to repeat Hoagland's perceptive assertion. "They can never constitute evidence for any hypothesis."

To dedicated ufologists, such a line of reasoning is denounced as a confusion between IFOs ("identifiable flying objects") and true UFOs. According to Dr. J. Allen Hynek whose Center for UFO Studies in Evanston, Illinois, finds that at least 95 per cent of all UFOs reported to it are in fact IFOs: "Experienced investigators quickly recognise IFOs for what they are . . . but sometimes it takes hard work to unmask the masquerader."

Sceptics such as aviation journalist Philip J. Klass take exception to Hynek's confidence and point to cases published by his own centre, cases which were solved only by strokes of unexpected luck on the part of researchers. All too often, these sceptics claim, the "hard work" prescribed by Hynek is absent—and the "sheer luck" which allowed the unmasking of some tricky IFOs masquerading as UFOs is not available. The result is that many (if not, as sceptics claim, all) of the official UFOs on the list of unsolved cases are still camouflaged IFOs.

Such a hazy line between IFOs (which provide only data about the limitations of the reliability of eyewitness testimony) and UFOs (which are alleged by ufologists to mark a potential breakthrough in human science) is an appallingly weak basis for the foundation of the new would-be science of ufology. That weakness is accentuated by another highly suspicious and non-scientific feature of ufology, an extremely cavalier attitude towards verification of data.

ADVERTISING TRICKS

Ufology is still struggling to achieve scientific and popular respectability, so it is perhaps understandable that public pronouncements of ufologists would be primarily in the persuasive rather than expository vein. It can thus be observed that all the traditional tricks of the Madison Avenue advertising executive's trade are followed: appeals to authority ("Jimmy Carter saw a UFO"; "our heroic astronauts have seen UFOs!"); assertions of the consequent ("the Universe is so large that other civilisations *must* exist out there!"); the bandwagon appeal ("Most Americans now believe in UFOs!"); the conspiratorial appeal ("The government knows all about it but is hiding the truth"); and the salvation appeal ("The people from space will come to bail us out of our self-inflicted miseries"). It is not necessary at first to examine the actual validity of such statements. What is important is to recognise them for what they are: tactics of illogical persuasion.

At the same time, most of what is commonly published about ufology is undeniably nonsense. UFO proponents such as Hynek are as adamant in the criticism of the news media exploitation of UFO stories as any sceptic could be. For the publishing industry and the news media, UFO stories are good business; they combine human interest, comic relief, scary stories, and swipes at government cover-ups and know-it-all scientists. It is based on such misinformation (and not a little disinformation) that the vast majority of the public has formed its attitudes about UFOs. To say, then, that "most American believe in UFOs"is to testify not to the scientific credentials of ufology but to the effectiveness of the media mythmakers.

Few choose to look behind the myths. The much-touted "Jimmy Carter UFO," for example, was *never* investigated by any of the ufologists who flaunted it or by any of the newsmen who advertised it—they simply passed it on as a good story, a useful anecdote. Yet when one sceptical young investigator named Robert Sheaffer tracked the case down, he uncovered gross inaccuracies in Carter's four-year-old recollections of the date and location of the event, and also came up with testimony from other witnessses which helped determine an entirely prosaic solution to the account. Nevertheless, the "Jimmy Carter UFO" is still constantly being referred to by UFO spokesmen who, due to an unconscious media blackout of sceptical work such as Sheaffer's, probably do not even know or care that it has been investigated and "solved."

Another glaring example of the total disregard for authenticity of evidence by most ufologists is the oft-repeated assertion that "astronauts have seen them too." Dozens of accounts have been collected of space pilots seeing and photographing UFOs; more than 20 such stories were featured in Hynek's *Edge of Reality*, a book which was billed as a "progress report,"on the state of ufology.

Yet not one of these cases has any relevance to "true UFOs," as they are for the most part frauds and hoaxes conjured up by unscrupulous writers and UFO buffs (several blatant photographic forgeries have been identified in these stories), or misunderstandings by citizens concerning the meaning of ordinary space jargon, or in a few cases, reports of passing satellites which in no way appear to be extraordinary. Yet with selective omission of explanatory data, with exaggeration, misquotation, or even fabrication of alleged "voice transcripts," and with deliberate accusations of "government cover-up," such stories form a major pillar of the public's "belief" in UFOs.

Hynek visited NASA's Houston space centre in July 1976 and was shown the original films and tapes involved in the most publicised space UFO stories. He later told colleagues that he deeply regretted including the UFO stories in his book without verifying them, and that he was satisfied that no "true UFOs" were among them. Referring to the astronaut-UFO stories in an interview with *Playboy* in Jamuary 1978, Hynek testified that, "I went to Houston and saw the photographs, and I must confess that I was not impressed."

The "Carter UFO" and the "astronaut UFOs" underscore a key problem in the acceptance of ufology as a science: ufologists in general have not been as willing as Hynek to retract endorsements of explained cases, and have preferred instead to continually recirculate and embellish the same stories. The authenticity of UFO reports, as portrayed in the popular press, therefore remains highly questionable— and justly so.

Such a problem with the "disproof" of UFO evidence points to yet another major weakness of the philosophical foundations of ufology. The burden of proof, which customarily lies with the claimants of supernormality (or, in a criminal trial, of the guilt of the accused, who is "innocent until proven guilty"), has been shifted to the sceptics, who are in the case of the UFOs required to *disprove* the evidence. In the Carter-UFO and the astronaut-UFOs, it was the sceptic who investigated and solved the cases—while ufologists assumed the cases were authentic until proven otherwise (and most *still* believe so).

And yet the rules of science are clear: extraordinary claims demand extraordinary proof. The thesis of ufology is an indictment against the ability of contemporary science to explain the Universe, and it must prove such an indictment as every other such proponent must prove it: the need for a modification of our current model of reality must be established beyond reasonable doubt.

The very foundation of ufology is contrary to this time-tested procedure. For ufologists, the mere existence of unsolvable cases is allegedly proof of the need to modify modern science. For ufology, extraordinary reports can be considered to be valid data until disproved. And, in the most devastating departure from scientific methodology, ufologists reject the concept of "falsifiability" of scientific theories.

No theory can be considered scientific until it can be formulated so as to be disprovable, or falsifiable. That is, the theory must explain a portion of the Universe in such a way that further observations or experiments will either fail or conform to the theory's predictions, or *will* conform to it (while, preferably, not conforming to traditional predictions). Einstein's prediction of the bending of star light observed near the Sun during a total eclipse is a famous example of such a procedure.

Yet after three decades of aimless speculation, no scientific theories worthy of the name have been produced by ufology. It is thus a sterile "science." Every wild speculation is touted as a "new theory," yet none of them makes predictions which would, by not coming true, discredit the theory. Here again, the processes of thought which characterise "ufology" cannot be classified as "scientific."

The most regrettable aspect of this current unscientific state for "ufology" is that it is not a judgement on the actual validity of many of the published speculations about what might be behind the "true UFO" sightings (if any exist). Alien spacecraft could well be visiting Earth, and there are at least a dozen valid reasons why "they" might decide not to make overt contact, while allowing Earthmen to catch glimpses of them. UFOs might well represent some other phenomenon, such as "psychic projections," "time machines," a terrestrial but undiscovered civilisation or life form, or many other similarly bizarre possibilities. The only thing that can be said scientifically is that none of these suggestions has been even suggested, much less proved in any rigorous sense.

The pity is that if such eventualities should come to pass, and the ufologists are proved "right," they will in all probability have impeded rather than accelerated the acceptance of that phenomenon by traditional science. This is because the new theories will most likely be championed by those ufologists already badly discredited by too many cries of "wolf!", by too many endorsements of what subsequently turned out to have been hoaxes, and by too many anti-scientific assertions and claims. They would be right only by accident, not by their virtue.

WHAT IS UFOLOGY?

If ufology is not a science, what then is it? It might be considered as a protest movement against the impersonality and specialisation of modern science, which has all but eliminated the role of the "citizen-scientist," the amateur investigator who in the past contributed substantially to the development of science through part-time dabbling. Belief in UFOs is also an undeniably attractive "ego trip," a posturing of inside information and secret lore, the possession of which puts its intimates apart from and above the rest of the unimaginative world. Such speculations demand more scientific attention of sociologists.

Nor would it be fair to judge ufology by the quality and quantity of the outright crackpots whom it attracts—other fields, such as medicine, religion, education and economics, have certainly attracted crackpots as well. Yet it cannot be overlooked that ufology seems to have attracted more than its fair share of cranks, and that it has failed to police adequately its own ranks in this regard.

Where is the "ufology" movement likely to be after *another* 30 years? Perhaps new evidence will finally appear which can stand up to scientific scrutiny. Perhaps self-styled ufologists will establish truly scientific standards of evidence, will accept the burden of proof, will produce "falsifiable" theories, and will seek to formulate their science on positive rather than negative logic. Perhaps something significant will come out of this after all.

Many sceptical observers join ufologists in hoping so, because if any of the claims of ufology prove valid it would indeed rate as a major scientific breakthrough, perhaps one of the most important such events in human history (even if not, the UFO movement would then "merely" be the most powerful public delusion of the century, which is in itself well worthy of sociological and psychological study). But in more cynical moments, such sceptics fall back upon the famous quotation attributed by Boswell to Samuel Johnson when he learned of the news of a friend's second marriage. "Ahh," Johnson is quoted as saying, "the triumph of hope over experience."

Trudy E. Bell. . . . .**The Grand Analogy:**
History of the Idea of Extraterrestrial Life

The author, a science historian, provides a capsule history of the idea of extraterrestrial life. The first part of her article, not reproduced here, covers the period from the first century B.C. to the invention of the telescope in the early 17th century.

The telescope revealed beyond doubt that the moon was a world much like the earth, with rugged mountains and large dark flat areas smooth as seas; clearly it was a solid opaque body that reflected the light of the sun and no light of its own. The changing phases of Venus were so much like the moon's that Venus, too, must be a body like the moon. And if these bodies were so much like the earth in some ways, could it be that indeed they were exactly like the earth in all ways?

A number of Seventeenth Century authors explored that question, cautiously speculative. By far the most famous book on the subject was the engaging *Entretiens sur la pluralite des mondes* published in 1686 (the year before Newton's *Principia*) by a 28-year-old playwright named Bernard le Bouvier de Fontenelle. The book is written in the form of a delightful dialogue over half a dozen starlit evenings between Monsieur L———— and a fictitious quick-minded Marchioness of G————. Both the flavor and the essence of the conversations are embodied in one particularly nice passage:

"I must tell you [says the monsieur], that in love and the mathematics, people reason much alike: allow ever so little to a lover, yet presently after you must grant him more; nay, more and more, which will at last go a great way; in like manner, grant but a mathematician one minute principle, he immediately draws a consequence, to which you must necessarily assent; and from this consequence another, till he leads you so far, whether you will or no, that you have much ado to believe him. . . . Now this way of arguing have I made use of. The moon, said I, is inhabited, because she is like the earth; and the other planets are inhabited, because they are like the moon; I find the fixed stars to be like our sun, therefore I attribute to them what is proper to him: you are now going too far to be able to retreat, therefore you must go forward with a good grace."

Fontenelle's *Plurality of Words,* as it was called, was read so avidly that it was translated from French into all the major languages of Europe; it had at least three separate English translations, one of which ran through six editions by 1737. One of its readers was none other than Christian Huygens, who actually felt that Fontenelle did not go far enough in his reasoning. Then in his 60s, Huygens put pen to paper and gave the world *Cosmotheoros* (Latin for "Theory of the Universe") in which he dispassionately and critically examined the possibility of life on other worlds. . . . [Huygens tried to determine the distance of stars and methodically reasoned from analogy with the earth that all the planets must have plants, animals, and intelligent life, all adapted to the heat or cold of their respective environments.]

Huygens's scientific reasoning about the existence of extraterrestrial life seemed to be confirmed by the rapid astronomical discoveries of the Enlightenment. Newton's laws of gravity established a physical connection between all the bodies in the universe, and his first law of motion established the existence of inertia and momentum, thus eliminating the last Aristotelian need for a finite universe and *Primum Mobile.* James Bradley's observations of the aberration of starlight conclusively demonstrated that the earth was indeed moving around the sun. Furthermore, William Herschel's observations of double stars revealed that light-years away from the earth, bodies were behaving according to the same laws of gravity and motion that our own solar system was, proving finally that there was no difference between celestial matter and terrestrial matter—the universe was indeed all of a piece.

What powerful tool that was! It implied for once and for all that reasoning about other planetary systems by analogy with our own was indeed a valid approach. Even more exciting, the nebular hypothesis of Immanuel Kant and later Pierre Simon Laplace that the sun and planets condensed out of a spinning cloud of gas and dust implied that planetary systems were a natural accompaniment to the formation of stars. These discoveries opened the way for a veritable flood of Eighteenth Century writings—ranging from scholarly treatises to cheerful essays in almanacs—setting out to prove the existence of extraterrestrial life and speculate what it was like.

Huygens's theological reasoning also threw open the way for others to demonstrate that—lo and behold!—the existence of a plurality of inhabited worlds actually glorified Scripture. In an influential work entitled *Astro-Theology* published in 1715, William Derham rushed in where Huygens dared not tread, populating all the bodies in the universe, even the sun and comets. "How can we say they are not inhabited?" he asked. "How can we place such limits on the infinitude of God's capabilities?" With such arguments the question of extraterrestrial life began migrating into a highly theological realm, until in the first half of the Nineteenth Century Thomas Dick unconsciously demonstrated the irony of Bruno's death by declaring in his *Sidereal Heavens:* ". . . though the Scriptures never directly or explicitly treat of this subject, the doctrine of a plurality of worlds *is embodied in many passages of the sacred writings*" (his italics).

Now, to be sure, not every astronomer felt that the existence of extraterrestrial life was a foregone conclusion. Although by the Nineteenth Century negative views on the subject were prone to attack, there were a minority of dissenters, the most notable of whom was the British philosopher William Whewell. In his *Plurality of Worlds* of 1851 Whewell stated that he was skeptical about the concept of extraterrestrial life on theological grounds because he thought it unnecessary: to him the creation of man was the great event of the universe and he did not think it at all derogatory to divine wisdom to have arranged all the other bodies of the universe to provide an elegant setting for the existence of such a being.

On scientific grounds Whewell did not settle for the assumption of his predecessors that life would arise everywhere and adapt itself to the conditions under which it existed. On the contrary, he felt that certain conditions were necessary for life to arise at all. Neptune, Uranus, Saturn, and Jupiter were simply too far from the sun and too cold and dark for life; moreover, their gravitational fields are so great that at best any life there would not have a skeleton, but would "be cartilaginous and glutinous masses . . . boneless, watery, pulpy creatures" floating in the liquid environment. On Mars he abstains from commenting: "(We) need not discuss the question whether there are intelligent beings on the surface of Mars . . . till we have better evidence that there are living things at all." Mercury and Venus he depopulates in a page as being too close to the sun.

"The earth, alone, is placed at the border where the conditions of life are combined; ground to stand upon; air to breathe; water to nourish vegetables, and thus, animals . . . ; and with this, a due supply of light and heat, and due energy of the force of weight. All these conditions are, in our conception, required for life; that all these conditions meet, elsewhere than in the earth's orbit, we see strong reason to disbelieve . . . That the earth is inhabited, is not a reason for believing that the other planets are so, but for believing they are not so."

In that passage Whewell distinguished himself as the first writer to describe what is called the zone of habitability. He also seems to be one of the first to recognize that life on a planet does not necessarily mean intelligent life, an assumption implicit in the writings of his predecessors.

The Nineteenth Century was a bustling, active, exciting era for astronomy. For the first time astronomers possessed big telescopes for gathering light from faint stars and for examining details on planets; for the first time they possessed spectroscopes for sifting the light to determine their chemical constitution. With the advent of tools for probing the physical secrets of the universe, theological arguments about the conditions on the planets began to have less force, and scientific arguments had more. . . . [Lowell's speculations about Mars and its canals built by an intelligent race are discussed.]

When the photographs and observations of Mars during its opposition in 1907 failed to reveal anything new, different, or exciting, however, popular interest in the planet began to wane. Moreover, that disappointment was only one in a series of disappointments about the planets. Whereas the discoveries of the Eighteenth Century had emphasized the kinship of the earth with the rest of the universe the wealth of astronomical data gathered in the Nineteenth Century pointed up the differences between the earth and the rest of the universe. It wasn't enough that they shared the same physics and chemistry. Spectroscopic observations indicated that Mars was a frigid desert, populated at most by lichens. Venus seemed to be a swamp, at best roamed by dinosaurs as in the earth's own past. The rest of the solar system was totally inhospitable: the moon was airless, Mercury was a heap of slag, Jupiter and the other giant planets were bloated balls of poisonous gases.

Even more disheartening, the prospects outside the solar system also looked grim. By the mid-1800s it had been observed that the sun, which contains the overwhelming majority of the mass in the solar system, has only a small fraction of the angular momentum; the rest was possessed by the planets. Since no way was known for the sun to get rid of angular momentum, that disparity constituted a real objection to the nebular hypothesis. To explain the fact, various catastrophic theories of planetary formation were proposed. One of the most popular was the Chamberlin-Moulton theory, which hypothesized that the planets condensed from material pulled out from the sun by the gravitational attraction of a star passing close by. The implication of all the catastrophic theories, however, was that the formation of a solar system was an exceedingly rare event. How much rarer must be life.

The result of such disappointments was that during the first half of the Twentieth Century the books and articles discussing the possibility of intelligent life in the universe were noticeably less exuberant—some cautious to the point of pessimism.

It is intriguing to note, however, that this pessimism in science coincided with the birth of the lusty, burgeoning genre of early modern science fiction, which had its heroes swashing their buckles in steaming Venusian swamps or on the shifting sands of Mars, rescuing voluptuous damsels in distress from the clutches of green and drooling monsters. Now, science fiction is very old: its roots go back at least to the Seventeenth Century, when the initial speculations about a plurality of inhabited worlds loosed the imaginations of Kepler, Cyrano, and later even Poe. But these older science fiction works were rather isolated phenomena, because, I suspect, the idea of life on other worlds was so widely accepted that people could satisfy their yearnings and curiosity about extraterrestrial life in books of speculative fact. Only when theological arguments lost weight and scientific arguments seemed to indicate that the probability of extraterrestrial life was slim, did science fiction in the modern sense begin to appear—almost as if thwarted hopes and dreams were channeled into speculative fiction.

In the short run the rise of science fiction had a negative effect on the concept of extraterrestrial life: it became associated with LGMs (Little Green Men) and the extravagant exploits of space opera. Moreover after 1947 with the widely publicized sighting by Kenneth Arnold of an unidentified flying object (UFO), the idea of extraterrestrial life was also co-opted by the flying saucer cults. To serious, conservative investigators, the idea of extraterrestrial life had not only been shelved by science, it had fallen off the shelf into bad company—and I suspect that all these associations were what conspired to make the idea temporarily distasteful.*

In spite of the fact that the idea of extraterrestrial life *per se* languished in the early Twentieth Century, astronomers, biologists, and engineers were independently making contributions that eventually met in powerful combination.

By 1931 the spectroscope revealed the curious fact that although hot, brilliant, massive stars were spinning rapidly on their axes, rotating once in a period of hours or days, there was a fairly sharp dividing line below which smaller, cooler stars were spinning very slowly, rotating perhaps only once per month—exactly like the sun. Where did all their angular momentum go? Might all the myriad of slowly spinning stars in the galaxy also be accompanied by systems of planets—exactly like the sun? Within the following decade or two, astronomers returned to the nebular hypothesis, with newly-discovered principles of magnetohydrodynamics playing a key role in solving the angular momentum problem.

---

* This hypothesis seems to be supported by the fact that today, now that extraterrestrial life is once again a reputable field for speculative fact, science fiction is being incorporated into mainstream literature.

In the early Twentieth Century radio developed, and in the 1930s it was discovered that the universe was alive with radio signals. Radio astronomy was born: astronomers began to "listen" to the stars and the gas and dust between them, penetrating regions blocked to the narrow range of visible light.

Meanwhile, biochemists were hypothesizing that life of the earth began spontaneously in a "hot, thin soup" of amino acids, sugars, proteins, and organic compounds in a lightning-stormy hydrogen-rich atmosphere of the primordial earth. Laboratory experiments seemed to verify this, implying that life might be an intrinsic property of molecules past a certain stage of complexity. And subsequently organic molecules were found deep inside certain meteorites and in clouds of dust in interstellar space, suggesting that carbon compounds tend to form even in hostile environments.

But perhaps most significant of all, on October 4, 1957, a Soviet rocket thundered off its launch pad, split the atmosphere, and injected a beeping satellite the size of a basketball into orbit around the earth, Sputnik. With that one decisive stroke the human race "slipped the surly bonds of earth"—and 12 years later reached up and touched the moon.

The impact of space travel on the idea of extraterrestrial life was dizzyingly profound. Suddenly perspective was altered: visiting other bodies in the universe was no longer a fantastic dream but was within the grasp of reality—and so for the first time, was the possibility of finding out first-hand whether there was indeed life on other worlds.

CAN WE FIND OUT?

The first human being had not even left the surface of the earth to venture into space when the new hope, the new optimism leapt up to embrace the stars. All the seemingly independent threads of investigation that led to the new optimism were gathered together into one bundle by Harlow Shapley. In 1958, in his delightful book *Of Stars and Men*, Shapley was the first to put numbers to the probability of life on other worlds. Suppose, he estimated, that only one star in a thousand has a planetary system, that only one of those systems in a thousand has a planet in the zone of habitability, that only one of *those* planets in a thousand has the proper chemical composition for life. Why, that meant that one out of a trillion (10^{12}) planets meets all tests for life; and since there are some one hundred million trillion (10^{20}) observable stars in the universe, then that meant there are a minimum of 100 million opportunities for life in the universe. Personally Shapley felt that the estimate was between 1,000 and one million times too *low*.

The effect of Shapley's book was electrifying. In 1959 Giuseppe Cocconi and Phillip Morrison published an article in *Nature* titled "Searching for Interstellar Communications" in which they suggested we listen for intelligent signals from several nearby sun-like stars at the radio wavelength of atomic hydrogen, 21 centimeters. With their last paragraph they threw the question of extraterrestrial life back into scientific repute:

"The reader may seek to consign these speculations wholly to the domain of science fiction.We submit, rather, that the foregoing line of argument demonstrates that the presence of interstellar signals is entirely consistent with all we now know, and that if signals are present the means of detecting them is now at hand . . . We therefore feel that a discriminating search for signals deserves a considerable effort. The probability of success is difficult to estimate; but if we never search, the chance of success is zero."

Although the idea of communicating with extraterrestrial beings is not a new one—Gauss, Littrow, and several other Nineteenth Century astronomers entertained various schemes for signalling Mars with light—the suggestions were isolated phenomena until the development of radio in the Twentieth Century.

Apparently the earliest discussion of the problem of building up a "lingua cosmica" was an article in 1920 by H. W. and C. Wells Nieman in *Scientific American*, called "What Shall we Say to Mars?" In it they suggested sending a series of signals that could be combined in such a way that it would form a pictorial message—a message remarkably similar in part to the two-and-a-half-minute message sent in 1974 from the Arecibo radio telescope in Puerto Rico toward the globular cluster M13 in Hercules. The problem of an interplanetary vocabulary was discussed at greater length by Lancelot Hogben in his article "Astroglossa, or First Steps in Celestial Syntax" in the *Journal of the British Interplanetary Society* in 1952, and by Hans Freudenthal eight years later in his book *Lincos: Design of a Language for Cosmic Intercourse.*

Today the problem is receiving considerable study, because only in the 1960s and 1970s has the technology become available for a serious search for extraterrestrial intelligence. In 1974 Carl Sagan pointed out that if on another planet there were another civilization only as advanced as ours with a radio telescope just like the one we already possess at Arecibo, the two radio telescopes could be essentially anywhere in the Milky Way galaxy and still communicate with each other.

Over the past 10 or 15 years scores of technical conferences, hundreds of books, thousands of articles and innumerable lectures have addressed the question of life on other worlds, ways of detecting it, and the implications—both exhilarating and threatening—that its discovery might have on our science and society. The search for it has begun. One of the principal purposes of the Viking mission to Mars was to search for evidence of microbial life—and the results were tantalizingly ambiguous. The plaques attached to the Pioneer spacecraft and the records of terrestrial sights and sounds included with the Voyager spacecraft are as much greeting cards addressed to "Occupant, Universe" as they are interstellar graffiti: "Homo sapiens was here."

On a very modest scale half a dozen astronomers under Stuart Bowyer at the Hat Creek Radio Observatory of the University of California have begun Project SERENDIP: Search for Extraterrestrial Radio Emissions from Nearby Developed Interstellar Populations.

Searches have also been conducted or are in progress at the National Radio Astronomy Observatory at Green Bank, West Virginia, the National Astronomy and Ionosphere Center at Arecibo, Puerto Rico, the Ohio State-Ohio Wesleyan Radio Observatory, Delaware, Ohio, the National Research Council Observatory at Algonquin Park, Canada, and at several observatories in the U.S.S.R.

The subject of searching for extraterrestrial intelligence has become sufficiently reputable that in the past three years an article on it was published in *Scientific American* and an entire number of the *Proceedings of the Royal Society of London* was occupied with "A Discussion on the Recognition of Alien Life." The sheer tonnage of wood pulp and volume-hours of warm air lavished on the subject can easily lead on to the happy assumption that intelligent extraterrestrial life not only exists but is friendly and eager to see us wave to it across the light-years. (Some uncritical minds even assume it has already contacted us.)

In backlash to such confident press, a number of authors have constructed detailed arguments based on contradictions in internal logic, devoted to showing that we have no reason at all to assume that life developed elsewhere in the universe and that even if it had, the structure of its society of the existence of interstellar travel might preclude us from discovering it or communicating with it all.

Arguments of this type impress me as being the modern-day equivalent of the medieval debates as to how many angels can dance on the head of a pin. On the basis of exactly zero data, careful mathematical formulae are devised to show how many aliens we cannot hope to detect. Although the arguments are phrased in terms of communicating with extraterrestrial life, however, the real issue being argued is nothing less than *the grand analogy* that forms the philosophical foundation of modern astronomy: the assumption that the laws of physics and chemistry and the mathematical probabilities in the universe are everywhere the same. Without that assumption, astronomy would consist only of gathering data about an infinite number of unrelated special cases. The grand analogy has been a fruitful tool for 350 years. If one truly wants to find out if extraterrestrial life exists—and I suspect that the authors of the negative arguments simply do not—one must begin somewhere, and the grand analogy is all we have. It's even been suggested that the search for extraterrestrial life would be an excellent test of our assumption about the universality of the universe.

On the other hand, the fact remains that we still have exactly zero direct evidence in favor of extraterrestrial life. No planet has ever been seen around another star, no LGM has ever radioed to us: "Mind if I drop in for tea?" Too much flashy overconfidence about the existence of extraterrestrial intelligence could whip up public fervor for a great search, only to create a bitter taste if success is not immediate. After all, if we look at all the wrong stars first, or listen at the wrong wavelengths, a search could take years, even decades.

Nonetheless, we have much circumstantial evidence about the universe that gives us hope that indeed there is a plurality of inhabited worlds. Moreover, that hope is held today for the same reason that it sprang eternal centuries ago: the grand analogy. *The difference is that today, for the first time in human history, we have the capability to stop speculating and to find out.*

Freeman Dyson . . . . **Extraterrestrials**

We cannot know if extraterrestrial intelligence exists, says Freeman Dyson, a physics professor at the Institute for Advanced Study in Princeton. He proposes a way to look for it, in case it does exist.

In the year 1918 a brilliant new star, called by astronomers Nova Aquilae, blazed for a few weeks in the equatorial sky. It was the brightest nova of this century. The biologist Haldane was serving with the British Army in India at the time and recorded his observation of the event:

> Three Europeans in India looking at a great new star in the Milky Way. These were apparently all of the guests at a large dance who were interested in such matters. Amongst those who were at all competent to form views as to the origin of this cosmoclastic explosion, the most popular theory attributed it to a collision between two stars, or a star and a nebula. There seem, however, to be at least two possible alternatives to this hypothesis. Perhaps it was the last judgement of some inhabited world, perhaps a too successful experiment in induced radioactivity on the part of some of the dwellers there. And perhaps also these two hypotheses are one, and what we were watching that evening was the detonation of a world on which too many men came out to look at the stars when they should have been dancing.

A few words are needed to explain Haldane's archaic language. He used the phrase "induced radioactivity" to mean what we now call nuclear energy. He was writing fifteen years before the discovery of fission made nuclear energy accessible to mankind. In 1924 scientifically educated people were aware of the enormous store of energy that is locked up in the nucleus of uranium and released slowly in the process of natural radioactivity. The equation $E = mc^2$ was already well known. But attempts to speed up or slow down natural radioactivity by artificial means had failed totally. The nuclear physicists of that time did not take seriously the idea that "induced radioactivity" might one day place in men's hands the power to release vast quantities of energy for good or evil purposes. Haldane had the advantage of being an outsider, a biologist unfamiliar with the details of nuclear physics. He was willing to go against the opinion of the experts in suggesting "induced radioactivity" as a possible cause of terrestrial or extraterrestrial disasters.

The example of Nova Aquilae raises several questions which we must answer before we can begin a serious search for evidence of intelligent life existing elsewhere in the universe. Where should we look, and how should we recognize the evidence when we see it? Nova Aquilae was for several nights the second brightest star in the sky. One had to be either very blind or very busy not to see it. Perhaps it was an artifact of a technological civilization, as Haldane suggested. How can we be sure that it was not? And how can we be sure that we are not now missing equally conspicuous evidence of extraterrestrial intelligence through not understanding what we see? There are many strange and poorly understood objects in the sky. If one of them happens to be artificial, it might stare us in the face for decades and still not be recognized for what it is.

In 1959 the physicists Cocconi and Morrison proposed a simple solution to the problem of recognition of artificial objects. They proposed that we listen for radio messages from extraterrestrial civilizations. If indeed such messages are being transmitted by our neighbors in space with the purpose of attracting our attention, the messages will be coded in a form which makes their artificiality obvious. Cocconi and Morrison solve the recognition problem by assuming that the beings who transmit the message cooperate with us in making it easy to recognize. The message by its very existence proves that its source must be artificial. A year after Cocconi and Morrison made their proposal, Edward Purcell carried their idea a stage further and described an interstellar dialogue of radio signals traveling to and fro across the galaxy:

> What can we talk about with our remote friends? We have a lot in common. We have mathematics in common, and physics, and astronomy. . . . So we can open our discourse from common ground before we move into the more exciting exploration of what is not common experience. Of course, the exchange, the conversation, has the peculiar feature of built-in delay. You get your answer back decades later. But you are sure to get it. It gives your children something to live for and look forward to. It is a conversation which is, in the deepest sense, utterly benign. No one can threaten anyone else with objects. We have seen what it takes to send *objects* around, but one can send information for practically nothing. Here one has the ultimate in philosophical discourse—all you can do is exchange ideas, but you can do that to your heart's content.

Founders of religions are not to be held responsible for the dogmas which their followers build upon their words. Cocconi and Morrison merely suggested that we listen for a certain type of message with radio telescopes. Purcell merely expressed in poetic language the joys of discovery and companionship that would be ours if we could achieve a two-way communication with an alien species. Everything that

Cocconi and Morrison and Purcell said was true. But in the subsequent twenty years their suggestions have hardened into a dogma. Many of the people who are interested in searching for extraterrestrial intelligence have come to believe in a doctrine which I call the Philosophical Discourse Dogma, maintaining as an article of faith that the universe is filled with societies engaged in long-range philosophical discourse. The Philosophical Discourse Dogma holds the following truths to be self-evident:

1. Life is abundant in the universe.

2. A significant fraction of the planets on which life exists give rise to intelligent species.

3. A significant fraction of intelligent species transmit messages for our enlightenment.

If these statements are accepted, then it makes sense to concentrate our efforts upon the search for radio messages and to ignore other ways of looking for evidence of intelligence in the universe. But to me the Philosophical Discourse Dogma is far from self-evident. There is as yet no evidence either for it or against it. Since it may be true, I am whole-heartedly in favor of searching for radio messages. Since it may be untrue, I am in favor of looking for other evidence of intelligence, and especially for evidence which does not require the cooperation of the beings whose activities we are trying to observe.

In recent years there have been some serious searches for radio messages. The technology of listening has been steadily improved. No messages have yet been detected, but the listeners are not discouraged. Their efforts have so far searched only a tiny fraction of the radio frequencies and directions in which messages might be coming. They have plans for continuing their searches in future with greatly increased efficiency. They do not need to build huge new radio telescopes to scan the sky for messages. All that they need is a modest allotment of time on existing telescopes, and a modest amount of money to build new data-processing receivers which allow a large number of frequencies to be searched in parallel. Several groups of radio astronomers are hoping to implement these plans. I support their efforts and hope they will be successful. If they are successful and actually detect an interstellar message, it will be the greatest scientific discovery of the century, a turning point in human history, a revolution in mankind's view of ourselves and our place in the universe. But unfortunately, to be successful they will need a great deal of luck. They will need political luck to get funds to build their instruments. And they will need scientific luck to get a cooperative alien to send them a message.

If the radio astronomers are unlucky or the aliens unhelpful, no messages will be heard. But the absence of messages does not imply the nonexistence of alien intelligences. It is important to think about other ways of looking for evidence of intelligence, ways which might still work if the Philosophical Discourse Dogma happens to be untrue. We should not tie our searches to any one hypothesis about the nature and motivation of the aliens. The commonwealth of aliens whispering their secrets to one another in a universe abuzz with radio messages is one possibility. Equally possible, perhaps more probable, is a sparsely populated and uncooperative universe, where life is rare, intelligence is very rare, and nobody outside is interested in helping us discover them. Even under these unfavorable conditions the search for intelligence is not hopeless. When we turn aside from radio messages, the problem which Cocconi and Morrison so neatly solved, of learning how to recognize artificial objects as artificial, becomes again the primary concern.

Let us go back to the example of Nova Aquilae. Nobody now takes seriously Haldane's idea that Nova Aquilae was a too successful experiment in nuclear physics. Why not? What has happened since 1924 to make this idea absurd? What happened was not, as one might have expected, that Haldane's alternative suggestion of an accidental collision as the cause of the nova turned out to be correct. In fact, nobody now believes any of the theories which Haldane mentioned. The reason is simply this. As a result of brilliant observational work done during the last twenty years, mostly by Robert Kraft at the Lick Observatory in California, we now know too much about novae to be satisfied with any theory which explains the outburst as some kind of accident. Kraft observed with meticulous care ten faint stars. Each of them is the dim remnant surviving after a nova explosion. One of them is Nova Aquilae. He discovered that certainly seven out of ten, and probably all ten of these objects have a peculiar structure which sets them apart from the other stars in the sky. Each of them is a double star consisting of one very small hot component and one rarefied cool component. Each of them has the two stars revolving around each other at such a short distance that they are effectively touching. The periods of revolution are all very short. For Nova Aquilae the period is three hours twenty minutes. We still do not understand in detail why double stars of this special type should be associated with nova explosions. One theory is that there is a steady rain of material from the cool component falling onto the surface of the hot component, and this infalling material is cooked to such a high temperature that it occasionally ignites like a hydrogen bomb. This theory may turn out to be right, or it may be superseded by a better theory. In any case, after Kraft's observations we cannot take seriously any theory of the explosions which does not also explain why they occur only in double stars of this special type. All of Haldane's suggestions fail this test. In particular, it is incredible that intelligent beings capable of conducting disastrous experiments in nuclear physics should appear, in many widely separated parts of the sky, always on planets attached to double stars of a rare and peculiar class.

I reject as worthless all attempts to calculate from theoretical principles the frequency of occurrence of intelligent life forms in the universe. Our ignorance of the chemical processes by which life arose on earth makes such calculations meaningless. Depending on the details of the chemistry, life may be abundant in the universe, or it may be rare, or it may not exist at all outside our own planet. Nevertheless, there are good scientific reasons to pursue the search for evidence of intelligence with some hope for a successful outcome. The essential point which works in our favor as observers is that we are not required to observe the effects of an average intelligent species. It is enough if we can observe the effects of the most spendthrift, the most grandiosely expansionist, or the most technology-mad society in the universe. Unless of course the species excelling all others in these characteristics happens to be our own.

It is easy to imagine a highly intelligent society with no particular interest in technology. It is easy to see around us examples of technology without intelligence. When we look into the universe for signs of artificial activities, it is technology and not intelligence that we must search for. It would be much more rewarding to search directly for intelligence, but technology is the only thing we have any chance of seeing. To decide whether or not we can hope to observe the effects of extraterrestrial technology, we need to answer the following question: What limits does Nature set to the size and scale of activities of an expansionist technological society? The societies whose activities we are most likely to observe are those which have expanded, for whatever good or bad reasons, to the maximum extent permitted by the laws of physics.

Now comes my main point. Given plenty of time, there are few limits to what a technological society can do. Take first the question of colonization. Interstellar distance looks forbiddingly large to human colonists, since we think in terms of our short human lifetime. In one man's lifetime we cannot go very far. But a long-lived society will not be limited by a human lifetime. If we assume only a modest speed of travel, say one hundredth of the speed of light, an entire galaxy can be colonized from end to end within ten million years. A speed of one percent of light velocity could be reached by a spaceship with nuclear propulsion, even using our present primitive technology. So the problem of colonization is a problem of biology and not of physics. The colonists may be long-lived creatures in whose sight a thousand years are but as yesterday, or they may have mastered the technique of putting themselves into cold storage for the duration of their voyage. In any case, interstellar distances are no barrier to a species which has millions of years at its disposal. If we assume, as seems to me probable, that advances in physical technology will allow ships to reach one half of light velocity, then intergalactic distances are no barrier either. A society pressing colonization to the limits of the possible will be able to reach and exploit all the resources of a galaxy, and perhaps of many galaxies.

What are the exploitable resources of a galaxy? The raw materials are matter and energy—matter in the form of planets, comets or dust clouds, and energy in the form of starlight. To exploit these resources fully, a technological species must convert the available matter into biological living space and industrial machinery arranged in orbiting shells around the stars so as to utilize all the starlight. There is enough matter in a planet of the size and chemical composition of Jupiter to form an artificial biosphere exploiting fully the light from a star of the size of our sun. In the galaxy as a whole there may not be enough planets to make biospheres around all the stars, but there are other sources of accessible matter which are sufficient for this purpose. For example, the distended envelopes of red-giant stars are accessible to mining operations and provide matter in quantity far more abundant than that contained in planets. The question remains whether it is technically feasible to build the necessary machinery to create artificial biospheres. Given sufficient time, the job can be done. To convince myself that it is feasible, I have made some rough engineering designs of the machinery required to take apart a planet of the size of the, earth and to reassemble it into a collection of habitable balloons orbiting around the sun. To avoid misunderstanding, I should emphasize that I do not suggest that we should actually do this to the earth. We shall have enough dead planets to experiment with so that we shall not need to destroy a live one. But in this chapter I am not concerned with what mankind may do in the future. I am only concerned with the observable effects of what other societies may have done in the past. The construction of an artificial biosphere completely utilizing the light of a star is definitely within the capabilities of any long-lived technological species.

Some science fiction writers have wrongly given me the credit for inventing the idea of an artificial biosphere. In fact, I took the idea from Olaf Stapledon, one of their own colleagues:

> Not only was every solar system now surrounded by a gauze of light traps, which focused the escaping solar energy for intelligent use, so that the whole galaxy was dimmed, but many stars that were not suited to be suns were disintegrated, and rifled of their prodigious stores of subatomic energy.

This passage I found in a tattered copy of Stapledon's *Star Maker* which I picked up in Paddington Station in London in 1945.

The Russian astronomer Kardashev has suggested that civilizations in the universe should fall into three distinct types. A type 1 civilization controls the resources of a planet. A type 2 civilization controls the resources of a star. A type 3 civilization controls the resources of a galaxy. We have not yet achieved type 1 status, but we shall probably do so within a few hundred years. The difference in size and power between types 1 and 2, or between types 2 and 3, is a factor of the order of ten billion, unimaginably large by human standards. But the process of exponential economic growth allows this immense gulf to be bridged remarkably rapidly. To grow by a factor of ten billion takes thirty-three doubling times. A society growing at the modest rate of one percent per year will make the transition from type 1 to type 2 in less than 2500 years. The transition from type 2 to type 3 will take longer than this, since it requires interstellar voyages. But the periods of transition are likely to be comparatively brief episodes in the history of any long-lived society. Hence Kardashev concludes that if we ever discover an extraterrestrial civilization, it will probably belong clearly to type 1, 2 or 3 rather than to one of the brief transitional phases.

In the long run, the only limits to the technological growth of a society are internal. A society has always the option of limiting its growth, either by conscious decision or by stagnation or by disinterest. A society in which these internal limits are absent may continue its growth forever. A society which happens to possess a strong expansionist drive will expand its habitat from a single planet (type 1) to a biosphere exploiting an entire star (type 2) within a few thousand years, and from a single star to an entire galaxy (type 3) within a few million years. A species which has once passed beyond type 2 status is invulnerable to extinction by even the worst imaginable natural or artificial catastrophe. When we observe the universe, we have a better chance of discovering a society that has expanded into type 2 or type 3 than one which has limited itself to type 1, even if the expansionist societies are as rare as one in a million.

Having defined the scale of the technological activities we may look for, I finally come to the questions which are of greatest interest to astronomers: What are the observable consequences of such activities? What kinds of observations will give us the best chance of recognizing them if they exist? It is convenient to discuss these questions separately for civilizations of type 1, 2 and 3.

A type 1 civilization is undetectable at interstellar distances except by radio. The only chance of discovering a type 1 civilization is to follow the suggestion of Cocconi and Morrison and listen for radio messages. This is the method of search that our radio astronomers have followed for the last twenty years.

A type 2 civilization may be a powerful radio source or it may not. So long as we are totally ignorant of the life style of its inhabitants, we cannot make any useful estimate of the volume or nature of their radio emissions. But there is one kind of emission which a type 2 civilization cannot avoid making. According to the second law of thermodynamics, a civilization which exploits the total energy output of a star must radiate away a large fraction of this energy in the form of waste heat. The waste heat is emitted into space as infrared radiation, which astronomers on earth can detect. Any type 2 civilization must be an infrared source with power comparable to the luminosity of a normal star. The infrared radiation will be mainly emitted from the warm outer surface of the biosphere in which the civilization lives. The biosphere will presumably be maintained at roughly terrestrial temperatures if creatures containing liquid water are living in it. The heat radiation from its surface then appears mainly in a band of wavelengths around ten microns (about twenty times the wavelength of visible light). The ten-micron band is fortunately a convenient one for infrared astronomers to work with, since our atmosphere is quite transparent to it.

After Cocconi and Morrison had started the scientific discussion of extraterrestrial intelligence, I made the suggestion that astronomers looking for artificial objects in the sky should begin by looking for strong sources of ten-micron infrared radiation. Of course it would be absurd to claim that evidence of intelligence has been found every time a new infrared source is discovered. The argument goes the other way. If an object in the sky is not an infrared source, then it cannot be the home of a type 2 civilization. So I suggested that astronomers should first make a survey of the sky to compile a catalog of infrared sources, and then look carefully at objects in the catalog with optical and radio telescopes. Using these tactics, the search for radio messages would have greatly improved chances of success. Instead of searching for radio messages over the whole sky, the radio astronomer could concentrate his listening upon a comparatively small number of accurately pinpointed directions. If one of the infrared sources turned out to be also a source of peculiar optical or radio signals, then one could begin to consider it a candidate for possible artificiality.

When I made this proposal twenty years ago, infrared astronomy had hardly begun. Only a few pioneers had started to look for infrared sources, using small telescopes and simple detecting equipment. Now the situation is quite different. Infrared astronomy is a major branch of astronomy. The sky has been surveyed and catalogs of sources exist. I do not claim any credit for this. The astronomers who surveyed the sky and compiled the catalogs were not looking for type 2 civilizations. They were just carrying one step further the traditional mission of astronomers, searching the sky to find out what is there.

Up to now, the infrared astronomers have not found any objects that arouse suspicions of artificiality. Instead they have found a wonderful variety of natural objects, some of them within our galaxy and others outside it. Some of the objects are intelligible and others are not. A large number of them are dense clouds of dust, kept warm by hot stars which may or may not be visible. When the hot star is invisible such an object is called a "cocoon star," a star hidden in a cocoon of dust. Cocoon stars are often found in regions of space where brilliant newborn stars are also seen, for example in the great nebula in the constellation Orion. This fact makes it likely that the cocoon is a normal but short-lived phase in the process of birth of a star.

Superficially, there seems to be some similarity between a cocoon star and a type 2 civilization. In both cases we have an invisible star surrounded by a warm opaque shell which radiates strongly in the infrared. Why, then, does nobody believe that type 2 civilizations are living in the cocoon stars that have now been discovered? First, the cocoons are too luminous. Most of them are radiating hundreds or thousands of times as much energy as the sun. Stars with luminosity as high as this are necessarily short-lived by astronomical standards. A type 2 civilization would be much more likely to exist around a long-lived star like the sun. The infrared radiation which it emits would be hundreds of times fainter than the radiation which we detect from most of the cocoons. A second reason for not believing that cocoons are artificial is that their temperatures are too high to be appropriate for biospheres. Most of them have temperatures higher than 300 degrees centigrade, far above the range in which life as we know it can exist. A third reason is that there is direct visual evidence for dense dust clouds in the neighborhood of cocoons. We have no reason to expect that a type 2 civilization would find it necessary to surround itself with a smoke screen. The fourth and most conclusive reason for regarding cocoons as natural objects is the general context in which they occur. One sees in the same region of space new stars being born and large diffuse dust clouds condensing. The cocoons must be causally related to these other natural processes with which they are associated.

I have to admit that in the twenty years since I made my suggestion, infrared astronomy, with all its brilliant successes, has failed to produce evidence of type 2 civilizations. Should we then give up hope of its ever doing so? I do not believe we should. We can expect to find candidates for type 2 civilizations only when we explore infrared sources a hundred times fainter than the spectacular ones which the astronomers have observed so far. An astronomer prefers to spend his time at the telescope studying in detail one conspicuously interesting object, rather than cataloguing a long list of dim sources for future investigation. I do not blame the astronomers for skimming the cream off the bright sources before returning to the tedious work of surveying the faint ones. We will have to wait a few years before we have a complete survey of sources down to the luminosity of the sun. Only when we have a long list of faint sources can we hope that candidates for type 2 civilizations will appear among them. And we shall not know whether to take these candidates seriously until we have learned at least as much about the structure and distribution of the faint sources as we have now found out about the bright ones.

A type 3 civilization in a distant galaxy should produce emissions of radio, light and infrared radiation with an apparent brightness comparable with those of a type 2 civilization in our own galaxy. In particular, a type 3 civilization should be detectable as an extragalactic infrared source. However, a type 3 civilization would be harder than a type 2 to recognize, for two reasons. First, our ideas about the behaviour of a type 3 civilization are even vaguer and more unreliable than our ideas about type 2. Second, we know much less about the structure and evolution of galaxies than we do about the birth and death of stars, and consequently we understand the naturally occurring extragalactic infrared sources even more poorly than we understand the natural sources in our galaxy. We understand the cocoon stars at least well enough to be confident that they are not type 2 civilizations. We do not understand the extragalactic infrared sources well enough to be confident of anything. We cannot expect to recognize a type 3 civilization for what it is until we have thoroughly explored the many strange and violent phenomena that we see occurring in the nuclei of distant galaxies.

Is it possible that a type 3 civilization could exist in our own galaxy? This is a question which deserves more serious thought than has been given to it. The answer is negative if we think of a type 3 civilization as overrunning the galaxy with ruthless efficiency and exploiting the light of every available star. However, other kinds of type 3 civilization are conceivable. One attractive possibility is a civilization based on vegetation growing freely in space rather than on massive industrial hardware. A type 3 civilization might use comets rather than planets for its habitat, and trees rather than dynamos for its source of energy. If such a civilization does not already exist, perhaps we shall one day create it ourselves. . . .

I do not believe we yet know enough about the stars, planets, life and mind to give us a firm basis for deciding whether the presence of intelligence in the universe is probable or improbable. Many biologists and chemists have concluded from inadequate evidence the development of intelligent life should be a frequent occurence in our galaxy. Having examined their evidence and heard their arguments, I consider it just as likely that no intelligent species other than our own has ever existed. The question can only be answered by observation.

From the discussion of Nova Aquilae, of civilizations of types 1, 2 and 3, and of the infrared sources, I draw the general conclusion that the best way to look for artificial objects in the sky is to look for natural objects in as many different ways as possible. It is not likely that we can guess correctly what an artificial object should look like. Our best chance is to search for a great variety of natural objects and to try to understand them in detail. When we have found an object that defies natural explanation, we may begin to wonder whether it might be artificial. A reasonable long-range program of searching for evidence of intelligence in the universe is indistinguishable from a reasonable long-range program of general astronomical exploration. We should go ahead with the exploration of the cosmos on all available channels, with visible light, radio, infrared, ultraviolet, x-rays, cosmic rays and gravitational waves. Only by observing on many channels simultaneously shall we learn enough about the objects which we find to tell whether they are natural or artificial. And our program of exploration will bring a rich harvest of discoveries of natural objects, whether or not we are lucky enough to find among them any artificial ones.

• DISCUSSION QUESTIONS •

1. In what ways might we communicate with extraterrestrials? What are the advantages of each?

2. What can we learn about approaching extraterrestrials from studying Champollion's decipherment of Egyptian hieroglyphics and the results of contacts between alien civilizations on Earth? What are the limitations of such activities?

3. Why might science be a universal language? How can a message be cast so that it will be understood by extraterrestrials?

4. How, according to Oberg, does "ufology" refuse to "play by the rules of scientific thought"?

5. What are Sagan's and Dyson's proposals on how to look for extraterrestrial intelligence?

6. What is Bell's "grand analogy"? Why do Sagan, Dyson, and Bell all say that it is important to look for extraterrestrial intelligence even if our chances for success are small?

• ADDITIONAL ACTIVITIES •

Optional Projects

1. Develop arguments for and against trying to contact extraterrestrial civilizations.

2. Compare Chang Hsieh's expressed opinion of "barbarians" with that of Columbus. Write a paper showing how each rose out of its culture.

Supplementary Bibliography

Alfred W. Crosby, Jr., *The Columbian Exchange*. Westport, Connecticut: Greenwood Press, 1972.
Presents the cultural forces that caused the Spanish to view Native Americans as so alien that enslaving them was justified.

Gerald Feinberg and _____ Shapiro, *Life Beyond Earth*. New York: William Morrow, 1980.
A comprehensive and highly readable survey of physical and chemical probabilities for life as we do not know it.

Cyril Ponnamperuma and A.G.W. Cameron, *Interstellar Communication: Scientific Perspectives*. Boston: Houghton Mifflin, 1974.
A collection of articles on extraterrestrial intelligence.

Maurice Pope, *The Story of Archaeological Decipherment*. New York: Charles Scribner's Sons, 1975.
Contains the story of Champollion's decipherment of Egyptian hieroglyphics.

Carl Sagan, "The Quest for Extraterrestrial Intelligence" from *Broca's Brain*. New York: Random House, 1979.
An article by Sagan on the possibility of extraterrestrial life and ways of searching for it.

Chapter XIII

WHO SPEAKS FOR EARTH?

• OVERVIEW •

WE ARE LIVING in an age unlike any other in the Earth's history. As we approach the end of the twentieth century, we find ourselves at a crossroads: the technology that has enabled us to send men to the moon and put spacecraft in orbit around the planets is also instrumental in the development of nuclear weapons whose potential for destruction is almost beyond our comprehension. We are also facing serious environmental problems, many of which may have already affected the ecological balance of life on the planet. Some writers warn that we are rapidly becoming an endangered species, that we may be rushing headlong toward destruction. Whether or not this is true, the threats of nuclear warfare, poverty, inadvertent climate modification, world hunger, and environmental pollution cannot be ignored. Clearly, we are living in an era that presents us with some basic choices and challenges us to reevaluate our priorities.

There is much to be learned from history. In the short time we have been on the Earth, human beings have made progress in almost every aspect of living. We have survived the evolutionary process only because we were able to adapt to our environment, and adapt the environment to our needs. Now, as we become more aware of our place in the cosmos, we begin to realize the fragility of that environment and the importance of preserving its basic integrity.

Although history is full of people who out of fear or ignorance or a lust for power destroyed things of value, there are many more examples of people whose courage and desire for knowledge advanced the cause of humanity. There is evidence in our history of compassion and intelligence, which suggests that we do have the capabilities of finding solutions to existing problems.

• LEARNING OBJECTIVES •

1. Describe and explain what Dr. Sagan believes to be the crucial dichotomy of 20th century technology.

2. List and describe some of the direct and indirect consequences of a global nuclear war on this planet.

3. Describe L.F. Richardson's theory based on his "Statistics of Deadly Quarrels" and the conclusions Dr. Sagan reaches from his study of this theory and subsequent data.

4. Outline some of Dr. Sagan's solutions to the current dilemma facing civilization in its "technological adolescence."

5. Review the twelve previous lessons and summarize cosmic evolution (in about three or four paragraphs).

• KEY TERMS AND NAMES •

Alexandrian Library	radiation
cosmic evolution	L.F. Richardson
mutation	

• ASSIGNMENT •

Watch COSMOS television series Program 13, "Who Speaks for Earth?"

Read Chapter 13, "Who Speaks for Earth?" in Carl Sagan's text, *Cosmos*, or other readings assigned by your instructor.

• READINGS •

Philip Morrison . . . . If the Bomb Gets Out of Hand

In the following selection, written in 1946, Philip Morrison gives a graphic first-hand account of the effects of the atomic bomb on the city of Hiroshima. Morrison is currently professor of physics at the Massachusetts Institute of Technology.

We sat in a small open wooden hut, like a booth at a church fair, listening to the Japanese General Staff major from Tokyo. Around us the ground was blackened. The trees were strangely bare for September beside the Inland Sea. The advance party of the American Army mission to study the effects of the atom bomb had come to Hiroshima. In the rubble of the castle grounds, the old headquarters of the Fifth Division, the local authorities had prepared for us a meeting with the men who had lived through the disaster of the first atomic bomb. The major was very young and very grave. He spoke slowly and carefully, like a man who wants to be properly translated and clearly understood. The story he told is worth hearing. It is the story of the first impact of the atomic bomb on the structure of a nation.

About a quarter-past seven on Monday morning, August 6, the Japanese early-warning radar net had detected the approach of some enemy aircraft headed for the southern part of Honshu, and doubtless for the ports of the Inland Sea. The alert was given, and radio broadcasting stopped in many cities, among them Hiroshima. The raiders approached the coast at very high altitude. At nearly eight o'clock the radar operators determined that the number of planes coming was very small—probably not more than three—and the air raid alert was lifted. The normal broadcast warning was given to the population that it might be advisable to go to shelter if B-29's were actually sighted, but that no raid was expected beyond some sort of reconnaissance. At 8:16 the Tokyo control operator of the Japan Broadcasting Corporation noticed that the Hiroshima station had gone off the air. He tried to use another telephone line to re-establish his program, but it too had failed. About twenty minutes later the Tokyo railroad telegraph center realized that the main line telegraph had stopped working just north of Hiroshima. And from some railway stops within ten miles of that city there had come unofficial and rather confused reports of a terrible explosion in Hiroshima. All these events were then reported to the air-raid defense headquarters of the General Staff. The military called again and again the Army wireless station at the castle in Hiroshima. There was no answer. Something had happened in Hiroshima. The men at headquarters were puzzled. They knew that no large enemy raid could have occurred; they knew that no sizeable store of explosives was in Hiroshima at that time.

The young major of the General Staff was ordered in. He was instructed to fly immediately by army plane to Hiroshima, to land, to survey the damage, and to return to Tokyo with reliable information for the staff. It was generally felt in the air-raid defense headquarters that nothing serious had taken place, that the nervous days of August, 1945, in Japan had fanned up a terrible rumor from a few sparks of truth. The major went to the airport and took off for the southwest. After flying for about three hours, still nearly one hundred miles from Hiroshima, he and his pilot saw a great cloud of smoke from the south. In the bright afternoon Hiroshima was burning. The major's plane reached the city. They circled in disbelief. A great scar, still burning, was all that was left of the center of a busy city. They flew over the military landing strip to land, but the installations below them were smashed. The field was deserted.

About thirty miles south of the wrecked city is the large naval base of Kure, already battered by carrier strikes from the American fleet. The major landed at the Kure airfield. He was welcomed by the naval officers there as the first official representative of aid from Tokyo. They had seen the explosion at Hiroshima. Truckloads of sailors had been sent up to help the city in this strange disaster, but terrible fires had blocked the roads, and the men had turned back. A few refugees had straggled out of the northern part of the town, their clothes and skin burned, to tell near-hysterical stories of incredible violence. Great winds blew in the streets, they said. Debris and the dead were everywhere. The great explosion had been for each survivor a bomb hitting directly on his house. The staff major, thrown into the grimmest of responsibilities, organized some two thousand sailors into parties, which reached the city about dusk. They were the first group of rescue workers to enter Hiroshima.

The major took charge for several days. The rail line was repaired, and trainloads of survivors were shipped north. The trains came first from Onomichi, where, about forty miles north, there was a large naval hospital. Soon the hospital was filled, and its movable supplies exhausted. Then the trains bore the injured still farther north, until there too the medical facilities were completely used up. Some sufferers were shipped twenty-four hours by train before they came to a place where they might be treated. Hospital units were mobilized by Tokyo to come from hundreds of miles to set up dressing stations in Hiroshima. One bomb and one plane had reduced a city of four hundred thousand inhabitants to a singular position in the war economy of Japan: Hiroshima consumed bandages and doctors, while it produced only trainloads of the burned and the broken. Its story brought terror to all the cities of the islands.

The experts in the science of the killing of cities have developed a concept which well describes the disaster of Hiroshima, the disaster which will come to any city which feels the atomic bomb. That is the idea of saturation. Its meaning is simple: if you strike at a man or a city, your victim defends himself. He hits you, he throws up flak, he fights the fires, he cares for the wounded, he rebuilds the houses, he throws tarpaulins over the shelterless machinery. The harder you strike, the greater his efforts to defend himself. But if you strike all at once with over-whelming force, he cannot defend himself. He is stunned. The city's flak batteries are all shooting as fast as they can; the firemen are all at work on the flames of their homes. Then your strike may grow larger with impunity. He is doing his utmost, he can no longer respond to greater damage by greater effort in defense. The defenses are saturated.

The atomic bomb is pre-eminently the weapon of saturation. It destroys so large an area so completely and so suddenly that the defense is overwhelmed. In Hiroshima there were thirty-three modern fire stations; twenty-seven were made useless by the bombing. Three-quarters of the fire-fighting personnel were killed or severely injured. At the same instant, hundreds, perhaps thousands, of fires broke out in the wrecked area. How could these fires be brought under control? There were some quarter of a million people injured in a single minute. The medical officer in charge of the public health organization was buried under his house. His assistant was killed, and so was *his* assistant. The commanding officer of the military was killed, and his aide, and his aide's aide, and in fact every member of his staff. Of 298 registered physicians, only thirty were able to care for the survivors. Of nearly twenty-four hundred nurses and orderlies, only six hundred were ready for work after the blast. How could the injured be treated or evacuation properly organized? The power substation which served the center of the city was destroyed, the railroad was cut, and the rail station smashed and burned. The telephone and telegraph exchange was wrecked. Every hospital but one in the city was badly damaged; not one was able to shelter its patients from the rain—even if its shell of concrete still stood—without roof, partitions, or casements. There were whole sections of the outer city undamaged, but the people there were unable to give effective aid, lacking leadership, organization, supplies, and shelter. The Japanese defenses had already been proved inadequate under the terrible fire raids of the B-29's, which had desolated so many of Japan's cities. But under the atomic bomb their strained defenses came to complete saturation. At Nagasaki, the target of the second atomic bomb, the organization of relief was even poorer. The people had given up.

A Hiroshima official waved his hand over his wrecked city and said: "All this from one bomb; it is unendurable." We knew what he meant. Week after week the great flights of B-29's from the Marianas had laid flame to the cities of all Japan. But at least there was a warning. You knew when the government announced a great raid in progress that, though Osaka people would face an infernal night, you in Nagoya could sleep. For the raids of a thousand bombers could not be hidden, and the fire raid had formed a pattern. But every day over any city of the chain there was a chance for a few American planes to come. These inquiring planes had been photographers or weather forecasters or even occasionally nuisance raiders; never before had a single plane destroyed a city. Now, all this was changed. From any plane casually flying almost beyond the range of flak there could come death and flame for an entire city. The alert would have to be sounded now night and day in every city. If the raiders were over Sapporo, the people of Shimonoseki, a thousand miles away, must still fear even one airplane. This is unendurable.

If war comes again, atomic war, there will not even be the chance for alerts. A single bomb can saturate a city the size of Indianapolis, or a whole district of a great city, like Lower Manhattan, or Telegraph Hill and the Marina, or Hyde Park and the South Shore. The bombs can come by plane or rocket in thousands, and all at once. What measures of defense can there be? To destroy the bombs in flight many measures will be attempted, but they cannot be a hundred per cent effective. It is not easy to picture what even one single bomb will do. We saw the test shot in the New Mexico desert, and we pored over and calculated the damage that a city would suffer. But on the ground at Hiroshima and Nagasaki there lies the first convincing evidence of the damage done by the present atomic bomb.

Niels Bohr. . . . . .Science and Civilization

Neils Bohr, whose research in atomic physics won him the Nobel Prize in 1922, stresses the urgent need for unity among scientists and cooperation among all nations in order to curtail the use of destructive atomic weapons. The following selection was published on August 11, 1945, just five days after the bombing of Hiroshima.

The possibility of releasing vast amounts of energy through atomic disintegration, which means a veritable revolution of human resources, cannot but raise in the mind of everyone the question of where the advance of physical science is leading civilization. While the increasing mastery of the forces of nature has contributed so prolifically to human welfare and holds out even greater promises, it is evident that the formidable power of destruction that has come within reach of man may become a mortal menace unless human society can adjust itself to the exigencies of the situation. Civilization is presented with a challenge more serious perhaps than ever before, and the fate of humanity will depend on its ability to unite in averting common dangers and jointly to reap the benefit from the immense opportunities which the progress of science offers.

In its origin science is inseparable from the collecting and ordering of experience, gained in the struggle for existence, which enabled our ancestors to raise mankind to its present position among the other living beings that inhabit our earth. Even in highly organized communities where, within the distribution of labor, scientific study has become an occupation by itself, the progress of science and the advance of civilization have remained most intimately interwoven. Of course, practical needs are still an impetus to scientific research, but it need hardly be stressed how often technical developments of the greatest importance for civilization have originated from studies aimed only at augmenting our knowledge and deepening our understanding. Such endeavors know no national borders, and where one scientist has left the trail another has taken it up, often in a distant part of the world. For scientists have long considered themselves a brotherhood working in the service of common human ideals.

In no domain of science have these lessons received stronger emphasis than in the exploration of the atom, which just now is bearing consequences of such overwhelming practical implications. As is well known, the roots of the idea of atoms as the ultimate constituents of matter go back to ancient thinkers searching for a foundation to explain the regularity which, in spite of all variability, is ever more clearly revealed by the study of natural phenomena. After the Renaissance, when science entered so fertile a period, atomic theory gradually became of the greatest importance to the physical and chemical sciences, although until half a century ago it was generally accepted that, owing to the coarseness of our senses, any direct proof of the existence of atoms would always remain beyond human scope. Aided, however, by the refined tools of modern technique, the development of the art of experimentation has removed such limitation and even yielded detailed information about the interior structure of atoms.

In particular, the discovery that almost the entire mass of the atom is concentrated in a central nucleus proved to have the most far-reaching consequences. Not only did it become evident that the remarkable stability of the chemical elements is due to the immutability of the atomic nucleus when exposed to ordinary physical agencies, but a novel field of research was opened up by the study of the special conditions under which disintegrations of the nuclei themselves may be brought about. Such processes, whereby the very elements are transformed, were found to differ fundamentally in character and violence from chemical reactions, and their investigation led to a rapid succession of important discoveries through which ultimately the possibility of large-scale release of atomic energy came into sight. This progress was achieved in the course of a few decades and was due not least to most effective international cooperation. The world community of physicists was, so to speak, welded into a single team, rendering it more difficult than ever to disentangle the contributions of individual workers.

The grim realities being revealed to the world these days will no doubt, in the minds of many, revive the terrifying prospects forecast in fiction. With all due admiration for such imagination, it is, however, most essential to appreciate the contrast between these fantasies and the actual situation confronting us. Far from offering any easy means to bring destruction forth, as it were by witchcraft, scientific insight has made it evident that use of nuclear disintegration for devastating explosions demands most elaborate preparations, involving a profound change in the atomic composition of materials found on earth. The astounding achievement of producing an enormous display of power on the basis of experience gained by the study of minute effects, perceptible only by the most delicate instruments, has in fact, besides a most intensive research effort, required an immense engineering enterprise, strikingly illuminating the potentialities of modern industrial development.

Indeed, not only have we left the time far behind where each man, for self-protection, could pick up the nearest stone, but we have even reached the stage where the degree of security offered to the citizens of a nation by collective defense measures is entirely insufficient. Against the new destructive powers no defense may be possible, and the issue centers on world-wide cooperation to prevent any use of the new sources of energy that does not serve mankind as a whole. The possibility of international regulation for this purpose should be ensured by the very magnitude and the peculiar character of the efforts that will be indispensable for the production of the formidable new weapon. It is obvious, however, that no control can be effective without free access to full scientific information and the granting of the opportunity of international supervision of all undertakings that, unless regulated, might become a source of disaster.

Such measure will, of course, demand the abolition of barriers hitherto considered necessary to safeguard national interests but now standing in the way of common security against unprecedented dangers. Certainly the handling of the precarious situation will demand the good will of all nations, but it must be recognized that we are dealing with what is potentially a deadly challenge to civilization itself. A better background for meeting such a situation could hardly be imagined than the earnest desire to seek a firm foundation for world security, so unanimously expressed by all those nations which only through united efforts have been able to defend elementary human rights. The extent of the contribution that agreement on this vital matter would make to the removal of obstacles to mutual confidence, and to the promotion of a harmonious relationship between nations can hardly be exaggerated.

In the great task lying ahead, which places on our generation the gravest responsibility toward posterity, scientists all over the world may offer most valuable services. Not only do the bonds created through scientific intercourse form some of the firmest ties between individuals from different nations, but the whole scientific community will surely join in a vigorous effort to induce in wider circles an adequate appreciation of what is at stake and to appeal to humanity at large to heed the warning that has been sounded. It need not be added that every scientist who has taken part in laying the foundation for the new development or who has been called upon to participate in work that might have proved decisive in the struggle to preserve a state of civilization where human culture can freely develop is prepared to assist, in any way open to him, in bringing about an outcome of the present crisis of humanity that is worthy of the ideals for which science through the ages has stood.

Albert Einstein. . . . . A Message to Intellectuals

In the following text of a speech delivered in 1948, Einstein appeals to members of the intellectual and scientific community to assume a more active role in finding solutions to the political conflicts that lead to war. Throughout his lifetime, Einstein was widely known (and sometimes criticized) for his pacifist views.

We meet today, as intellectuals and scholars of many nationalities, with a deep and historic responsibility placed upon us. We have every reason to be grateful to our French and Polish colleagues whose initiative has assembled us here for a momentous objective: to use the influence of wise men in promoting peace and security through the world. This is the age-old problem with which Plato, as one of the first, struggled so hard: to apply reason and prudence to the solution of man's problems instead of yielding to atavist instincts and passions.

By painful experience we have learnt that rational thinking does not suffice to solve the problems of our social life. Penetrating research and keen scientific work have often had tragic implications for mankind, producing, on the one hand, inventions which liberated man from exhausting physical labor, making his life easier and richer; but on the other hand, introducing a grave restlessness into his life, making him a slave to his technological environment, and—most catastrophic of all—creating the means for his own mass destruction. This, indeed, is a tragedy of overwhelming poignancy!

However poignant that tragedy is, it is perhaps even more tragic that, while mankind has produced many scholars so extremely successful in the field of science and technology, we have been for a long time so inefficient in finding adequate solutions to the many political conflicts and economic tensions which beset us. No doubt, the antagonism of economic interests within and among nations is largely responsible to a great extent for the dangerous and threatening condition in the world today. Man has not succeeded in developing political and economic forms of organization which would guarantee the peaceful coexistence of the nations of the world. He has not succeeded in building the kind of system which would eliminate the possibility of war and banish forever the murderous instruments of mass destruction.

We scientists, whose tragic destination has been to help in making the methods of annihilation more gruesome and more effective, must consider it our solemn and transcendent duty to do all in our power in preventing these weapons from being used for the brutal purpose for which they were invented. What task could possibly be more important for us? What social aim could be closer to our hearts? That is why this Congress has such a vital mission. We are here to take counsel with each other. We must build spiritual and scientific bridges linking the nations of the world. We must overcome the horrible obstacles of national frontiers.

In the smaller entities of community life, man has made some progress toward breaking down anti-social sovereignties. This is true, for example, of life within cities and, to a certain degree, even of society within individual states. In such communities tradition and education have had a moderating influence and have brought about tolerable relations among the peoples living within those confines. But in relations among separate states complete anarchy still prevails. I do not believe that we have made any genuine advance in this area during the last few thousand years. All too frequently conflicts among nations are still being decided by brutal power, by war. The unlimited desire for ever greater power seeks to become active and aggressive wherever and whenever the physical possibility offers itself.

Throughout the ages, this state of anarchy in international affairs has inflicted indescribable suffering and destruction upon mankind; again and again it has depraved the development of men, their souls and their well-being. For given time it has almost annihilated whole areas.

However, the desire of nations to be constantly prepared for warfare has, however, still other repercussions upon the lives of men. The power of every state over its citizens has grown steadily during the last few hundred years, no less in countries where the power of the state has been exercised wisely, than in those where it has been used for brutal tyranny. The function of the state to maintain peaceful and ordered relations among and between its citizens has become increasingly complicated and extensive largely because of the concentration and centralization of the modern industrial apparatus. In order to protect its citizens from attacks from without a modern state requires a formidable, expanding military establishment. In addition, the state considers it necessary to educate its citizens for the possibilities of war, an "education" not only corrupting to the soul and spirit of the young, but also adversely affecting the mentality of adults. No country can avoid this corruption. It pervades the citizenry even in countries which do not harbor outspoken aggressive tendencies. The state has thus become a modern idol whose suggestive power few men are able to escape.

Education for war, however, is a delusion. The technological developments of the last few years have created a completely new military situation. Horrible weapons have been invented, capable of destroying in a few seconds huge masses of human beings and tremendous areas of territory. Since science has not yet found protection from these weapons, the modern state is no longer in a position to prepare adequately for the safety of its citizens.

How, then, shall we be saved?

Mankind can only gain protection against the danger of unimaginable destruction and wanton annihilation if a supranational organization has alone the authority to produce or possess these weapons. It is unthinkable, however, that nations under existing conditions would hand over such authority to a supranational organization' unless the organization would have the legal right and duty to solve all the conflicts which in the past have led to war. The functions of individual states would be to concentrate more or less upon internal affairs; in their relation with other states they would deal only with issues and problems which are in no way conducive to endangering international security.

Unfortunately, there are no indications that governments yet realize the situation in which mankind finds itself makes the adoption of revolutionary measures a compelling necessity. Our situation is not comparable to anything in the past. It is impossible, therefore, to apply methods and measures which at an earlier age might have been sufficient. We must revolutionize our thinking, revolutionize our actions, and must have the courage to revolutionize relations among the nations of the world. Clichés of yesterday will no longer do today, and will, no doubt, be hopelessly out of date tomorrow. to bring this home to men all over the world is the most important and most fateful social function intellectuals have ever had to shoulder. Will they have enough courage to overcome their own national ties to the extent that is necessary to induce the peoples of the world to change their deep-rooted national traditions in a most radical fashion?

A tremendous effort is indispensable. If it fails now, the supranational organization will be built later, but then it will have to be built upon the ruins of a large part of the now existing world. Let us hope that the abolition of the existing international anarchy will not need to be bought by a self-inflicted world catastrophe the dimensions of which none of us can possibly imagine. The time is terribly short. We must act now if we are to act at all.

Richard E. Leakey and Roger Lewin. . . Mankind in Perspective

In this excerpt from the book Origins, *anthropologists Leakey and Lewin stress the fundamental oneness of humanity and voice a note of optimism and promise for the future of our civilization.*

Fundamental though it is, this issue of human conflict is but one of many in a world in precarious balance on the thin edge of the threat of global war as the supposed guarantor of global peace. War, on a scale both large and small, has etched itself deep in the annals of human history, and there are those who declare that because of our biological heritage such conflict is inevitable. This unfounded claim is based on a misunderstanding of the nature of such basic animal behaviors as territoriality and aggression, and an equal ignorance of the forces that nurtured the evolution of humanity. In this respect there is a certain irony in the spectacular success of the Viking mission, since its target, Mars, has so long been identified with the god of War!

If it were truly the case that the human animal is unswervingly propelled toward open conflict with members of its own species, then the prospects for long-term tenure of technological society on earth would be very poor indeed. With the means of mass destruction at hand, it would be merely a matter of time before their use dealt a blow to life on earth from which it might never recover. Those who argue that humans are innately aggressive must therefore be pointing to the inevitability of such an event. Unfortunately, it does not necessarily follow that a humanity not harboring inbuilt aggressiveness will avoid reaching the same end, as our recent history and current political posturing so clearly warns us. The possibility of a massive international confrontation is real.

How, then do we explain international conflict and the real threat of global confrontation within the context of the human community in which there is no powerful undercurrent of aggression waiting to surge to the surface? . . .

Evolution has endowed human beings with two remarkable characteristics, each of which alone would make us very special animals: first, the enormous capacity to learn about and interpret the world around us; and second, the ability to structure and manipulate the environment in arbitrary ways so as to create culture. Add these two together, combine them with a degree of social cooperation found elsewhere only in some insect societies, and one finishes up with an extraordinary product: an animal with the potential to achieve virtually anything. . . .

Precisely because evolution produced an animal capable of tackling whatever challenge the environment might offer, the answer must be that very few behavioral patterns are rigidly built into the human brain. Obviously our brains are not jumbled networks of nerve cells with no overall structure. The *anatomy* of the human brain is very well ordered, but it is built in such a way as to maximize *behavioral* adaptability. Within reasonable biological limits, humans, it is fair to say, could adapt to living in almost limitless numbers of ways. Indeed, this flexibility is manifest in the rich pattern of cultures expressed throughout the world.

Throughout the later stages of human evolution, from about three million years onwards, there was, however, one pattern of social behavior that became extremely important, and we can therefore expect the forces of natural selection would have ensured its becoming deeply embedded in the human brain: this is cooperation. . . .

To insist that blind cooperation is a universal aspect of human behavior would, of course, be to negate the flexibility and independence of the human mind. What is in us is a very readily-tapped tendency for group identification and group endeavor. Most communities have social rules and customs (the stuff of culture) that provide a framework through which 'groupness' is expressed. The rules and customs of different communities may vary, and ethnic groups may express their identification through such material channels as self-decoration or domestic architecture. But, throughout, the goal is the same: the sense of belonging to and therefore contributing to the group. We all experience such an urge, and it may extend from the need to be 'accepted' by a group as small as perhaps three or four people at school, in college, or within the local community, all the way to supporting a national sports team along with tens of thousands of other fans.

It is possible to argue that this urge for group identification is at the root of much of the conflict we have seen in the world: war would not be possible if people were not inclined to rally round their flag and fight for the good of the country, whatever that 'good' may be. To say, however, that the biological heritage of group identification and cooperation is the *cause* of war would be the same as claiming that guns are the cause of war. Both simply represent the *means* by which war is waged. War only became possible when there was something to fight about;

and here we must look back to the agricultural revolution, the transition from hunting and gathering to farming. . . .

With the advent of permanent settlement comes the birth of materialism as well. Sedentary life in villages allows the accumulation of non-essential objects, and it is with such objects that marks of status and wealth are often associated. Experience tells us that accumulation of wealth breeds the desire for more as often as it satiates the appetite. The phenomenon is more than simply collecting items for their own sake: it is a kind of psychomaterialism, a phenomenon akin to the lust for power. And, once again, power is possible only when there is a large body of people over which to exercise it. Clearly, the possibilities of seeking, holding, and expanding power were much greater after the agricultural revolution than before. And there are two basic routes to the expansion of power: skillful political maneuvering, or successful military operations. . . .

Affluent countries may inflict suffering on the poorer communities through incompetence as well as by design. The unthinking way in which Western medicine is foisted upon societies that are totally unsuited either to operate or cope with the fruits of its 'success'—those fruits being an expanded population—is potentially as harmful in the long term as economic exploitation. The technologically advanced must try to forget the notion that they have all the answers, and that what is good for them is good for everybody. This is not necessarily true. Indeed, it may well be that the economic and social strategy which has brought wealth to many Western countries is in the long run a certain recipe for global disaster. The high standard of material affluence enjoyed in Europe and the U.S. may well be *too* high to be feasible on a world-wide scale: the drain on the planet's resources, and the accompanying rape of the environment, could be too great to sustain a population of even four thousand million (the present level) for more than a hundred years or so. And it is inconceivable that the differentials that currently exist between the rich and poor countres can be part of a long-term strategy of economic survival. If those differentials persist, global tensions will rapidly pass exploding point.

One issue that ties together the question of material resources and of standards of living is the global planning of energy. We can now be certain that at the current rate of usage the world's reserves of oil and gas will be exhausted well within this century. We know, too, that there is enough coal to supply our energy-hungry world for many centuries. But it may also turn out that in order to survive we will have to leave that coal buried and unburned. The problem is that, as with other fossil fuels (oil and gas), coal when it is burned releases carbon dioxide. Over the long term, a large build-up of carbon dioxide in the atmosphere could alter the world's climate sufficiently to disrupt seriously the pattern of agriculture. Moreover, agricultural production in the U.S., China and the Soviet Union is so finely balanced with demand, particularly for grain, that even the slightest *normal* variation in weather can cause havoc. The results of a global warming of 2.5°C, the anticipated outcome of a dramatic rise in the carbon dioxide level within sixty years, are virtually unimaginable. . . .

From day to day, life on earth may seem in good enough order (provided one is a member of the affluent minority!) but in the perspective of biological time we have to face the fact that one day humanity *will* disappear. There is no escaping that fact. The question is, when?

At its most dramatic, the end of the planet earth could take place as a cosmological accident, sending all its passengers into oblivion. If such an event were to overtake us, that would be simply bad luck on a grand scale. More to the point is the question, can mankind thrive for a respectably long tenure without being destroyed by its own hand? The species to which we all belong, *Homo sapiens sapiens*, is perhaps fifty thousand years old, a mere infant in biological terms. It is quite possible that the path of evolution that brought us to our special position in the animal world, a position in which our inventiveness and culture allow us to manipulate our environment to an unprecedented degree, is soon to run into a dead end. Will the evolutionary step that handed over to an animal so much power and control over its environment turn out to have been the greatest biological blunder of all time? Can it be that the creation of the human species carried with it the seeds of ultimate destruction?

The future of the human species depends crucially on two things: our relationships with one another, and our relationship to the world around us. The study of human origins can offer important emphasis in the way we view these two issues.

First, we are one species, one people. Every individual on this earth is a member of *Homo sapiens sapiens*, and the geographical variations we see among peoples are simply biological nuances on the basic theme. The human capacity for culture permits its elaboration in widely different and colorful ways. The often very deep differences between those cultures should not be seen as divisions between people. Instead, cultures should be interpreted for what they really are: the ultimate declaration of belonging to the human species.

It is a truism to say that politics are international. But this being so, it follows that any attempt to achieve long-term stability for humanity can come only through a global determination and will. It is not our intention to suggest how global politics might be run, with a world government or whatever other machinery might be appropriate. Rather, we wish to suggest that unless there is an acceptance of the oneness of the human race, a real spirit of brotherhood, the political machinery, however sophisticated, will grind to a halt. The deep human drive for cooperation lends itself to achieve that aim. Just as the human propensity for group cooperation has in the past been harnessed to wage war between nations, it is now imperative that the same basic drive be channeled into a global effort to rescue humanity from itself.

An evolutionary perspective of our place in the history of the earth reminds us that *Homo sapiens sapiens* has occupied the planet for the tiniest fraction of that planet's four and a half thousand million years of existence. In many ways we are a biological accident, the product of countless propitious circumstances. As we peer back through the fossil record, through layer upon layer of long-extinct species, many of which thrived far longer than the human species is ever likely to do, we are reminded of our mortality as a species. There is no law that declares the human animal to be different, as seen in this broad biological perspective, from any other animal. There is no law that declares the human species to be immortal.

Unquestionably, mankind *is* special, and in many ways too. In past history, animals became extinct because for whatever reason the environment that had previously nurtured their birth turned hostile: perhaps the climate shifted, or competition from other species became too severe. Humans are the first animals capable of manipulating the global environment to a substantial degree. So, although through our evolution we have escaped many of the vicissitudes of the natural environment by becoming in some measure independent of it, we now have in our hands the engines of our own destruction. There is now a critical need for a deep awareness that, no matter how special we are as an animal, we are still part of the greater balance of nature. Unless we achieve such awareness the answer to the question of when the human species might disappear will be: 'sooner rather than later'.

Make no mistake: the human species *is* capable of gaining a keen awareness of its place in the global domain; and there is absolutely no reason why the world's population cannot operate in sympathy and harmony—and humility too—with the planet on which we are so recently evolved. During that relatively brief span evolutionary pressures forged a brain capable of profound understanding of matters animate and inanimate: the fruits of intellectual and technological endeavour in this latter quarter of the twentieth century give us just an inkling of what the human mind can achieve. The potential is enormous, almost infinite. We can, if we so choose, do virtually anything: arid lands will become fertile; terrible diseases will be cured by genetic engineering; touring other planets will become routine; we may even come to understnd how the human mind works!

No one with even the merest whiff of imagination would deny these predictions. What is at issue is whether nations can live peaceably with nations and with an understanding and deep respect for the natural world they inhabit so that one day these, and other, predictions may be fulfilled.

The answer, emphatically, is Yes. We certainly have the intellectual equipment with which to achieve it. And although the cultural spiral propelled successively by the Agricultural, Industrial, and Technological Revolutions is now spinning at a dizzying rate, we can clear our heads and measure short-term goals against the perspective of long-term existence. We are One People, and we can all strive for one aim: the peaceful and equitable survival of humanity.

To have arrived on this earth as the product of a biological accident, only to depart through human arrogance, would be the ultimate irony.

———————————

Bertrand Russell. **Science and Values**

In the following essay, noted philosopher Bertrand Russell discusses the various uses of knowledge and points out the dangers inherent in the search for power. He concludes by calling for a new moral outlook in which science is committed to the preservation of the highest human values. This essay was originally published in 1931.

The impulse towards scientific construction is admirable when it does not thwart any of the other major impulses that give value to human life, but when it is allowed to forbid all outlet to everything but itself it becomes a form of cruel tyranny. There is, I think, a real danger lest the world should become subject to a tyranny of this sort, and it is on this account that I have not shrunk from depicting the darker features of the world that scientific manipulation unchecked might wish to create.

Science in the course of the few centuries of its history has undergone an internal development which appears to be not yet completed. One may sum up this development as the passage from contemplation to manipulation. The love of knowledge to which the growth of science is due is itself the product of a twofold impulse. We may seek knowledge of an object because we love the object or because we wish to have power over it. The former impulse leads to the kind of knowledge that is contemplative, the latter to the kind that is practical. In the development of science the power impulse has increasingly prevailed over the love impulse. The power impulse is embodied in industrialism and in governmental technique. It is embodied also in the philosophies known as pragmatism and instrumentalism. Each of these philosophies holds, broadly speaking, that our beliefs about any object are true in so far as they enable us to manipulate it with advantage to ourselves. This is what may be called a governmental view of truth. Of truth so conceived science offers us a great deal; indeed there seems no limit to its possible triumphs. To the man who wishes to change his environment science offers astonishingly powerful tools, and if knowledge consists in the power to produce intended changes, then science gives knowledge in abundance.

But the desire for knowledge has another form, belonging to an entirely different set of emotions. The mystic, the lover, and the poet are also seekers after knowledge—not perhaps very successful seekers, but none the less worthy of respect on that account. In all forms of love we wish to have knowledge of what is loved, not for purposes of power, but for the ecstasy of contemplation. "In knowledge of God standeth our eternal life," but not because knowledge of God gives us power over Him. Wherever there is ecstasy or joy or delight derived from an object there is the desire to know that object—to know it not in the manipulative fashion that consists of turning it into something else, but to know it in the fashion of the beatific vision, because in itself and and for itself it sheds happiness upon the lover. In sex love as in other forms of love the impulse to this kind of knowledge exists, unless the love is purely physical or practical. This may indeed be made the touchstone of any love that is valuable. Love which has value contains an impulse towards that kind of knowledge out of which the mystic union springs.

Science in its beginnings was due to men who were in love with the world. They perceived the beauty of the stars and the sea, of the winds and the mountains. Because they loved them their thoughts dwelt upon them, and they wished to understand even more intimately than a mere outward contemplation made possible. "The world," said Heraclitus, "is an ever-living fire, with measures kindling and measures going out." Heraclitus and the other Ionian philosophers, from whom came the first impulse to scientific knowledge, felt the strange beauty of the world almost like a madness in the blood. They were men of Titanic passionate intellect, and from the intensity of their intellectual passion the whole movement of the modern world has sprung. But step by step, as science has developed, the impulse of love which gave it birth has been increasingly thwarted, while the impulse of power, which was at first a mere camp-follower, has gradually usurped command in virtue of its unforeseen success. The lover of nature has been baffled, the tyrant over nature has been rewarded. As physics has developed, it has deprived us step by step of what we thought we knew concerning the intimate nature of the physical world. Colour and sound, light and shade, form and texture, belong no longer to that external nature that the Ionians sought as the bride of their devotion. All these things have been transferred from the beloved to the lover, and the beloved has become a skeleton of rattling bones, cold and dreadful, but perhaps a mere phantasm. The poor physicists, appalled at the desert that their formulae have revealed, call upon God to give them comfort, but God must share the ghostliness of His creation, and the answer that the physicists think they hear to their cry is only the frightened beating of their own hearts. Disappointed as the lover of nature, the man of science is becoming its tyrant. What matters it, says the practical man, whether the outer world exists or is a dream, provided I can make it behave as I wish? Thus science has more and more substituted power-knowledge for love-knowledge, and as this substitution becomes completed science tends more and more to become sadistic. The scientific society of the future as we have been imagining it is one in which the power impulse has completely overwhelmed the impulse of love, and this is the psychological source of the cruelties which it is in danger of exhibiting. . . .

The scientific society in its pure form, which is what we have been trying to depict, is incompatible with the pursuit of truth, with love, with art, with spontaneous delight, with every ideal that men have hitherto cherished, with the sole exception of ascetic renunciation. It is not knowledge that is the source of these dangers. Knowledge is good and ignorance is evil: to this principle the lover of the world can admit no exception. Nor is it power in and for itself that is the source of danger. What is dangerous is power wielded for the sake of power, not power wielded for the sake of genuine good. The leaders of the modern world are drunk with power: the fact that they can do something that no one previously thought it possible to do is to to them a sufficient reason for doing it. Power is not one of the ends of life, but merely a means to other ends, and until men remember the ends that power should subserve, science will not do what it might to minister to the good life. But what then are the ends of life, the reader will say. I do not think that one man has a right to legislate for another on this matter. For each individual the ends of life are those things which he deeply desires, and which if they existed would give him peace. Or, if it be thought that peace is too much to ask this side of the grave, let us say that the ends of life should give delight or joy or ecstasy. In the conscious desires of the man who seeks power of its own sake there is something dusty: when he has it he wants only more power, and does not find rest in contemplation of what he has. The lover, the poet and the mystic find a fuller satisfaction than the seeker after power can ever know, since they can rest in the object of their love, whereas the seeker after power must be perpetually engaged in some fresh manipulation if he is not to suffer from a sense of emptiness. I think therefore that the satisfactions of the lover, using that word in its broadest sense, exceed the satisfactions of the tyrant, and deserve a higher place among the ends of life. When I come to die I shall not feel that I have lived in vain. I have seen the earth turn red at evening, the dew sparkling in the morning, and the snow shining under a frosty sun; I have smelt rain after drought, and have heard the stormy Atlantic beat upon the granite shores of Cornwall. Science may bestow these and other joys upon more people than could otherwise enjoy them. If so, its power will be wisely used. But when it takes out of life the moments to which life owes its value, science will not deserve admiration, however cleverly and however elaborately it may lead men along the road to despair. The sphere of values lies outside science, except in so far as science consists in the pursuit of knowledge. Science as the pursuit of power must not obtrude upon the sphere of values, and scientific technique, if it is to enrich human life, must not outweigh the ends which it should serve. . . .

I do not mean to deny that scientific technique may in time build an artificial world in every way preferable to that in which men have hitherto lived, but I do say that if this is to be done it must be done tentatively and with a realization that the purpose of government is not merely to afford pleasure to those who govern, but to make life tolerable for those who are governed. Scientific technique must no longer be allowed to form the whole culture of the holders of power, and it must become an essential part of men's ethical outlook to realize that the will alone cannot make a good life. Knowing and feeling are equally essential ingredients both in the life of the individual and in that of the community. Knowledge, if it is wide and intimate, brings with a realization of distant times and places, an awareness that the individual is not onmipotent or all-important, and a perspective in which values are seen more clearly than by those to whom a distant view is impossible. Even more important than knowledge is the life of the emotions. A world without delight and without affection is a world destitute of value. These things the scientific manipulator must remember, and if he does his manipulation may be wholly beneficial. All that is needed is that men should not be so intoxicated by new power as to forget the truths that were familiar to every previous generation. Not all wisdom is new, nor is all folly out of date.

Man has been disciplined hitherto by his subjection to nature. Having emancipated himself from this subjection, he is showing something of the defects of slave-turned-master. A new moral outlook is called for in which submission to the powers of nature is replaced by respect for what is best in man. It is where this respect is lacking that scientific technique is dangerous. So long as it is present, science, having delivered man from bondage to nature, can proceed to deliver him from bondage to the slavish part of himself. The dangers exist, but they are not inevitable, and hope for the future is at least as rational as fear.

• DISCUSSION QUESTIONS •

1. Is a world government possible? Is it desirable? What benefits and/or drawbacks would it present? What are some of the reasons for the limited success of the United Nations? What could inspire national governments to give up their power to make war?

2. Do you think the destruction of the planet is inevitable? When, if at all, might it take place? Do you think nuclear war can be prevented? If so, what steps would have to be taken?

3. Is war a biological imperative for the human species?

4. What are the ethical questions confronting scientists working for the military? What, in your opinion, is the responsibility of scientists in the nuclear age?

5. What is the value of space exploration? Has your exposure to *Cosmos* changed your opinion on this issue?

6. What do you consider to be the most pressing problems of our era? Do you believe we have the tools and resources to conquer these problems? What does Sagan mean when he says the need for scientific literacy is a desperate global need?

7. What is the historical and scientific significance of the Alexandrian Library? What factors were responsible for its ultimate destruction? Can you think of any parallels between what happened in Alexandria and events that are taking place in modern times?

8. What relationship did L.F. Richardson find between the number of people killed in a war and the likelihood of its occurrence? What do Richardson's data suggest about the possibility of a global catastrophe within the near future?

• ADDITIONAL ACTIVITIES •

Optional Projects

1. Write a paper outlining possible plans for restructuring present economic, political, social, and religious institutions in order to maximize the possibility of human survival.

2. Write a dialogue between yourself and an extraterrestrial observer, in which you attempt to explain the rationale behind the global arms race.

3. Using other sources if necessary, write a paper describing how the earth's ecology is presently being affected by human activity. Consider the implications of this activity for the future of the planet as a human habitat.

Supplementary Bibliography

Jacob Bronowski, *The Common Sense of Science*. Cambridge, Mass.: Harvard University Press, 1958.
A book about the essential nature of science, how it affects our lives and how its methods can be used to solve problems of everyday living.

B. Commoner, *Science and Survival*. New York: Viking, 1967.
Provides a good background on the history of the environmental movement.

Freeman Dyson, *Disturbing the Universe*. New York: Harper & Row, 1979.
A collection of essays on various topics in science. Includes chapters on peacemaking, nuclear weapons, and the ethics of defense.

R.L. Heilbroner, *An Inquiry into the Human Prospect*. New York: W.W. Norton, 1974.
In this short and somewhat disturbing book, a well-know futurist warns of the serious problems the future holds.

Carl Sagan, *The Cosmic Connection*. New York: Dell, 1975.
A stimulating book that speculates about the possibilites of making contact with extraterrestrial beings. Written for the popular reading audience.

Glossary

aberration of starlight A difference between the observed position and true position of a star, an effect of the earth's motion.

Alexandrian Library (300 B.C.-300 A.D.) The most famous library of antiquity; under the Ptolemies, was the center of Hellenistic culture, containing at least 700,000 volumes.

Amalthea A tiny potato-shaped moonlet of Jupiter.

amino acids A constituent of all proteins; the fundamental building blocks of life.

Anaxagoras 500-428 B.C. Greek philosopher and astronomer who studied the phases of the moon, the size of the sun, and the behavior of meteors; was among the first to postulate that the heavenly bodies were composed of ordinary matter.

Anaximander (611-547 B.C.) Greek philosopher and scientist who invented the sundial, made a map of the known world, and determined the length of the year and the seasons.

Arecibo Observatory Located in Arecibo, Puerto Rico, the site of a giant, disc-shaped radio telescope.

Aristarchus (310-230 B.C.) One of the last of the old Ionian scientists; best known for his belief that the sun, rather than the earth, was at the center of the planetary system.

artificial selection The process whereby a new variation of plant or animal is produced by the repeated crossing of desirable genotypes.

asteroid A small planet, less than 500 miles in diameter and orbiting in space between Mars and Jupiter.

asthenosphere The hot, amorphous and sometimes molten layer of a planet lying just below the lithosphere.

Big Bang A now widely accepted theory that hypothesizes that the universe was "born" and began expanding some 15 to 20 billion years ago when all space, time, matter, and energy were compressed into a gigantic, high-density fireball.

bit A unit of computer information representing a choice between two alternatives.

black hole A region of extremely warped space-time caused by an intense gravitational field.

blue star A young, vigorous, short-lived star.

Brahe, Tycho (1546-1601) Danish astronomer who studied the motions of the planets, sun, and moon, observed the locations of stars, and was one of the first to reject heliocentric cosmology.

brainstem The part of the brain linking the spinal cord with the forebrain and cerebrum.

Bruno, Giordano (1548-1600) Italian philosopher who believed in the infinity of the universe and was burned at the stake by the Inquisition.

Callisto An outer moon of Jupiter.

Cambrian explosion The period in terrestrial evolution, which began some 600 million years ago, characterized by an enormous proliferation of new and more complex lifeforms.

catastrophism A philosophy emphasizing the importance of sudden and violent events in causing changes, particularly in evolutionary processes.

cerebral cortex In humans, the convoluted surface layer of gray matter covering the cerebral hemispheres; the seat of coordination of high nervous activity, including thought and intuition.

Champollion (1790-1832) French Egyptologist who deciphered the Rosetta Stone, thus unlocking the secrets of Egyptian hieroglyphics.

chaos From the Greek, the state of things when chance is supreme.

chloroplast The chlorophyll-bearing body in cells that is the site of photosynthesis.

Chryse The region on the Martian surface chosen for the Viking 1 landing.

comet An object with a nucleus generally considered to be "dirty ice," which travels in an eccentric orbit around the sun and when near the sun shows a coma and a tail.

contact binaries Two proximal stars whose atmospheres are elongated by their mutual gravity and whose star stuff is intermingled.

Copernicus, Nicolaus (1473–1543) Polish astronomer whose heliocentric (sun-centered) model of the planetary system revolutionized astronomy.

corpus callosum A band of fibers uniting the cerebral hemispheres of the brain.

cosmic background radiation Remnants of radiation from the Big Bang, detected by radio telescopes.

cosmic ray A stream of atomic nuclei that enter the earth's atmosphere at very high speeds.

cosmology The study of the physical universe as a whole.

cosmos Derived from the Greek word meaning order of the universe, refers to a harmonious and systematic universe whose constituent objects are interconnected and obey the same physical laws.

crater A depression on the surface of an object in space, usually formed by an impact.

Cydonia The region on the Martian surface chosen for the Viking 2 landing.

Cygnus X-1 An X-ray source and member of a binary system; possibly a black hole.

Darwin, Charles (1809–1882) English naturalist best known for his formulation of the theory of evolution by natural selection.

Democritus (460–370 B.C.) Greek philosopher who invented the word "atom" and conceived the idea that everything in the universe is composed of atoms that move about in space and form into bodies.

DNA (deoxyribonucleic acid) A long chain of molecules, found in the nuclei of cells, that contain the genetic information of life.

Doppler effect The change in wavelength that is caused by the motion of an object or some other source of waves, relative to an observer.

Einstein, Albert (1879-1955) German-Swiss-American physicist whose theory of quantum mechanics won him the Nobel Prize in 1922.

electron A subatomic particle that has a negative charge and normally moves about the nucleus of an atom.

element A fundamental substance that consists of atoms of only one kind. At present, more than 100 elements have been discovered. Singly or combined, they constitute all matter.

Empedocles (fl. 444 B.C.) Greek philosopher and scientist who identified four immutable elements in the universe—earth, air, fire, and water—and made observations about the nature of the physical world, particularly about the behavior and motion of light and air, that anticipated modern physics.

epicycle The orbit in which a planet moves and which has a center that is itself carried around at the same time on the circumference of a larger orbit.

Eratosthenes (273–192 B.C.) Greek geographer and philologist who determined that the earth was round, measured its circumference, and calculated the approximate distance of the sun from the earth; served as a librarian and encyclopedist at the Alexandrian Library (235–195 B.C.).

Europa An inner moon of Jupiter.

galaxy A collection of gas, dust, and stars, usually containing millions of solar systems; there are estimated to be some 100 billion galaxies in the universe.

Galilean satellites Four moons of Jupiter first observed by Galileo: Io, Europa, Ganymede, and Callisto.

Galileo (1564-1642) Italian astronomer, physicist, and philosopher, best known for his invention of the telescope, whose observations of the stars and planets helped promote the Copernican revolution.

gamma ray A form of light composed of high-energy photons with short, high-freqency wavelengths.

Ganymede An outer moon of Jupiter.

genetic code The self-reproducing record of the specific protein pattern of an organism.

geocentric Earth-centered.

Goddard, Robert (1882–1945) American physicist and rocket pioneer.

gradualism A philosophy emphasizing the importance of steady, slow changes, particularly in evolutionary processes.

greenhouse effect The process by which a solid body traps and absorbs the sun's radiation, leading to higher temperatures. On earth, the warming of lower layers of the atmosphere tends to increase with greater concentrations of carbon dioxide.

Halley, Edmond (1656–1742) English astronomer who discovered that the "comets" which appeared in 1531, 1607, and 1682 were actually one comet, later named "Halley's comet."

heliocentric Sun-centered.

heliopause Outer boundary of the solar system.

Hubble, Edwin American astronomer whose discovery that light from distant galaxies is increasingly redshifted depending on the distance of the galaxy from earth helped lay the groundwork for the Big Bang theory.

Humason, Milton Assistant to Hubble who helped discover the Big Bang.

Huggins, William (1824–1910) English astronomer and pioneer in the use of the spectroscope to analyze stellar light.

Huygens, Christiaan (1629–1695) Dutch mathematician, physicist, and astronomer.

inverse square law A law formulated by Newton that explains why the planets orbit the sun in regular elliptical orbits.

Io Inner moon of Jupiter.

Ionians A group of Greek scientists and natural philosophers living in the six centuries before the birth of Christ who made seminal discoveries in astronomy, physics, geography, medicine, biology, mathematics, and other sciences.

isotropy Exhibiting properties (such as the velocity of light transmission) with the same values when measured along axes in all directions.

Jupiter The largest of the planets in our solar system, and the fifth planet from the sun.

Kepler, Johannes (1571–1630) German astronomer whose formulation of the laws of planetary motion helped establish the validity of the Copernican model of the solar system.

law of interia A law formulated by Newton; the tendency of a moving object to continue moving in a straight line unless something influences it, and moves out it of its path.

law of universal gravitation Newton's law which explains the force in nature by which two masses attract each other.

lenticular cloud A cloud shaped like a lens, sometimes mistaken for an extraterrestrial spaceship.

light year The distance light travels in a year, at a speed of 300,000 kilometers per second.

limbic system A group of structures of the brain concerned with motivation and emotion.

lithosphere The relatively rigid and solid outer layer of a planet.

Local Group The collection of two dozen or so galaxies, of which our own Milky Way is a member, that forms a subcluster.

Lowell, Percival (1855–1916) American astronomer who predicted the planet Pluto and was an active proponent of the theory that Mars was inhabited.

Lucretius (98–55 B.C.) Roman poet who outlined a complete science of the universe based on the philosophies of Emocritus and Epicurus.

Mariner 9 American spacecraft that photographed Mars and its two moons in 1971.

Mars The fourth planet from the sun.

Mars Jar A container in which the environment of Mars is simulated.

Mars 3 Soviet spacecraft which landed on Mars in 1971.

Mars 6 Soviet spacecraft which landed on Mars in 1974.

Mercury The planet closest to the sun.

meteor A track of light observed when extraterrestrial matter enters the earth's atmosphere and burns up; considered by some astronomers to be a fragment of a comet.

meteorite A piece of interplanetary matter that has impacted on earth; considered by some astronomers to be a fragment of an asteroid.

Michell, John (1724–1793) English astronomer, physicist, and geologist who founded seismology and created the notion of black holes.

Milky Way A rotating, spiral galaxy made up of dust, gas, and some 250 billion suns, of which our own sun is one, estimated to be about 100,000 light years in diameter.

Miller, Stanley American biochemist who, with Harold Urey in the 1950s, recreated the essential building blocks of life in a laboratory setting.

mitochondria Enzyme-rich organelles found in the cytoplasm of cells that play an important part in cell metabolism.

mutation An abrupt change in a gene or chromosome that accounts for differences between one generation of species and the next; plays an essential role in the process of evolution.

natural selection Outlined by Darwin, a process whereby only those forms of plant and animal life that are best adapted to reproduction and the environment survive the evolutionary process.

Neptune The eighth planet from the sun.

neuron Nerve cell.

neutrino A massless, chargeless elementary particle that travels with the speed of light and can pass through matter.

neutron Subatomic particle having no charge and whose mass is approximately equal to that of the proton.

neutron star A dead star of very high density composed entirely of neutrons.

Newton, Isaac (1642–1727) English mathematician and natural philosopher who invented calculus and discovered the law of the composition of light and the law of universal gravitation.

nova A star, possibly a member of a binary star, that suddenly increases in luminosity hundreds or thousands of times.

nucleic acid Any of two types of acid—RNA and DNA—that carry genetic information.

nucleosynthesis In stellar evolution, the production of a chemical element from hydrogen nuclei.

nucleotide A molecule that is the basic component of DNA and RNA.

nucleus In atoms, the heaviest part of the atom, composed mostly of protons and neutrons. Electrons revolve around the nucleus.

Parmenides Eleatic philosopher (c. 500) who argued that what is inconceivable is impossible, even if the senses tell one that it has, in fact, happened.

particulate ring A ring of particles in orbit around a planet.

photon A unit of electromagnetic energy.

photosynthesis The biological process in which plants convert carbon dioxide and water into carbohydrates by absorbing light and energy from the sun into chlorophyll.

Pioneer Venus Pioneer 11 and 12 space probes that studied the atmosphere of Venus in 1978.

planetary nebulae A shell of gas around an extremely hot star.

Pluto The ninth planet from the sun.

principle of covariance At the heart of Einstein's special theory of relativity, the concept of ultimate equality of all observers.

proton A heavy subatomic particle with a positive energy charge; one of the two main constituents (the other being the neutron) of the atom.

ptolemies A succession of Alexandrian rulers who supported the development of the Alexandrian Library.

pulsar A small but powerful radio source in space transmitting signals at regular, short intervals.

Ptolemy (second century A.D.) Alexandrian astronomer and geographer who formulated the rules of astrology, named the stars, discovered how to predict eclipses, and developed a geocentric model to explain the motions of the planets.

Pythagoras (fl. 540–510 B.C.) Greek philosopher and mathematician best known for his so-called Pythagorean theorem and for his quasi-mystical view of the harmonious nature of the universe.

quark A subatomic particle having a small electrical charge; may be a constituent of known elementary particles.

quasar A highly redshifted, star-like object that has a high energy output and that emits blue and ultraviolet light and radio waves; an acronym for quasi-stellar radio source.

radiation The emission and transmission of energy in the form of particles and waves.

radioactivity A property of some elements (for example, uranium) of emitting alpha or beta, and sometimes gamma, rays through the disintegration of nuclei.

radio astronomy Making astronomical observations through the use of radio wavelengths.

R complex The part of the brain "capping" the brainstem; the seat of aggression, ritual, territoriality, and social hierarchy.

red giant A large, cool, highly luminous elderly star.

red shift The shift of a spectrum, particularly of spectral lines, to longer wavelengths.

ring galaxy A ring-shaped galaxy, probably resulting from the collision of two galaxies.

Rosetta Stone A stone bearing inscriptions in Egyptian hieroglyphics, demotic characters, and Greek. Discovered in 1799, it gave the first clue to the decipherment of hieroglyphics.

Rutherford, Ernest (1871–1937) British physicist who developed a model of the atom.

Saturn The sixth planet from the sun.

Schiaparelli, Giovanni (1835–1910) Italian astronomer who observed *canali* (lines) on Mars.

solar wind A continuous flow of atomic particles ejected from the sun into interplanetary space.

Soviet Venera expeditions A series of eight expeditions sent by the Soviets to Mars.

spiral galaxy (spiral arms) A type of galaxy characterized by arms that unwind like a pinwheel.

supernova A stellar explosion in which a star suddenly increases in luminosity by hundreds of thousands or more times.

terraforming The process of changing the environment of a previously uninhabitable extraterrestrial body so that it can support life.

Thales (624–546 B.C.) Greek philosopher regarded by some as the founder of Greek philosophy and science; measured the height of a pyramid and believed that the world was made not by gods but by the interaction of material forces in nature.

Titan Moon of Saturn.

trilobites Tiny, insect-like organisms that flourished in vast herds on the ocean floors some 500 billion years ago.

Tsiolkovsky, Konstantin (1856–1935) Soviet rocket pioneer who anticipated solutions to problems of spaceflight.

Uranus The seventh planet from the sun.

Urey, Harold With Stanley Miller, recreated the basic building blocks of life in the laboratory.

Venus The second planet from the sun.

Viking 1 and 2 (1976) U.S. expeditions to Mars which conducted important biological and other experiments.

viroids The smallest-known living organisms, composed of less than 10,000 atoms.

Voyager 1 and 2 Two interstellar probes launched in 1977, which encountered Jupiter in 1979.

Wallace, Alfred Russel (1823–1913) English naturalist who debunked Lowell's Mars theories and formulated a theory of evolution by natural selection independently of Charles Darwin.

white dwarf A star in a final stage of its evolution that has exhausted all or almost all of its nuclear fuel and collapsed to small size with high surface temperature and density.

yellow dwarf A middle-aged star, like our own sun.

Timeline

600 B.C.	Beginning of the "new awakening" in Ionian philosophy and science on the Greek island of Samos.
624-546 B.C.	Thales developed methods to measure the heights of pyramids; postulated that the world was created by the interaction of material forces in nature.
611-547 B.C.	Anaximander invented the sundial, made a map of the known world, and determined the length of the year and the seasons.
540-510 B.C.	Pythagoras formulated the Pythagorean theorem and established a school of followers known as the Pythagoreans.
528-500 B.C.	Anaxagoras studied the behavior of celestial bodies; was one of the first to postulate that they were composed of ordinary matter.
460-370 B.C.	Democritus invented the word "atom" and conceived the idea that everything in nature is composed of atoms.
444 B.C.	Empedocles identified and characterized the behavior of the "four immutable elements" in nature—earth, air, water, and fire.
310-230 B.C.	Aristarchus postulated that the sun, not the earth, was at the center of the universe.
300 B.C.	The Alexandrian Library was founded in the city of Alexandria.
273-192 B.C.	Eratosthenes determined the earth was round, measured its circumference, and calculated the approximate distance of the earth from the sun.
98-55 B.C.	Lucretius wrote *The Nature of the Universe*, an exposition of the teachings of Democritus and Epicurus.
66 A.D.	First recorded appearance of what is now called "Halley's comet."
100-500	Printing developed in China.
200	Ptolemy published the *Almagest*, in which he described his geocentric model of the universe and laid down the tenets of modern astrology.
300	The Alexandrian Library was destroyed under Theodosios the Great.
1054	Crab supernova was observed in China, the American Southwest, and Moslem countries.
1066	Appearance of a comet, later identified as Halley's comet, associated with the invasion of England by William the Conqueror.
1178	Canterbury monks observed possible lunar impact, June 25.
1450	Invention of movable type revolutionized printing in Europe.
1492	Columbus landed in the New World.
1521	Cortez defeated the Aztecs.
1543	Publication of Copernicus' *On the Revolution of Heavenly Bodies*, in which he outlined his heliocentric model of the universe.

1573	Tycho Brahe published *De Nova Stella*, an account of his discovery of the "new star" in Cassiopeia.
1583	Galileo invented the telescope.
1600	Italian philosopher Giordano Bruno burned at the stake.
1609-1618	Johannes Kepler published his three laws of planetary motion.
1610	Galileo discovered Jupiter's satellites and sun spots.
1637	Galileo discovered the moon's libration.
1687	Isaac Newton published his *Mathematical Principles of Natural Philosophy*, in which he advanced the theory of universal gravitation and the law of inertia.
1690	Publication of Huygen's *The Celestial Worlds Discover'd*.
1765	Edmund Halley determined the regular return of "his" comet every 76 years.
1783	John Michell conceived the notion of black holes.
1785	La Perouse encountered Native Americans in Alaska.
1799	Rosetta Stone uncovered.
1824	Jean Francois Champollion published *Precis du systeme hieroglyphique des anciens egyptiens*, in which he described his decipherment of the Rosetta Stone.
1858	Alfred Russel Wallace sent an abstract outlining his theory of natural selection to Charles Darwin.
1859	Publication of Charles Darwin's *Origin of Species*, in which he described his theory of evolution by natural selection.
1877	Giovanni Schiaparelli announced his discovery of *canali* on Mars.
1879	Albert Einstein was born in Ulm, Germany.
1894	Percival Lowell published *Mars*, in which he speculated about canals on Mars.
1897	H.G. Wells published his science fiction novel *War of the Worlds*, a description of a Martian invasion of earth.
1905	Einstein published a paper titled "On the Electrodynamics of Moving Bodies," in which he outlined his theory of special relativity.
1905	Tunguska event, possible cometary impact in Siberia.
1910	Appearance of Halley's comet.
1916	Einstein published a paper titled "The Foundations of General Relativity," in which he outlined his theory of relativity.
1922	Einstein won the Nobel Prize for his work on quantum mechanics.
1924	Edwin Hubble proved at Mount Wilson Observatory that there were other galaxies besides our own in the universe.
1926	Robert Goddard demonstrated the first successful liquid-fuel rocket, which traveled 184 feet.

1932	Discovery of the neutron.
1938	Radio broadcast of *War of the Worlds* created panic in the United States.
1948	Two-stage rocket launching of V-2/WAC Corporal.
1953	Stanley Miller and Harold Urey created the essential building blocks of life in the laboratory.
1953	Watson and Crick discovered the structure of DNA.
1955	Einstein died in Princeton, New Jersey.
1957	Soviet *Sputnik*, first earth satellite, was launched.
1961	First manned orbital space flight by Soviet Yuri Gagarin in *Vostok 1*.
1961	Betty and Barney Hill allegedly encountered a spacecraft manned by extraterrestrials.
1962	U.S. *Mariner 2* flew by Venus.
1965	Cosmic background radiation was first registered. U.S. *Mariner 4* returned to Earth, bringing back 22 televised pictures of Mars.
1966	Soviet *Venera 3* landed on Venus; failed to return data.
1967	*Venera 4* measured temperature, pressure, and composition of Venusian atmosphere. *Mariner 5* flew by Venus and measured the structure of its upper atmosphere.
1969	First successful landing on Venus, by Soviet *Venera 5* and *6*. *Mariner 6* flyby of Mars; data was collected about spectra of Martian atmosphere and surface. Neil A. Armstrong walked on the moon. Astronomers in Arizona observed pulsar in Crab nebula.
1971	*Mariner 9*, the first spacecraft to go into orbit around another planet (Mars), returned more than 7,000 pictures. *Mars 3* orbiter returned data but descent vehicle failed after landing on Mars. Uhuru X-ray observatory spotted Cygnus X-1.
1972	Soviet *Venera 8* landed on Venus and survived for 50 minutes.
1973	*Pioneer 10* encountered Jupiter system and returned more than 300 pictures.
1974	*Mars 4* and *5* orbited Mars and returned photographs. *Mars 6* descent vehicle failed at touchdown. *Mariner 10* conducted first probe of Mercury and transmitted data from Venus and Mercury to earth.
1976	*Viking 1* and *2* descent vehicles successfully landed on Martian surface and conducted several experiments.
1978	*Pioneer 11* and *12* studied atmosphere of Venus.
1979	*Voyagers 1* and *2* encountered Jupiter system, to travel on past Saturn and into interstellar space.
1986	Halley's comet to reappear.

Suggested General Reading Materials

Basic Introductory Astronomy Textbooks:

George Abell, *Exploration of the Universe.* New York: Holt, Rinehart and Winston, 1964.

Donald Goldsmith, *The Universe.* Menlo Park, Calif.: Benjamin-Cummings, 1976.

William J. Kaufmann III, *Astronomy: The Structure of the Universe.* New York: Macmillan, 1977.

Jay M. Pasachoff, *Astronomy: From the Earth to the Universe.* Philadelphia: W.B. Saunders Company, 1979.

Magazines and Periodicals:

Astronomy. 411 East Mason Street, Milwaukee, Wisconsin 53202.

Good, richly illustrated astronomy articles for the nontechnical reader.

Cosmic Search. Radio Observatory, P.O. Box 293, Delaware, Ohio 43015.

Another new periodical that publishes excellent articles on astronomy and insightful interviews with well-known astronomers.

Mercury. Astronomical Society of the Pacific, 1290 24th Avenue, San Francisco, California 94122.

Publishes review articles, bibliographies, interdisciplinary articles, interviews, and summaries of current research in astronomy.

National Geographic. Washington, D.C. 20036.

Publishes good, beautifully illustrated articles on various popular topics in astronomy once or twice each year.

Natural History. Membership Services, Box 600, Des Moines, Iowa 50340.

Contains regular short articles on astronomy, frequently written by well-known astronomers.

Omni. 909 Third Avenue, New York, New York 10022.

A new publication featuring good articles on various astronomical subjects.

Science News. 1719 N Street N.W., Washington D.C. 20036.

Contains articles on new discoveries as well as general topics in astronomy. Published weekly.

Scientific American. 415 Madison Avenue, New York, New York 10017.

Features good astronomy articles, often written by prominent astronomers, about every other issue. Published monthly.

Sky and Telescope. Sky Publishing Company, 49-50-51 Bay State Road, Cambridge, Massachusetts 02138.

Written for the amateur astronomer; contains articles on current topics in astronomy as well as hints on how to observe the skies and descriptions of telescopes. Excellent photographs.

Smithsonian. 900 Jefferson Drive, Washington, D.C. 20560.

Occasionally features excellent articles on current topics in astronomy.

ACKNOWLEDGEMENTS (continued)

XIII. WHO SPEAKS FOR EARTH?

Philip Morrison, "If the Bomb Gets Out of Hand," from *One World or None* edited by Dexter Masters and Katherine Way. Published by McGraw-Hill Book Company, 1946. Reprinted by permission.

Niels Bohr, "Science and Civilization," from *One World or None* edited by Dexter Masters and Katherine Way. Published by McGraw-Hill Book Company, 1946. Reprinted by permission.

Albert Einstein, "A Message to Intellectuals," from *Einstein on Peace* (New York: Schocken Books), pp. 493–496. Reprinted by permission of the estate of Albert Einstein.

Richard E. Leakey and Roger Lewin, excerpts from *Origins* by Richard E. Leakey and Roger Lewin. Copyright © Richard E. Leakey and Roger Lewin, 1977. Reprinted by permission of E.P. Dutton.

Bertrand Russell, "Science and Values," reprinted from *The Scientific Outlook* by Bertrand Russell, with the permission of W.W. Norton & Company, Inc. Copyright 1931 by Bertrand Russell. Copyright Renewed 1959 by Bertrand Russell. Published in Canada by George Allen & Unwin Ltd. and reprinted by permission.